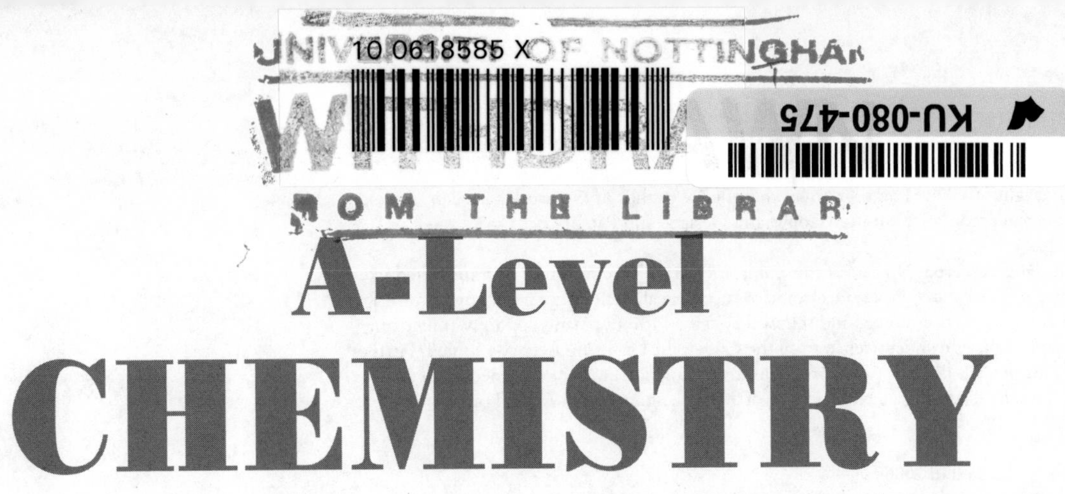

A-Level CHEMISTRY

FOURTH EDITION

Answers Key

E.N. Ramsden

B.Sc., Ph.D., D.Phil.

Formerly of Wolfreton School, Hull

Stanley Thornes (Publishers) Ltd.

First published in 2000 by

Stanley Thornes (Publishers) Ltd
Ellenborough House
Wellington Street
Cheltenham
GL50 1YW

00 01 02 03 04 / 10 9 8 7 6 5 4 3 2 1

A catalogue record of this book is available from the British Library.

ISBN 0 7487 5300 1

Typeset by Mathematical Composition Setters Ltd, Salisbury, Wiltshire
Printed and bound in Great Britain by Redwood Books, Trowbridge, Wiltshire

CONTENTS

ANSWERS

PART 1: THE FOUNDATION 1

PART 2: PHYSICAL CHEMISTRY 15

PART 3: INORGANIC CHEMISTRY 28

PART 4: ORGANIC CHEMISTRY 43

SYNOPTIC QUESTIONS

ANSWERS TO SYNOPTIC QUESTIONS

ACKNOWLEDGEMENTS

The author and publishers are grateful to the following Awarding Bodies for kind permission to reproduce examination questions:

AQA for the Associated Examining Board (AEB) and the Northern Examinations and Assessment Board (NEAB)
EDEXCEL for London Examinations (L and L(N))
Hong Kong Examinations Authority
Northern Ireland Council for the Curriculum Examinations and Assessment (CCEA)
OCR for Oxford and Cambridge Local Examinations Board (O & C) and the University of Cambridge Local Examinations Syndicate (C)
Welsh Joint Education Committee (W)

DISCLAIMER

The above Awarding Bodies accept no responsibility whatsoever for the accuracy or method of working in the answers given. These are the sole responsibility of the author.

ANSWERS

PART 1: THE FOUNDATION

CHAPTER 1 THE ATOM

Checkpoint 1.2: Particles

This is a revision of the particulate theory of matter.

1. The crystal consists of particles. Some particles break away from the solid crystal – dissolve – and spread through the water. The pink colour of some particles is in this way spread through the solution.
2. Chlorine and air consist of particles. The particles are in constant motion. When chlorine and air are mixed, the particles of chlorine and the particles of the gases which make up air move about until they are evenly distributed through the whole of the space.
3. A particle of smoke is bombarded from all directions by particles (molecules) of air. At any instant, the number of particles of air hitting the smoke particle is greatest in one direction and the smoke particle is moved in that direction.
4. Solid ⟶ liquid. The particles vibrate more energetically about their mean positions in the solid as the temperature rises. Eventually some particles break free from the solid structure: the solid melts.
   Liquid ⟶ gas. In a liquid, particles can move independently but are held in the liquid by intermolecular forces of attraction. As the temperature rises, some particles gain enough energy to break free from these forces of attraction: they enter the gas phase.
5. In nuclear fission, atomic nuclei are split, and nuclei of different elements are formed; see § 1.10.6

Checkpoint 1.8: Atoms

1. *(a)* 19p, 19e, 20n *(b)* 13p, 13e, 14n *(c)* 56p, 56e, 81n *(d)* 88p, 88e, 138n
2. *(a)* 6p, 6e, 6n *(b)* 6p, 6e, 8n *(c)* 1p, 1e *(d)* 1p, 1e, 1n *(e)* 1p, 1e, 2n *(f)* 38p, 38e, 49n *(g)* 38p, 38e, 52n *(h)* 92p, 92e, 143n *(i)* 92p, 92e, 146n
3. The atoms of an element all have the same atomic number – the number of protons. They may differ in the number of neutrons and therefore have different mass numbers. For example, chlorine atoms all have 17 protons, but some have 18 neutrons, giving mass number 35 and some have 20 neutrons, giving mass number 37. The atoms of the same atomic number and different neutron number are called isotopes. They do not differ chemically because chemical behaviour is determined by the electron configuration, and isotopes, having the same number of protons, have also the same number of electrons and the same electron configuration. The isotopes of hydrogen ^{1}H, ^{2}H and ^{3}H are rather exceptional in that some differences in the rates of their chemical reactions are observed.
4. It was found [see § 1.6] that the mass of an atom was greater than the mass of protons in it. The existence of uncharged particles, neutrons, with the same mass as a proton, was postulated. The mass of an atom = mass of protons + mass of neutrons + mass of electrons, with the electrons contributing very little to the mass.

   The neutron was hard to find because, being uncharged, it is not deflected in a magnetic field (unlike α-rays and β-rays) and because it does not make zinc sulphide fluoresce.

Checkpoint 1.9: Mass spectrometry

1. Refer to Figure 1.9B. For *(a)* see notes 1 and 2, for *(b)* note 3, for *(c)* note 4 and for *(d)* notes 5, 6 and 7.
2. Mass number = number of protons + number of neutrons in an atom of a nuclide; see § 1.6, 1.7. Isotopes are nuclides with the same proton number and different mass numbers; see § 1.8.

   $$\text{Relative atomic mass} = \frac{\text{mass of one atom of an element}}{1/12 \text{ mass of one atom of carbon-12}}$$

   See § 3.4.

   $$\text{Mean } A_r = \left(\frac{75.77}{100} \times 34.97\right) + \left(\frac{24.23}{100} \times 36.96\right) = 35.45$$

3. $CH_2\,Cl_2$
   The peak at 84 is due to $CH_2\,^{35}Cl_2$; that at 86 to $CH_2\,^{35}Cl\,^{37}Cl$; that at 88 to $CH_2\,^{37}Cl_2$.
   Since the ratio $^{35}Cl : ^{37}Cl = 3:1$,
   the ratio $^{35}Cl_2 : ^{37}Cl_2 = 9:1$ and $^{35}Cl\,^{37}Cl : ^{37}Cl_2 = 6:1$
4. The average atomic mass is obtained by finding the sum of

   $$\left(\frac{\text{height of peak}}{100} \times \text{mass number}\right) = 207.2\text{ u}$$

*Checkpoint 1.10 A: Nuclear reactions I

1. ^{35}Cl, ^{37}Cl
2. The half-life of the radioactive isotope is one year (the time taken for 8 g to decay to 4 g). In the same time, 6 g will decay to 3 g.
3. *(a)* $^{14}_{7}N$ *(b)* $^{17}_{8}O$ *(c)* $^{226}_{88}Ra$ $^{222}_{86}Rn$ *(d)* $^{73}_{33}As$ $^{73}_{32}Ge$ *(e)* $^{27}_{14}Si$ *(f)* $^{1}_{0}n$

Questions on Chapter 1

1. See § 1.9.1. The ion with the highest value of m/z is usually the molecular ion. Some large molecules are split up and do not give molecular ions.
2. 64 and 73; $^{13}C_2\,^{1}H_5\,^{35}Cl$, $^{12}C_2\,^{1}H_5\,^{37}Cl$, $^{13}C_2\,^{1}H_3\,^{2}H_2\,^{35}Cl$, $^{12}C\,^{13}C\,^{1}H_4\,^{2}H\,^{35}Cl$
3. There are equal numbers of the molecules:
   $^{1}H^{1}H$, $^{1}H^{2}H$, $^{1}H^{3}H$, $^{2}H^{1}H$, $^{2}H^{2}H$, $^{2}H^{3}H$, $^{3}H^{1}H$, $^{3}H^{2}H$, $^{3}H^{3}H$
   Therefore, for peaks of mass = 2, 3, 4, 5, 6
   Ratio of heights = 1 : 2 : 3 : 2 : 1
4. See § 1.5.
5. Peaks at 49 ($^{14}N^{35}Cl$), 51 ($^{14}N^{37}Cl$), 84 ($^{14}N^{35}Cl_2$), 86 ($^{14}N^{35}Cl^{37}Cl$), 88 ($^{14}N^{37}Cl_2$), 119 ($^{14}N^{35}Cl_3$), 121 ($^{14}N^{35}Cl_2\,^{37}Cl$), 123 ($^{14}N^{35}Cl^{37}Cl_2$), 125 ($^{14}N^{37}Cl_3$)
6. $^{228}_{90}Z$
7. Subtracting mass numbers and atomic numbers gives (1) a β-particle, $^{0}_{-1}e$ and (2) an α-particle, $^{4}_{2}He$. Atomic numbers show that X is one group after Pb, that is, in Group 5 and Y is one group before Pb, that is, Group 3. If Y loses a β-particle, Z must be $^{208}_{82}Z$ and in the same group as Pb, Group 4.
8. *(a)* $a = 35$, $b = 16$, **X** = S *(b)* $c = 4$, $d = 2$, **Y** = He
9. In the molecules, $^{79}Br^{79}Br$ (158), $^{79}Br^{81}Br$ (160), $^{81}Br^{81}Br$ (162), the ^{79}Br isotope is slightly more abundant than ^{81}Br; therefore the peak at 158 is slightly higher than that at 160 which is slightly higher than that at 162.
10. The peak at $m/e = 46$ is the molecular peak. The peak at $m/e = 47$ is due to $^{12}C^{13}CH_5OH$. The peak at 45 is due to $C_2H_5O^+$, 31 to CH_2OH^+, 29 to $C_2H_5^+$ and 27 to $C_2H_3^+$.

11. 44, 46, 48. There are 4 times as many ^{16}O atoms as ^{18}O atoms; therefore the number of $^{12}C^{16}O^{16}O$ molecules = 4 × the number of $^{12}C^{16}O^{18}O$ molecules = 16 × the number of $^{12}C^{18}O^{18}O$ molecules.
12. The empirical formula, calculated as in § 3.8 is C_4H_8O.
The peak at $m/e = 72$ has the maximum value of m/e and is the molecular ion, therefore, the molecular formula is C_4H_8O.
The peak at 15 is probably CH_3.
We are told that the compound possesses a >C=O group or a —CHO group.
The peak at 29 could be $CH_3CH_2^+$ or CHO^+.
The peak at 43 could be $CH_3CH_2CH_2^+$.
The peak at 57 could be $C_2H_5CO^+$ or $CH_2CH_2CHO^+$.
Combining the fragments gives $CH_3CH_2CH_2CHO$.
13. *(a)* See § 1.9 and Figure 1.9A.
(b) (i) Magnesium has three isotopes, all with at. no. = 12 and with A_r = 24, 25 and 26.
(ii) [(1.000 × 24) + (0.127 × 25) + (0.139 × 26)]/1.266 = 24.320
14. *(a)* (i) see § 1.7 (b) § 3.4
(c) m = mass of particles in atomic mass units, u. z = charge on particles in elementary charge units
(d) (i) $^{58}_{28}Ni^+$
(ii) [(69/100) × 58] + [(27/100 × 60] + [(4/100 × 62)] = 58.70
(e) Ni : (Ar) $4s^2 3d^8$, Ni^{2+} : (Ar) $3d^8$.
15. *(a)* ^{12}C is taken as the standard; see § 3.4
(b) $1.0078 - (9.1091 \times 10^{-28} \times 6.0225 \times 10^{23}) = 1.0078 - 5.486 \times 10^{-4} = 1.00725$
(c) (i) See § 1.9 and Figure 1.9B.
(ii) to avoid fragmentation with loss of the molecular ion
(iii) acceleration; see Figure 1.9B, Note 3.
(d) The difference is the relative atomic mass of one electron $(9.1091 \times 10^{-28} \times 6.0225 \times 10^{23}) = 5.486 \times 10^{-4}$ compared with A_r(Li) = 6.94. The difference is negligible for most purposes.
16. *(a)* electron. The neutron is uncharged and therefore not deflected. The electron is lighter than the proton and therefore deflected more.
(b) Only positively charged particles are accelerated by the electric field [see Figure 1.9B(3)]. Only positive ions are deflected by the electromagnet [Figure 1.9B(4)].
(c) $x\%\ ^{10}B + (100 - x)\%\ ^{11}B = 10.8 \Rightarrow x = 20$
Ratio $^{10}B : ^{11}B = 1 : 4$
(d) Ratio B : H = (81.2/10.8) : (18.8/1) = 1 : 2.5
Empirical formula is B_2H_5
Empirical formula mass = 26.6 therefore molecular formula is B_4H_{10}.
Highest $m/z = {}^{11}B_4H_{10} = 54$
17. *(a)* (i) $^{222}_{86}Rn$ (ii) $^{14}_{7}N$ (iii) $^{60}_{28}Ni$
(b) (i) See § 1.10.5 (ii) An isotope injected into the body should have a half-life long enough to allow a diagnosis to be made but no longer.
(c) $^{241}_{95}Am \xrightarrow{^{0}_{-1}\beta} {}^{241}_{96}X \xrightarrow{^{0}_{-1}\beta} {}^{241}_{97}Y \xrightarrow{^{4}_{2}He} {}^{237}_{95}Am$
Loss of two beta particles and one alpha particle
(d) (i) 24.32
(ii) CH_3^+ has $m/e = 15$; CH_3CO^+ has $m/e = 43$.
(iii) $C_2H_5^+$ has $m/e = 29$, suggesting propanal.
18. *(a)* See § 1.7
(b) See Figure 1.9B notes (1) for electron gun and (4) for magnet.
(c) (i) $^{20}_{10}Ne$ (ii) $^{22}_{10}Ne^{2+}$
(iii) [(17.8 × 20) + (1.7 × 22)]/19.5 = 20.2

CHAPTER 2 THE ATOM: THE ARRANGEMENT OF ELECTRONS

Checkpoint 2.7A: The Periodic Table I

1. Francium is the last member of the alkali metals, Group 1. One can predict that it will resemble the other members of the group in being a solid, metallic element, even more reactive than other members of the group in the reactions listed in Table 2.7A.
2. Astatine, in Group 7, is a halogen. One can predict that it will be a solid, like iodine, of low melting temperature, a non-metallic element and the least reactive of the halogens in the reactions shown in Table 2.7B.
3. Beryllium is the first member of the alkaline earths in Group 2. Reactivity increases down the group so one can predict than beryllium will react slowly with water (even more slowly than does magnesium) to form hydrogen and a solution of the alkali, beryllium hydroxide. See Table 2.7A for the reaction of beryllium with water.
4. Radium is the last member of the alkaline earths in Group 2.
(a) The chloride $RaCl_2$ is ionic.
(b) The oxide RaO is a strong base.
(c) One can predict that the reaction with water will be fast, to form hydrogen and a solution of the alkali radium hydroxide.

Checkpoint 2.7B: The Periodic Table II

1. Li_2O basic, BeO basic, B_2O_3 amphoteric, C oxides acidic or neutral; see Table 2.7C.
2. Li, Be giant metallic structure
N, O, F individual diatomic molecules
Ne individual monatomic molecules
3. Ga, Group 3, Ga_2O_3
Ge, Group 4, Ge O_2
As, Group 5, As_2O_5, As_2O_3
Se, Group 6, SeO_3,
4. *(a)* Melting temperatures of elements indicate the strength of bonds between elements. (b) From Na ⟶ Mg ⟶ Al the number of valence electrons increases and the metallic bond increases in strength. (c) Intermolecular forces are weak in argon.
5. These elements have metallic bonds with free electrons available to conduct electricity.

Checkpoint 2.8: Electronic configurations

1. Calcium has $Z = 20$; therefore each isotope has 20 protons, and Ca-40 has 20 neutrons, Ca-42 has 22n, Ca-43 has 23n, Ca-44 has 24n, Ca-46 has 26n and Ca-48 has 28 neutrons.

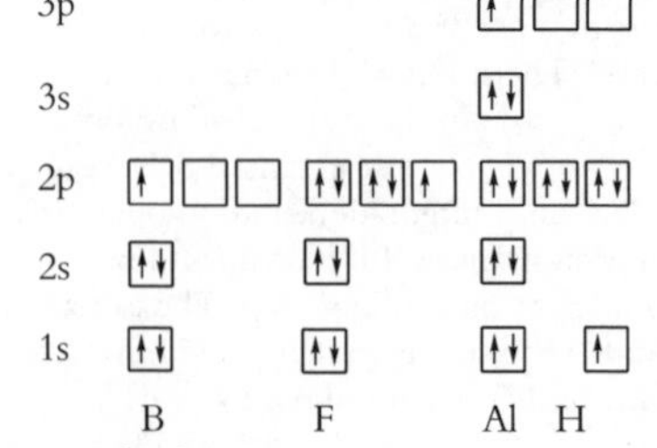

4. 4 $1s^2 2s^2$ — Group 2
7 $1s^2 2s^2 2p^3$ — Group 5
18 $1s^2 2s^2 2p^6 3s^2 3p^6$ — Group 0
27 $1s^2 2s^2 2p^6 3s^2 3p^6 3d^7 4s^2$ — Transition metal
37 $1s^2 2s^2 2p^6 3s^2 3p^6 3d^{10} 4s^2 4p^6 5s^1$ — Group 1
5. Na^+ 11 $1s^2 2s^2 2p^6$
Mg^{2+} 12 $1s^2 2s^2 2p^6$
Al 13 $1s^2 2s^2 2p^6 3s^2 3p^1$
Si 14 $1s^2 2s^2 2p^6 3s^2 3p^2$
P 15 $1s^2 2s^2 2p^6 3s^2 3p^3$

S	16	$1s^2 2s^2 2p^6 3s^2 3p^4$
S^{2-}	16	$1s^2 2s^2 2p^6 3s^2 3p^6$
Cl	17	$1s^2 2s^2 2p^6 3s^2 3p^5$
Cl^-	17	$1s^2 2s^2 2p^6 3s^2 3p^6$
Ar	18	$1s^2 2s^2 2p^6 3s^2 3p^6$

Checkpoint 2.9: The Periodic Table III

1. *(a)* He, Ne, Ar, Kr, Xe, Rn *(b)* Group 0
   (c) (i) a full outer shell of 2 (He) or 8 electrons
   (ii) They are chemically unreactive, except for Kr and Xe which react with fluorine.
2. The alkaline solution indicates Group 1 or Group 2. The slow reaction indicates Group 2.
3. Y forms ions Y^-; therefore Y is in Group 7.
4. The strongly alkaline solution indicates Group 1 or Group 2. The vigorous reaction indicates Group 1.

Questions on Chapter 2

1. The light which is emitted has frequencies which correspond to electrons moving from an orbit to an orbit of lower energy. The orbits are of certain energies only [§2.3] and the transitions between them correspond to certain energies only and certain wavelengths only. The orbits further away from the nucleus have higher energy levels than orbits close to the nucleus, and they are closer together so transitions between them involve smaller changes in energy than transitions between orbitals closer to the nucleus.
2. Your discussion should include the following points. The hydrogen atom has one electron. To explain why the emission spectrum of hydrogen consists of many lines of different frequencies, Bohr theorised that the electron can occupy many different orbits of different energies [§2.3.1]. The orbits are described by quantum numbers. The orbits of lowest energy are closest to the nucleus and have principal quantum number 1. An electron in one of these orbits is in its ground state – the state of lowest energy.

   Sommerfield [§2.3.4] suggested that each principle quantum number, *n*, governs a circular orbit and a set of elliptical orbits. The second quantum number, l, governs the shape of the elliptical orbits and has values 0, 1, 2, 3, 4, etc. Each value of l is assigned a letter; for l = 0, the orbit is an s- orbit.

   The concept of orbits was replaced by orbitals; see the wave theory of the atom, §2.4.1.

   Thus the electron of the hydrogen atom is in its ground state, with principle quantum number 1 and second quantum number 0.
3. *(a)* See §2.3.2 for the convergence method.
   (b) The plot shows a big jump between the 3rd electron and the 4th electron; therefore it is likely that three electrons only are removed and BCl_3 is formed.
4. *(a), (b)* Compare with Figure 2.2D; energy and frequency increase from A to G.
   (c) See §2.3.1
   (d) Within a series [see Figure 2.3C] the transitions are to orbitals of the same principal quantum number.
5. *(a)* When hydrogen is excited by an electric discharge [see Figure 2.2B] hydrogen molecules form atoms. The atoms acquire energy and move to higher energy levels. Later they emit the acquired energy in the form of light; see §2.2.
   (b) The hydrogen emission spectrum is in the red region, at lower frequency than the tungsten emission spectrum which is in the yellow region at higher frequency.
   (c), (d) see §2.3.2
6. *(a)* Different numbers of neutrons, same numbers of protons and electrons
   (b) ${}^{7}_{3}X$
   (c) (i) $(Ar)4s^2$ (ii) Group 5
   (d) (i) $B \longrightarrow B^+ + e^-$
   (ii) The second electron must be removed against the attraction of B^+.
   (iii) The first three electrons are removed from the outer shell, the $2s^2 2p$ electrons. The fourth electron is a 1s electron, much nearer to the positively charged nucleus.
7. *(a)* (i) Mg has 2 valence electrons; therefore the metallic bond is stronger than in Na with only one valence electron.
   (ii) between T_m of Cl and zero K
   (iii) Intermolecular forces in Ar are weak and Ar does not liquefy until a few degrees above zero K. There is a difference of only a few kelvins between T_m and T_b.
   (b) $2P(s) + 5O_2(g) \longrightarrow 2P_2O_5(s)$
   (c) $Na_2O(s) + H_2O(l) \longrightarrow 2NaOH(aq)$; pH 13–14
   $SO_3(s) + H_2O(l) \longrightarrow H_2SO_4(aq)$; pH 0–1
8. *(a)* $[(20 \times 90.82) + (21 \times 0.26) + (22 \times 8.92)] \times 10^{-2} = 20.18$
   (b) (i) $(3.03/20.18) \times 22.4 \times (298/273)\ dm^3 = 3.67\ dm^3$.
   (ii) $3.67 \times (1.01 \times 10^5 / 5.05 \times 10^5)\ dm^3 = 0.734\ dm^3$
   (c) (i) In He($1s^2$) the 1s electron is removed. This is closer to the nucleus than the 2p electrons removed when Ne($1s^2 2s^2 2p^6$) ionises.
   (ii) Be($1s^2 2s^2$), Li($1s^2 2s$), B($1s^2 2s^2 2p$)
   I.E. (Be) > I.E. (Li) because some stability is associated with the full $2s^2$ sub-shell in Be.
   (iii) N ($1s^2 2s^2 2p^3$), O($1s^2 2s^2 2p^4$) I.E.(N) > I.E.(O) because removal of one electron from the oxygen atom leaves a half-full p subshell, and there is stability associated with half-filled subshells. In N, in contrast, the removal of one electron disturbs a half-full p subshell and takes more energy.
   (d) [↑↓] 1s [↑↓] 2s [↑↓|↑↓|↑↓] 2p
   O^{2-}: $1s^2 2s^2 2p^6$; Ne
9. *(a)* See §§ 1.7, 1.8
   (b) (i) $Na^+ \longrightarrow Na^{2+} + e^-$
   (ii) I. A Group 1, B Group 6
   II. The second electron is removed against the attraction of A^+.
   (c) (i) $1s^2 2s^2 2p^6 3s^2 3p$
   (ii) The 3p electron is easiest to remove (electron no. 1), followed by the $3s^2$ electrons (nos. 2, 3), then by the $2s^2 2p^6$ electrons (nos 4–11) and finally by the $1s^2$ electrons which are nearest to the nucleus (nos. 12, 13).
   (d) (i)

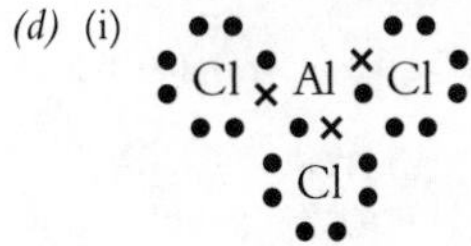

   (ii)

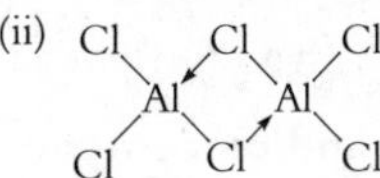

   (iii) $Al_2Cl_6(s) + H_2O(l) \longrightarrow 2[Al(H_2O)_6{}^{3+}](aq) + 6Cl^-(aq)$
10. *(a)* (i) Si: between values of Al and P; Cl: between values of S and Ar
   (ii) Na: (Ar)3s, Mg: $(Ar)3s^2$. The electrons are removed from the same 3s sub-shell, but in Mg there is a higher charge on the nucleus.
   (iii) Al: $(Ar)3s^2 3p$. The p electron is further from the nucleus and easier to remove than the s electron in Mg.
   (b) (i) decrease
   (ii) As the nuclear charge increases across the period the electrons are more tightly held.
   (c) (i) 4 (ii) 2 (iii) 1 (iv) 2

CHAPTER 3 EQUATIONS AND EQUILIBRIA

Checkpoint 3.2: Formulae

1. *(a)* 12 *(b)* 14 *(c)* 5 *(d)* 8 *(e)* 12 *(f)* 30 *(g)* 13 *(h)* 14 *(i)* 17 *(j)* 39
2. *(a)* NaOH *(b)* HCl *(c)* NH_3 *(d)* NaCl *(e)* CaO *(f)* $Ca(OH)_2$ *(g)* $CaCO_3$ *(h)* H_2SO_4 *(i)* HNO_3

Checkpoint 3.3: Equations

1. *(a)* $Fe_2O_3(s) + 3C(s) \longrightarrow 2Fe(s) + 3CO(g)$
   (b) $Fe_2O_3 + 3CO(g) \longrightarrow 2Fe(s) + 3CO_2(g)$
   (c) $4NH_3(g) + 5O_2(g) \longrightarrow 4NO(g) + 6H_2O(l)$
   (d) $2Cr(s) + 6HCl(aq) \longrightarrow 2CrCl_3(aq) + 3H_2(g)$
   (e) $Fe_3O_4(s) + 4H_2(g) \longrightarrow 3Fe(s) + 4H_2O(l)$
   (f) $C_3H_8(g) + 5O_2(g) \longrightarrow 3CO_2(g) + 4H_2O(l)$
2. *(a)* $H_2(g) + CuO(s) \longrightarrow Cu(s) + H_2O(l)$
   (b) $C(s) + CO_2(g) \longrightarrow 2CO(g)$
   (c) $Mg(s) + H_2SO_4(aq) \longrightarrow H_2(g) + MgSO_4(aq)$
   (d) $Cu(s) + Cl_2(g) \longrightarrow CuCl_2(s)$
   (e) $2Hg(l) + O_2(g) \longrightarrow 2HgO(s)$
   (f) $Fe(s) + S(s) \longrightarrow FeS(s)$
3. *(a)* $Ca(s) + 2H_2O(l) \longrightarrow H_2(g) + Ca(OH)_2(aq)$
   (b) $Fe(s) + 2HCl(aq) \longrightarrow H_2(g) + FeCl_2(aq)$
   (c) $2Fe(s) + 3Cl_2(g) \longrightarrow 2FeCl_3(s)$
   (d) $2Al(s) + 3Cl_2(g) \longrightarrow 2AlCl_3(s)$
   (e) $Zn(s) + H_2O(g) \longrightarrow ZnO(s) + H_2(g)$
   (f) $4Na(s) + O_2(g) \longrightarrow 2Na_2O(s)$
4. *(a)* $FeSO_4(aq) + 2NaOH(aq) \longrightarrow Fe(OH)_2(s) + Na_2SO_4(aq)$
   $Fe^{2+}(aq) + 2OH^-(aq) \longrightarrow Fe(OH)_2(s)$
   (b) $AgNO_3(aq) + NaBr(aq) \longrightarrow AgBr(s) + NaNO_3(aq)$
   $Ag^+(aq) + Br^-(aq) \longrightarrow AgBr(s)$
   (c) $Pb(NO_3)_2(aq) + 2NaI(aq) \longrightarrow PbI_2(s) + 2NaNO_3(aq)$
   $Pb^{2+}(aq) + 2I^-(aq) \longrightarrow PbI_2(s)$

Checkpoint 3.5: Relative molecular mass

1. 40, 74.5, 40, 74, 63, 123.5, 80, 159.5, 146

Checkpoint 3.6: The Avogadro constant

1. £ 150 million million
   The answer is obtained from $6 \times 10^{23}/4 \times 10^{12}$
2. *(a)* 1 mol = 39 g (b) 1300 g : 39 g × $2 \times 10^{25}/6 \times 10^{23}$
3. 2.7×10^{-7} p:
   £8.20 is the price of 1 g of gold
   = 1/198 mol gold = $6 \times 10^{23}/198$ atoms of gold.
   The price of 10^{12} atoms of gold is
   £$(8.20 \times 10^{12}/6 \times 10^{23}) \times 198 = 2.7 \times 10^{-7}$ p

Checkpoint 3.7: The mole

1. *(a)* 72 g *(b)* 8 g *(c)* 16 g *(d)* 8 g *(e)* 64 g
2. *(a)* 0.33 mol *(b)* 0.25 mol *(c)* 2.0 mol *(d)* 0.010 mol *(e)* 0.33 mol
3. *(a)* 88 g *(b)* 980 g *(c)* 117 g *(d)* 37 g
4. *(a)* 482 g mol^{-1} *(b)* 342 g mol^{-1} *(c)* 368 g mol^{-1}
5. *(a)* 2.5×10^{-3} mol *(b)* 5.00×10^{-2} mol *(c)* 5.40×10^{-2} mol
6. *(a)* 3.0×10^{19} *(b)* 7.5×10^{16} *(c)* 3.0×10^{11}

Checkpoint 3.10: Formulae and percentage composition

The method of finding empirical formulae is given in § 3.8. In (3), remember to subtract to obtain the mass of oxygen in the oxide and the mass of chlorine in each chloride. In (4), the ratio of amount of salt : amount of water is found by dividing the mass of anhydrous salt by its molar mass (120 g mol^{-1} for $MgSO_4$) and the mass of water by its molar mass (18 g mol^{-1}).

1. *(a)* 72% *(b)* 39% *(c)* 80%
2. *(a)* CO_2 *(b)* C_3O_2 *(c)* $Na_2S_2O_3$ *(d)* Na_2SO_4
3. *(a)* MgO *(b)* $CaCl_2$ *(c)* $FeCl_3$
4. $a = 7, b = 2, c = 1/2$

Checkpoint 3.11; Masses of reacting solids

1. 94 tonnes.
   The answer is found by substituting relative atomic masses in $Al_2O_3 \longrightarrow 2Al$.
2. 25.4%
   Since the % of S in $BaSO_4 = 100 \times 32/(137 + 32 + 64)\%$ = 13.7%; mass of S in compound = 0.137 × 0.1852 g and the % of S in the compound can be calculated.
3. 21.0 g, 93%
4. 21.2 g, 96%

Checkpoint 3.12: Reacting volumes of gases

1. 2.80 dm^3 at stp
   The equation:
   $Mg(s) + H_2SO_4(aq) \longrightarrow MgSO_4(aq) + H_2(g)$ shows that 1 mol Mg (24 g) gives 1 mol H_2 (24 dm^3 at rtp).
2. 26.8 g
   The equation shows that 1 mol glucose (180 g) gives 6 mol CO_2 (6 × 24 dm^3 at rtp).
   The mass of glucose reacting must be 180 × 20.0/ (6 × 24) g
3. 26.1 g NaCl, 43.8 g H_2SO_4.
   To give 10.0/ 24.0 mol HCl requires 10.0/24.0 mol NaCl (Mr = 58.5) + 10.0/24.0 mol H_2SO_4 (Mr = 98)

Checkpoint 3. 13 A: Concentration

1. *(a)* 0.20 M *(b)* 0.020 M *(c)* 0.20 M *(d)* 8 M
   The concentration is found from:
   $$\left(\frac{\text{Mass of solute/g}}{\text{Molar mass of solute/g mol}^{-1}}\right) \Big/ \text{Volume of solution/dm}^3 = \text{concentration/mol dm}^{-3}$$
2. *(a)* 10 g *(b)* 0.365 g *(c)* 4.9 g *(d)* 0.14 g
   The amount of solute is found from:
   Amount of solute = Concentration of solution × Volume

Checkpoint 3.13B: Solutions

1. *(a)* For accurate work, Jerry would use a pipette or a burette to measure volumes and a volumetric flask to make up the solution. To dilute by a factor of 10, Jerry would measure 50.0 cm^3 of acid in a burette or a pipette and make it up to the mark in a 500 cm^3 volumetric flask. He could take two 50.0 cm^3 measures and make up to 1000 cm^3 in a volumetric flask. He could take 25.0 cm^3 either in a pipette or in a burette and make up to 250 cm^3 in a volumetric flask.
   (b) For approximate work, a measuring cylinder is sufficiently accurate. Jerry could take 50 cm^3 of acid in a measuring cylinder. He will know that the volume is between 49 cm^3 and 51 cm^3. He can pour into distilled water in a volumetric flask and make up to 500 cm^3. For rough work, he could use a graduated beaker instead of a volumetric flask.
2. The burette would have to be dry before you filled it. If you tried to rinse out water with concentrated acid, heat would be generated (enthalpy of dilution) and this could crack the burette.
   - Any carelessness in filling that resulted in concentrated acid on the outside of the burette would mean acid on your fingers when you handle the tap. Any leakage from the tap would put concentrated acid on your fingers.
   - There would be a loss of hydrogen chloride or sulphur trioxide or nitrogen dioxide etc from the acid solution, which you would inhale.
   - Rinsing out the burette with water after use would generate heat and make hot acid splash out of the burette or crack the burette.
3. *(a)* 6 dm^3 *(b)* 1 dm^3 *(c)* measuring cylinder *(d)* Add the measured volume of acid to distilled water with stirring, make up to 6 dm^3. Approximate volumes will suffice for 2 M bench acid.

For work of this kind the approximate method of dilution would suffice. The technician has to dilute 1.0 dm^3 of concentrated acid to 6.0 dm^3 of bench acid. He or she could take 330 cm^3 of concentrated acid in a measuring cylinder, pour into 1.0 dm^3 of distilled water with stirring, and make up to 2.0 dm^3. He or she would repeat this twice – unless a larger graduated container were available.

4. 140 cm^3
5. *(a)* It can be obtained pure and it is stable in air, e.g. it does not absorb water from the atmosphere while you are weighing it.
   (b) 0.42 g
   (c) Weigh out 0.42 g, dissolve in distilled water in a 500 cm^3 volumetric flask and make up to the mark.
6. *(a)* Measure 62.5 cm^3 of 4.00 M acid in a burette. Dissolve in distilled water and make up to 1.00 dm^3 in a volumetric flask.
   (b) Measure 235 cm^3 of glacial ethanoic acid in a measuring cylinder. Pour gradually into distilled water. Make up to 2 dm^3 in a graduated beaker.

Checkpoint 3.14: Titration

The method for questions 1 and 2 is given in § 3.14, that is, amount of NaOH = amount of HCl.

1. 0.15 M
2. *(a)* 0.25 M *(b)* 10.0 cm^3
3. *(a)* 2 *(b)* 0.24 M
   From the equation:
   $Na_2CO_3(aq) + 2HCl(aq) \longrightarrow 2NaCl(aq) + CO_2(g) + H_2O(l)$
   1 mol Na_2CO_3 is neutralised by 2 mol HCl and amount of HCl = 2 × amount of Na_2CO_3
4. *(a)* The ratio (volume of acid neutralised/price) is highest for Stopit.
   (b) One would consider taste, whether the tablet could be chewed, swallowed or dissolved in water and how quickly it acted.
5. Since amount of NaOH = amount of $H^+(aq)$, the concentration of hydrogen ion in the water is 1.0×10^{-5} mol dm^{-3}.
6. 98.9%.
   The amount of HCl used in the titration is given by
   Amount of solute = Volume of solution × Concentration
   This is equal to the amount of NaOH in 25.0 cm^3 of solution, which gives the amount of NaOH in 1.00 dm^3 of solution. From this the mass of pure NaOH can be found since

   Mass = Amount × Molar mass

   The percentage purity = (mass of pure NaOH/5.00 g) × 100%
7. $n = 10$.
   From the equation:

   $Na_2CO_3(aq) + 2HCl(aq) \longrightarrow 2NaCl(aq) + CO_2(g) + H_2O(l)$

   1 mol of Na_2CO_3 requires 2 mol of HCl.
   The amount of HCl used in titration can be found since

   Amount of Na_2CO_3 = 1/2 × Amount of HCl

   This is the amount of Na_2CO_3 in 25.0 cm^3 of solution and gives the amount and thence the mass of Na_2CO_3 in 1.00 dm^3 of solution. The difference between the mass of crystals and the mass of Na_2CO_3 gives the mass of water in the crystals. n is the ratio (amount of water/amount of Na_2CO_3).
8. Amount of HCl = $44.1 \times 10^{-3} \times 0.100$ mol = 4.41×10^{-3} mol
   Amount of NH_3 = 4.41×10^{-3} mol
   Amount of $(NH_4)_2SO_4$ = 2.205×10^{-3} mol
   Mass of $(NH_4)_2SO_4$ = 132 g mol^{-1} × 2.205×10^{-3} mol = 0.291 g
   % = 100 × 0.291/0.500 = 58.2%

Checkpoint 3.15: Redox reactions

1. *(a)* $Sn^{2+}(aq) \longrightarrow Sn^{4+}(aq) + 2e^-$
   (b) $2Cl^-(aq) \longrightarrow Cl_2(aq) + 2e^-$
   (c) $H_2S(aq) \longrightarrow S(s) + 2H^+(aq) + 2e^-$
   (d) $SO_3^{2-}(aq) + H_2O(l) \longrightarrow SO_4^{2-}(aq) + 2H^+(aq) + 2e^-$
   (e) $H_2O_2(aq) \longrightarrow O_2(g) + 2H^+(aq) + 2e^-$
2. *(a)* $Br_2(aq) + 2e^- \longrightarrow 2Br^-(aq)$
   (b) $MnO_2(s) + 4H^+(aq) + 2e^- \longrightarrow Mn^{2+}(aq) + 2H_2O(l)$
   (c) $PbO_2(s) + 4H^+(aq) + 2e^- \longrightarrow Pb^{2+}(aq) + 2H_2O(l)$
   (d) $2IO^-(aq) + 4H^+(aq) + 2e^- \longrightarrow I_2(aq) + 2H_2O(l)$
   (e) $2ClO_3^-(aq) + 12H^+(aq) + 10e^- \longrightarrow Cl_2(aq) + 6H_2O(l)$
3. *(a)* $2Fe^{3+}(aq) + 2I^-(aq) \longrightarrow 2Fe^{2+}(aq) + Sn^{4+}(aq)$
   (b) $2Fe^{3+}(aq) + Sn^{2+}(aq) \longrightarrow 2Fe^{2+}(aq) + I_2(aq)$
   (c) $2MnO_4^-(aq) + 16H^+(aq) + 10Cl^-(aq) \longrightarrow$ $2Mn^{2+}(aq) + 8H_2O(l) + 5Cl_2(aq)$
   (d) $2MnO_4^-(aq) + 16H^+(aq) + 5H_2O_2(aq) \longrightarrow$ $2Mn^{2+}(aq) + 8H_2O(l) + 5O_2(aq)$
   (e) $2MnO_4^-(aq) + 16H^+(aq) + 10I^-(aq) \longrightarrow$ $2Mn^{2+}(aq) + 8H_2O(l) + 5I_2(aq)$
   (f) $Cr_2O_7^{2-}(aq) + 14H^+(aq) + 6I^-(aq) \longrightarrow$ $2Cr^{3+}(aq) + 7H_2O(l) + 3I_2(aq)$
   (g) $Cr_2O_7^{2-}(aq) + 14H^+(aq) + 6Fe^{2+}(aq) \longrightarrow$ $2Cr^{3+}(aq) + 7H_2O(l) + 6Fe^{3+}(aq)$
   (h) $2MnO_4^-(aq) + 16H^+(aq) + 5Sn^{2+}(aq) \longrightarrow$ $2Mn^{2+}(aq) + 8H_2O(l) + 5Sn^{4+}(aq)$
   (i) $Cr_2O_7^{2-}(aq) + 8H^+(aq) + 3SO_3^{2-}(aq) + 3H_2O(l) \longrightarrow$ $2Cr^{3+}(aq) + 7H_2O(l) + 3SO_4^{2-}(aq)$
   (j) $2MnO_4^-(aq) + 6H^+(aq) + 5SO_3^{2-}(aq) \longrightarrow$ $2Mn^{2+}(aq) + 3H_2O(l) + 5SO_4^{2-}(aq)$
   (k) $MnO_4^-(aq) + 8H^+(aq) + 5Fe^{2+}(aq) \longrightarrow$ $Mn^{2+}(aq) + 4H_2O(l) + 5Fe^{3+}(aq)$
   (l) $Cr_2O_7^{2-}(aq) + 14H^+(aq) + 3Sn^{2+}(aq) \longrightarrow$ $2Cr^{3+}(aq) + 7H_2O(l) + 3Sn^{4+}(aq)$
   (m) $PbO_2(s) + 4H^+(aq) + 4Cl^-(aq) \longrightarrow$ $PbCl_2(aq) + 2H_2O(l) + Cl_2(g)$
   (n) $ClO_3^-(aq) + 4H^+(aq) + 4I^-(aq) \longrightarrow$ $ClO^-(aq) + 2H_2O(l) + 2I_2(aq)$
   (o) $Br_2(aq) + 2I^-(aq) \longrightarrow 2Br^-(aq) + I_2(aq)$
   (p) $2Cl_2(aq) + IO^-(aq) + 2H_2O(l) \longrightarrow$ $4Cl^-(aq) + IO_3^-(aq) + 4H^+(aq)$
   (q) $Br_2(aq) + H_2S(aq) \longrightarrow S(s) + 2Br^-(aq) + 2H^+(aq)$

Checkpoint 3.16A: Oxidation number

1. 0, +1, 0, +2, +1, 0, 0, 0, −3, −1, 0, +1, 0, −1
2. +2, +1, −2, +4, +6, +2, +4, +3, +6, +2, +4, +5
3. *(a)* +2, +4, +4, +1, +3, +5, +5
   (b) +2, +3, +4, +7, +6
   (c) +3, +3, +5, +3
   (d) +6, +6, +6
   (e) −1, +1, +5, 0, +3, +1

Checkpoint 3.16 B: Equations and oxidation numbers

1. *(a)* Change in ox. no. of Mn = +7 to +2 = −5
   Change in ox. no. of Fe = +2 to +3 = +1
   Therefore $5Fe^{2+}$ can be oxidised by one MnO_4^-. Adding $8H^+$ to combine with the 4O in MnO_4^- gives
   $MnO_4^-(aq) + 8H^+(aq) + 5Fe^{2+}(aq) \longrightarrow$ $Mn^{2+}(aq) + 5Fe^{3+}(aq) + 4H_2O(l)$
   (b) Change in ox. no. of Sn = +7 to +2 = −5
   Change in ox. no. of N = +2 to +3 = +1
   Therefore $4HNO_3$ oxidise 1 Sn.
   $Sn(s) + 4HNO_3(aq) \longrightarrow SnO_2(s) + 4NO_2(g) + 2H_2O(l)$
   (c) Change in ox. no. of Cu = +2 to +1 = −1
   Change in ox. no. of I = −1 to 0 = +1
   Therefore 1 Cu^{2+} oxidises 1 I^-.
   $2Cu^{2+}(aq) + 2I^-(aq) \longrightarrow 2Cu(s) + I_2(aq)$
   (d) Change in ox. no. of Cl = 0 to −1 = +1
   This is disproportionation, and $Cl_2 \longrightarrow Cl^- + ClO^-$
   $Cl_2(aq) + 2OH^-(aq) \longrightarrow Cl^-(aq) + ClO^-(aq) + H_2O(l)$

(*e*) Change in ox. no. of Zn = 0 to +2 = +2
Change in ox. no. of Fe = +3 to +2 = −1
Therefore $2Fe^{3+}$ oxidise 1 Zn.
$Zn(s) + 2Fe^{3+}(aq) \longrightarrow Zn^{2+}(aq) + 2Fe^{2+}(aq)$

(*f*) Change in ox. no. of I = 0 to −1 = −1
Change in ox. no. of S = +2 to +2.5 = +0.5
Therefore 1 I oxidises $1S_2O_3^{2-}$.
$I_2(aq) + 2S_2O_3^{2-}(aq) \longrightarrow 2I^-(aq) + S_4O_6^{2-}(aq)$

2. $ICl_3 + 3KI \longrightarrow 2I_2 + 3KCl$; +3
3. (*a*) −2, −1, −2, 0 (*b*) 0, +5, +2, +2 (*c*) +2, +6, +3, +3
(*d*) +2, 0, +2.5, −1 (*e*) +5, −1, −1, −1, +1, −1 (*f*) +6, +6
The species with an increase in oxidation number have been oxidised.
(*a*) $H_2O_2(aq + 2I^-(aq) + 2H^+(aq) \longrightarrow I_2(aq) + 2H_2O(l)$
(*b*) $3Cu(s) + 2NO_3^-(aq) + 8H^+(aq) \longrightarrow 3Cu^{2+}(aq) + 2NO(g) + 4H_2O(l)$
(*c*) $Fe^{2+}(aq) + Cr_2O_7^{2-}(aq) + 14H^+(aq) \longrightarrow Fe^{3+}(aq) + 2Cr^{3+}(aq) + 7H_2O(l)$
(*d*) $2S_2O_3^{2-}(aq) + I_2(aq) \longrightarrow S_4O_6^{2-}(aq) + 2I^-(aq)$
(*e*) $KIO_3(aq) + 2KI(aq) + 6HCl(aq) \longrightarrow 3KCl(aq) + 3ICl(aq) + 3H_2O(l)$
(*f*) $2CrO_4^{2-}(aq) + 2H^+(aq) \longrightarrow Cr_2O_7^{2-}(aq) + H_2O(l)$

Checkpoint 3.18: Redox titrations

1. 96%.
The equation is

$$Cr_2O_7^{2-}(aq) + 14H^+(aq) + 6Fe^{2+}(aq) \longrightarrow 2Cr^{3+}(aq) + 7H_2O(l) + 6Fe^{3+}(aq)$$

From the amount of $Cr_2O_7^{2-}$ used in titration, the amount of Fe^{2+} can be found and hence the mass of Fe in the iron wire and the % purity.

2. 5.50×10^{-2} mol dm^{-3}, 30.8 cm^3 O_2
From the equation:

$$MnO_4^-(aq) + 6H^+(aq) + H_2O_2(aq) \longrightarrow Mn^{2+}(aq) + O_2(g) + 4H_2O(l)$$

one can calculate the amount of MnO_4^- required. The amount of H_2O_2 is equal to this amount and from it the concentration of H_2O_2 can be found.
Amount of O_2 = Amount of H_2O_2 = Amount of MnO_4^-.

3. 95.0%
The equation is:

$$2S_2O_3^{2-}(aq) + I_2(aq) \longrightarrow 2I^-(aq) + S_4O_6^{2-}(aq)$$

The amount of thiosulphate used in titrating the excess of iodine is calculated. The excess of iodine is half this amount. The amount of iodine added to the sample of thiosulphate is calculated. By subtraction, the amount of iodine used by the thiosulphate is obtained. This gives the amount of thiosulphate in the sample and the % purity of the sample.

4. 60.0 cm^3
The equations are:

$$MnO_4^-(aq) + 8H^+(aq) + 5Fe^{2+}(aq) \longrightarrow Mn^{2+}(aq) + 5Fe^{3+}(aq) + 4H_2O(l)$$
$$2MnO_4^-(aq) + 16H^+(aq) + 5C_2O_4^{2-}(aq) \longrightarrow 2Mn^{2+}(aq) + 10CO_2(g) + 8H_2O(l)$$

and by addition:

$$3MnO_4^-(aq) + 24H^+(aq) + 5FeC_2O_4(aq) \longrightarrow 3Mn^{2+}(aq) + 5Fe^{3+}(aq)\ 10CO_2(g) + 12H_2O(l)$$

The amount of iron(II) ethanedioate can be calculated. The amount of MnO_4^- = 3/5 × this amount. Since
Volume of solution = Amount of solute/Concentration,
the volume of solution can be calculated.

Checkpoint 3.20: Equilibrium

1. When NaOH is added, it reacts with the acids on the RHS of the equilibrium and displaces the equilibrium from left to right. As a result the brown colour of bromine decreases. Addition of a little acid reverses the change.
2. (*a*) Addition of water displaces the equilibrium from left to right. The white colour of BiOCl becomes visible.
(*b*) Adding a little concentrated hydrochloric acid drives the equilibrium from right to left.

Questions on Chapter 3

1. (*a*) An equation which shows the relationship between the amounts of products and reactants in a chemical reaction; see § 3.11.
(*b*) Oxidation is the acceptance of electrons from another substance.
(*c*) Reduction is the donation of electrons to another substance; see § 3.15.1.
(*d*) Part of a substance is oxidised while part is reduced; see § 3.16.2.
2. (*a*) Zn is oxidised to Zn^{2+}; H^+ is reduced to H.
(*b*) Cl_2 is reduced; H is oxidised.
(*c*) In $NH_4^+NO_3^- \longrightarrow N_2O$
(+3) (+5) (+1)
disproportionation occurs.
(*d*) I in IO_3^- is reduced from ox. no. +5 to ox. no. 0 in I_2.
I^- is oxidised from ox. no. −1 to ox. no. 0 in I_2.
(*e*) Cr retains ox. no. +6 throughout.
(*f*) Cu disproportionates from ox. no. +1 in Cu^+ to ox. no. 0 in Cu and ox. no. +2 in Cu^{2+}.
3. 30.0 cm^3
From the equation

$$2NaOH(aq) + H_2SO_4(aq) \longrightarrow Na_2SO_4(aq) + 2H_2O(l)$$

Amount of NaOH = 2 × Amount of H_2SO_4
The volume can be found from

Volume = Amount of solute/Concentration

4. (*a*) In a system at equilibrium, no change in the properties is occurring; see § 3.20.
(*b*) In dynamic equilibrium, the system is in motion.
5. 20.0%
First the amount of sulphuric acid used in titration is calculated.

$$2NH_3(aq) + H_2SO_4(aq) \longrightarrow (NH_4)_2SO_4(aq)$$

From this the amount of ammonia in 25.0 cm^3 of solution is calculated and hence the amount of ammonia in 500 cm^3 of solution. From the amount follows the mass of NH_3 in a 25.0 g measure of household ammonia and hence the percentage.

6. 20.1%
The amount of thiosulphate in the titration is calculated:

$$I_2(aq) + 2S_2O_3^{2-}(aq) \longrightarrow 2I^-(aq) + S_4O_6^{2-}(aq)$$

The amount of iodine is half this amount and is equal to the amount of arsenic. Thus the mass of arsenic can be found and hence the percentage of arsenic.

7. (*a*) $SO_3^{2-}(aq) + H_2O(l) \longrightarrow SO_4^{2-}(aq) + 2H^+(aq) + 2e^-$ Oxidation
(*b*) $Cr_2O_7^{2-}(aq) + 14H^+(aq) + 6e^- \longrightarrow 2Cr^{3+}(aq) + 7H_2O(l)$ Reduction
(*c*) $I_2(aq) + 2e^- \longrightarrow 2I^-(aq)$ Reduction
(*d*) $2S_2O_3^{2-}(aq) \longrightarrow S_4O_6^{2-}(aq) + 2e^-$ Oxidation
(*e*) $Fe^{2+}(aq) \longrightarrow Fe^{3+}(aq) + e^-$ Oxidation
(*f*) $MnO_4^-(aq) + 8H^+(aq) + 5e^- \longrightarrow Mn^{2+}(aq) + 4H_2O(l)$ Reduction

8. *(a)* $2S_2O_3^{2-}(aq) + I_2(aq) \longrightarrow S_4O_6^{2-}(aq) + 2I^-(aq)$
(b) $2MnO_4^-(aq) + 5SO_3^{2-}(aq) \longrightarrow 2Mn^{2+}(aq) + 5SO_4^{2-}(aq)$
(c) $6Fe^{2+}(aq) + Cr_2O_7^{2-}(aq) \longrightarrow 6Fe^{3+}(aq) + 2Cr^{3+}(aq)$

9. *(a)* 3.20×10^8 mol *(b)* 3.20×10^8 mol
(c) 7.7×10^9 dm^3 SO_2
(d) Gypsum is used in the manufacture of cement and of plaster of Paris and in the manufacture of the fertiliser ammonium sulphate.

10. *(a)* Both: in the first Cu^{2+} is reduced and I^- is oxidised, in the second I_2 is reduced and $S_2O_3^{2-}$ is oxidised.
(b) starch solution
(c) (i) 3.0×10^{-3} mol (ii) 1.5×10^{-3} mol
(iii) 1.905 g (3.0×10^{-2} mol) (iv) 95%

11. *(a)* to remove copper
(b) acidic
(c) a change from colourless to pink
(d) $Sn^{2+}(aq) \longrightarrow Sn^{4+}(aq) + 2e^-$
$MnO_4^-(aq) + 8H^+(aq) + 5e^- \longrightarrow Mn^{2+}(aq) + 4H_2O(l)$
(e) $2MnO_4^-(aq) + 16H^+(aq) + 5Sn^{2+}(aq) \longrightarrow 2Mn^{2+}(aq) + 5Sn^{4+}(aq) + 8H_2O(l)$
(f) 12.0%

12. *(a)* $Na \longrightarrow Na^+ + e^-$; $\Delta H = +500$ kJ mol^{-1}
(b) (i) ionic (ii) basic
(iii) $Na_2O(s) + H_2O(l) \longrightarrow 2NaOH(aq)$
(c) (i) -1
(ii) $Na_2O_2(s) + H_2SO_4(aq) \longrightarrow H_2O_2(aq) + Na_2SO_4(aq)$
(d) Amount of $H_2O_2 = 20.0 \times 10^{-3} \times 0.100 = 2.00 \times 10^{-3}$ mol
Amount of $Cr_2O_7^{2-} = 6.66 \times 10^{-4}$ mol
$M = 14.7/294 = 0.0500$ mol dm^{-3}
$V = (6.66 \times 10^{-4}/0.0500)$ dm^3 = 13.3 cm^3
(e) (i) $Ni(OH)_2(s)$ (ii) $[Ni(NH_3)_6]^{2+}(aq)$
(iii) $Ni(OH)_2(s) + 4NH_3(aq) \longrightarrow [Ni(NH_3)_4]^{2+}(aq) + 2OH^-(aq)$
(iv) displacement

13. *(a)* see metallic bond; § 6.3
(b) Ag: 92.5/107.87 = 0.858 and Cu: 7.5/63.54 = 0.118
% = 87.9% Ag and 12.1% Cu
(c) (i) $AgNO_3(aq) + NaCl(aq) \longrightarrow AgCl(s) + NaNO_3(aq)$
(ii) Mass of Ag = (107.868 × 1.519)/(107.868 + 35.453) = 1.14325 g
% Ag = 91.8%

14. *(a)* See § 3.6
(b) 24 g Mg $\longrightarrow$ 33.33 g Mg_3N_2 = 0.3333 mol Mg_3N_2 and 3 mol Mg $\longrightarrow$ 1 mol Mg_3N_2
(c) (i) $2Mg(s) + O_2(g) \longrightarrow 2MgO(s)$
$3Mg(s) + N_2(g) \longrightarrow Mg_3N_2(s)$
(d) (i) Mass of Mg = 6.00 g and mass of product = 9.50 g therefore 1 mol Mg (24 g) $\longrightarrow$ 38.0 g product
(ii) Let a = mass of MgO and $(38 - a)$ = mass of Mg_3N_2.
1 mol Mg $\longrightarrow$ a mol MgO + 1/3 $(1 - a)$ mol Mg_3N_2
24 g Mg $\longrightarrow$ $a \times 40$ g MgO + 1/3 $(1 - a) \times 100$ g Mg_3N_2 = 38.0 g
$40a + 33.3 - 33.3a = 38.0$ and $a = 0.70$ mol
Mass of MgO = 0.70 × 40 = 28.0 g
Mass of Mg_3N_2 = 38.0–28.0 = 10.0 g
(iii) Amount of MgO/ Amount of Mg_3N_2 = 0.70/0.30 = 2.3
(iv) N_2 is less reactive than O_2

15. *(a)* (i) It loses electrons. (ii) +4 and +6
(iii) $SO_2(g) + 2H_2O(l) \longrightarrow SO_4^{2-}(aq) + 4H^+(aq) + 2e^-$
(iv) $MnO_4^-(aq) + 8H^+(aq) + 5e^- \longrightarrow Mn^{2+}(aq) + 4H_2O(l)$
(b) Amount of $KMnO_4 = 100 \times 10^{-3} \times 0.01 = 1.0 \times 10^{-3}$ mol $KMnO_4$
Amount of $SO_2 = (5/2) \times 1.0 \times 10^{-3} = 2.5 \times 10^{-3}$ mol
Mass of $SO_2 = 2.5 \times 10^{-3} \times 64 \times 2 = 0.32$ g m^{-3}

16. *(a)* (i) N has ox. state −3 in NH_3, 0 in N_2; therefore NH_3 is oxidised
Cl has ox. state 0 in Cl_2, −1 in HCl; therefore Cl is reduced.
(ii) Cu has ox. state +2 in CuO, +2 in $CuCl_2$ therefore it is neither oxidised nor reduced. Cl has ox. state −1 in HCl and −1 in $CuCl_2$; therefore it is neither oxidised nor reduced.
(b) (i) $MnO_4^- + 8H^+ + 5e^- \longrightarrow Mn^{2+} + 4H_2O$
$C_2O_4^{2-} \longrightarrow 2CO_2 + 2e^-$
$2MnO_4^- + 16H^+ + 5C_2O_4^{2-} \longrightarrow 2Mn^{2+} + 8H_2O + 10CO_2$
(ii) Amount of $MnO_4^- = 30.4 \times 10^{-3} \times 0.200$ mol = 6.08×10^{-4} mol
Amount of $C_2O_4^{2-}$ in 25.0 cm^3 = $(5/2) \times 6.08 \times 10^{-4} = 15.20 \times 10^{-4}$ mol
Mass of $C_2O_4^{2-}$ in 250 cm^3 = 1.338 g and % = 69.3%

17. *(a)* (i) Mass spectrometry; see § 1.9
(ii) same number of protons, different number of neutrons
(iii) (121 × 0.5725) + (123 × 0.4275) = 121.9
(b) (i) +3
(ii) 2 mol $Sb_2S_3 \longrightarrow$ 1 mol $Sb_4O_6 \longrightarrow$ 3 mol CO_2
10 mol $Sb_2S_3 \longrightarrow$ 15 mol CO_2 = 360 dm^3 CO_2

18. *(a)* (i) (Ox. no. of N) + 3(−2) = −1: Ox. no. of N = +5
(ii) (Ox. no. of N) + 2(−2) = −1: Ox. no. of N = +3
(b) KNO_3 (M_r = 101) $\longrightarrow$ KNO_2 (M_r = 85)
therefore 1.55 g $KNO_3 \longrightarrow$ 1.304 g KNO_2
(c) (i) Amount of $MnO_4^- = 28.9 \times 10^{-3} \times 0.0150 = 4.335 \times 10^{-4}$ mol
(ii) $10 \times 4.335 \times 10^{-4} \times 5/2 = 0.010\ 84$ mol
(iii) 85 × 0.010 84 = 0.9214 g
(iv) (0.9214/1.304) × 100 = 70.7%

19. *(a)* (i) $HCO_3^-(aq) + H_2O(l) \rightleftharpoons CO_3^{2-}(aq) + H_3O^+(aq)$
(ii) $HCO_3^-(aq) + H_3O^+(aq) \longrightarrow CO_2(g) + 2H_2O(l)$
(b) (i) 58 g $Mg(OH)_2$ need 2 mol HCl(aq)
1.00 g $Mg(OH)_2$ needs 3.448×10^{-2} mol HCl
$V = (3.448 \times 10^{-2}/0.100)$ dm^3 = 345 cm^3

20. *(a)* reducing agent
(b) sulphuric acid (HCl is oxidised by MnO_4^-)
(c) purple to pale pink
(d) Amount of $KMnO_4 = 18.1 \times 10^{-3} \times 0.0200$ mol $= 3.62 \times 10^{-4}$ mol
Amount of $H_2O_2 = (5/2) \times 3.62 \times 10^{-4}$ mol = 9.05×10^{-4} mol
$[H_2O_2] = (9.05 \times 10^{-4})/25.0 \times 10^{-3} = 0.0362$ mol dm^{-3}

21. *(a)* Amount of thiosulphate = $40.0 \times 10^{-3} \times 0.0500$ mol = 2.00×10^{-3} mol
(b) $I_2(aq) + 2S_2O_3^{2-}(aq) \longrightarrow 2I^-(aq) + S_4O_6^{2-}(aq)$
(c) Amount of $I_2 = 1.00 \times 10^{-3}$ mol
(d) Amount of $Cu^{2+} = 20.0 \times 10^{-3} \times 0.100$ mol = 2.00×10^{-3} mol
(e) $2Cu^{2+} \longrightarrow I_2$
$2Cu^{2+}(aq) + 2I^-(aq) \longrightarrow 2Cu^+(aq) + I_2(aq)$
For I^- change in ox. no. = 2(−1) to 0 = +2
For Cu^{2+}, change in ox. no. = 2(+2) to 2(+1) = −2

CHAPTER 4: THE CHEMICAL BOND

Checkpoint 4.2: Electrical conductors

1 *(a)* (i) distilled water (a poor conductor), aqueous ethanol (a poor conductor), copper, steel, sugar solution (a poor conductor), brass, molten magnesium chloride, sodium hydroxide solution, silver
(ii) solid wax, molten wax, ethanol, wood, sodium chloride crystals, sugar crystals, tetrachloromethane, poly(ethene), solid sodium hydroxide, PVC, petrol
(b) $MgCl_2$, NaOH, NaCl

2. See § 4.2.3 for explanations.

3. *(a)* Electrostatic attraction draws positive ions towards the negative electrode and negative ions towards the positive electrode; see Figure 4.2B.
(b) In a solid, the ions are not free to move.

4. • Copper(II) compounds contain Cu^{2+} ions which are blue.
- Dichromates(VI) contain $Cr_2O_7^{2-}$ ions which are orange.
- When the solute is ionic, the solution contains ions, which are free to move. Positive ions move to the negative electrodes, where they accept electrons, and negative ions move towards the positive electrodes, where they give electrons, thus causing a stream of electrons to flow from the positive electrode to the negative electrode through the external circuit.
- Copper ions are positively charged. They move to the negative electrode, where they accept electrons to form copper atoms.
- Chloride ions are negatively charged. They move to the positive electrode, where they give electrons to become chlorine atoms which join to form chlorine molecules.
- Salts consist of regular three-dimensional arrangements of ions.

Checkpoint 4.3A: Bonding in ionic compounds

1. *(a)* *(b)*

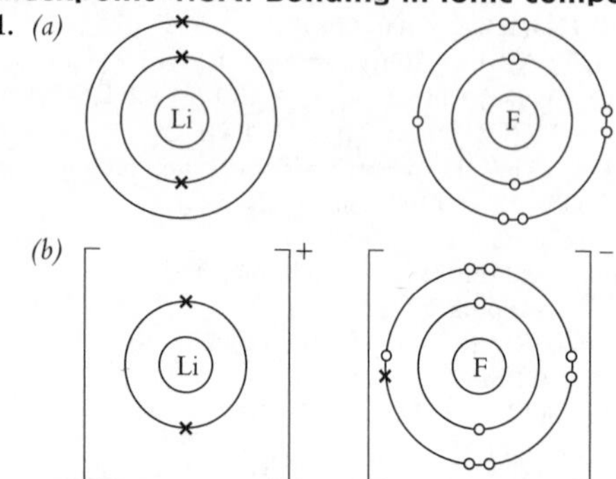

2. Sodium atoms have the electron configuration $Na(1s^22s^22p^63s)$.
Sodium ions have the electron configuration $Na^+(1s^22s^22p^6)$.
Chlorine atoms have the electron configuration $Cl(1s^22s^22p^63s^23p^5)$.
Chloride ions have the electron configuration $Cl^-(1s^22s^22p^63s^23p^6)$.

3.

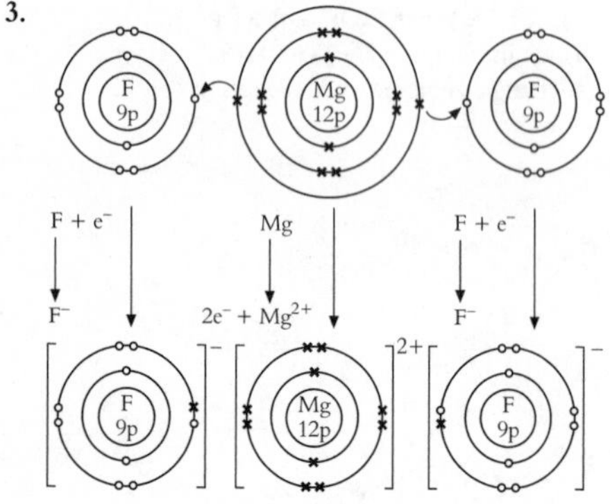

4. *(a)* *(b)* *(c)* *(d)* *(e)*

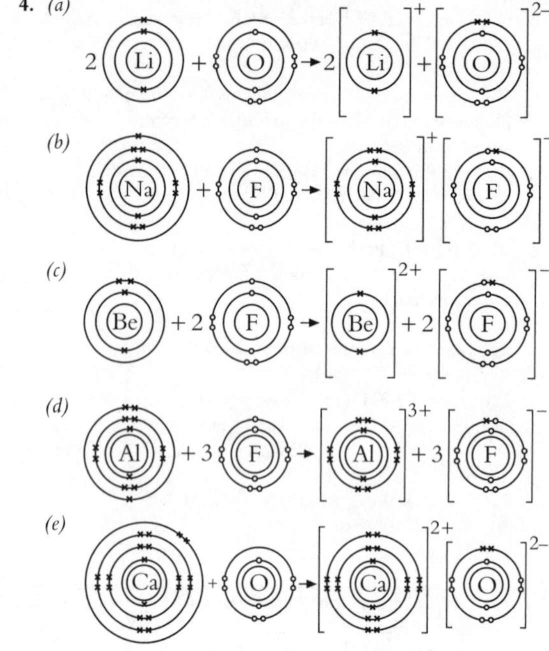

5. *(a)* The charge and the mass (Na^+ 11 u, Ne 10 u)
(b) The charge and the mass (Cl^- 17 u, Ar 18 u)

6. Gp 2, Gp 3, Gp 2, Gp 7, Gp 5, Gp 6, Gp 1, Gp 2

Checkpoint 4.3 B: Formulae of ionic compounds

1. *(a)* AgCl *(b)* KNO_3 *(c)* $AgNO_3$ *(d)* $ZnBr_2$ *(e)* MgI_2 *(f)* $CuBr_2$ *(g)* NH_4Cl *(h)* $(NH_4)_2SO_4$ *(i)* $Ca(OH)_2$ *(j)* $AlCl_3$ *(k)* $NaHCO_3$ *(l)* Na_2SO_3 *(m)* $Fe(OH)_2$ *(n)* $Fe(OH)_3$ *(o)* Al_2O_3.

2. *(a)* aluminium iodide *(b)* copper(II) carbonate *(c)* zinc hydroxide *(d)* silver bromide *(e)* copper(II) nitrate *(f)* iron(II) bromide *(g)* iron(III) bromide *(h)* aluminium oxide *(i)* potassium manganate(VII) *(j)* sodium silicate *(k)* trisodium phosphate(V) *(l)* potassium nitrite *(m)* potassium dichromate(VI) *(n)* calcium phosphate *(o)* sodium sulphite *(p)* barium sulphite *(q)* calcium hydrogencarbonate

Checkpoint 4.3C: Ions

1. *(a)* Mg_3N_2 *(b)* AlF_3 *(c)* Al_2S_3 *(d)* FeO *(e)* Fe_2O_3 *(f)* $Co_2(SO_4)_3$ *(g)* $Ni(NO_3)_2$

2. $Li^+(1s^2)$ (He)
$N^{3-}(1s^22s^22p^6)$ (Ne)
Be^{2+} $(1s^2)$ (He)
K^+ $(1s^22s^22p^63s^23p^6)$ (Ar)
S^{2-} $(1s^22s^22p^63s^23p^6)$ (Ar)

3. Mn^{2+} $(1s^22s^22p^63s^23p^63d^5)$
Cu^+ $(1s^22s^22p^63s^23p^63d^{10})$
Cu^{2+} $(1s^22s^22p^63s^23p^63d^9)$
Zn^{2+} $(1s^22s^22p^63s^23p^63d^{10})$

Checkpoint 4.4: Bonding in covalent compounds

1.

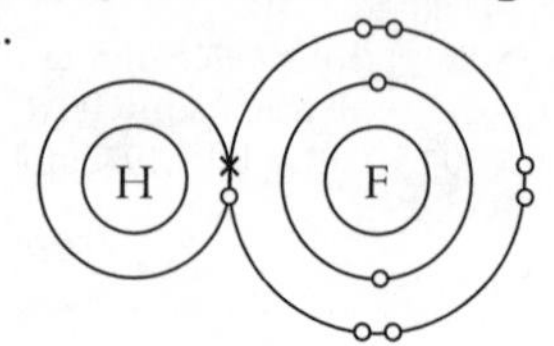

2.

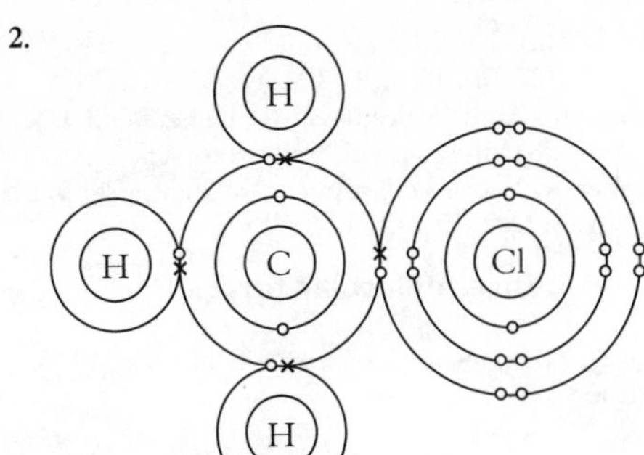

3.

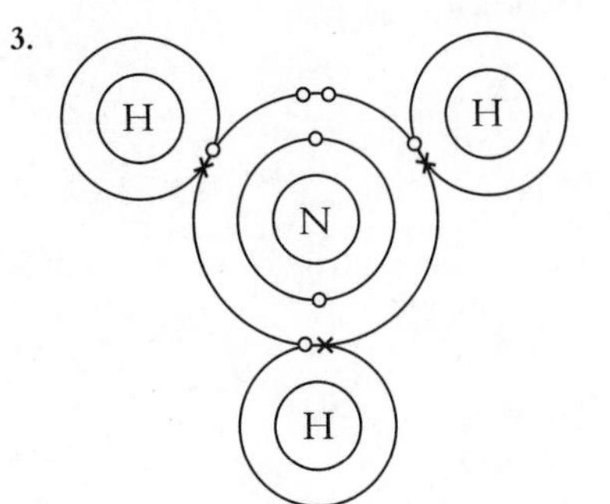

4.

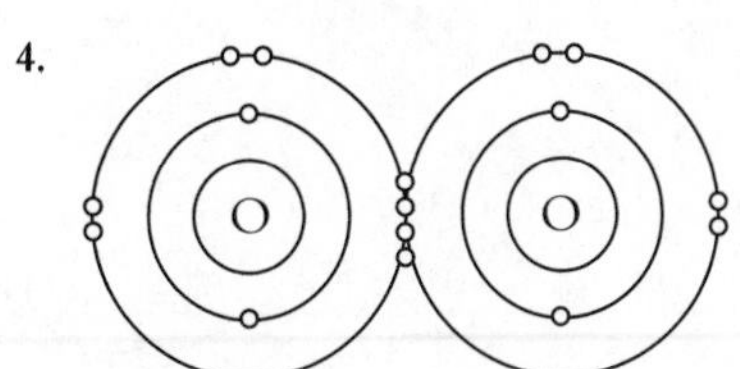

5.

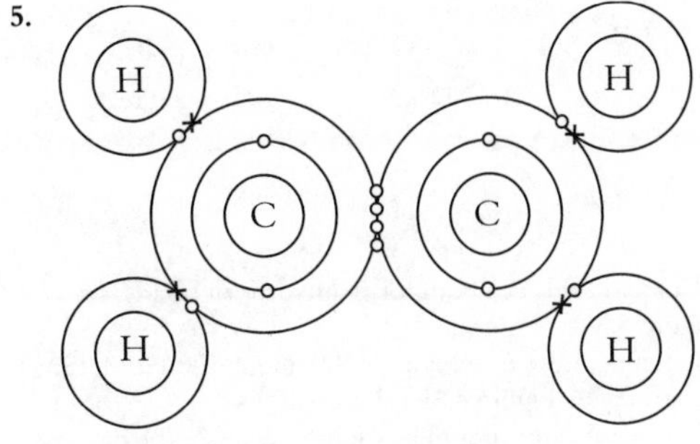

Checkpoint 4.5: Chemical bonds

1. When the elements are widely separated in the Periodic Table they form ionic bonds.
(a) ionic *(b)* ionic *(c)* ionic *(d)* ionic *(e)* covalent *(f)* covalent *(g)* covalent
2. The substances could be elements or compounds – ionic or covalent (molecular or macromolecular).
A could be a non-metallic element or a covalent compound.
B is probably an ionic compound because it has a high melting temperature.
C could be a non-metallic element or a covalent compound. The high melting temperature indicates a covalent macromolecular compound.
D could be a molecular covalent compound or a covalent polymer or a non-metallic element.
E could be a non-metallic element or a molecular covalent compound.

Checkpoint 4.6: The covalent bond

In these diagrams the bonding electrons are shown, but the inner orbitals have been omitted.

1. *(a)*

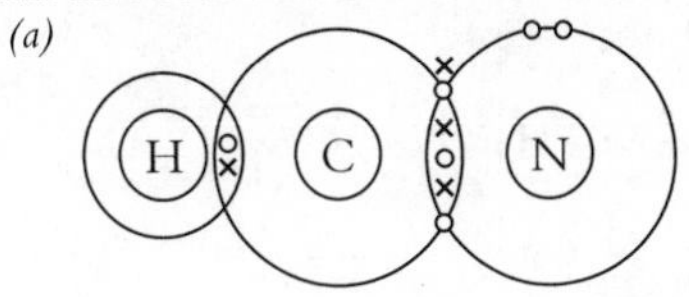

(b)

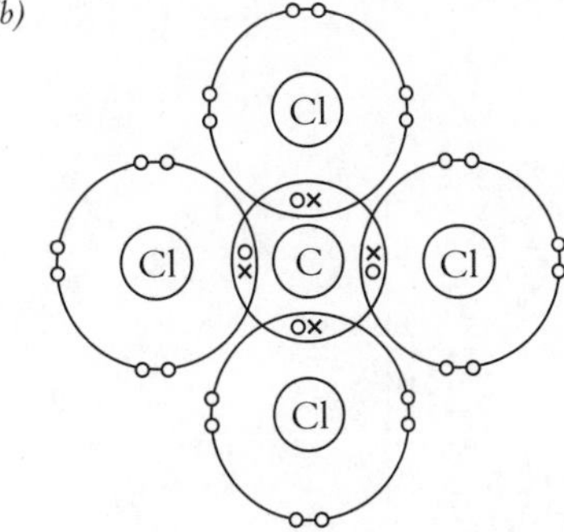

(c)

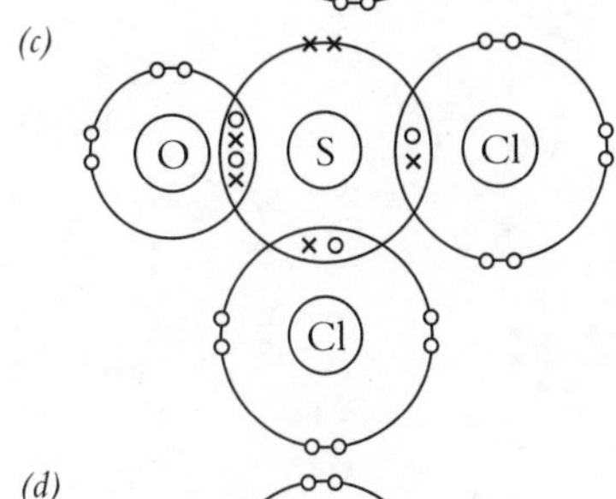

(d)

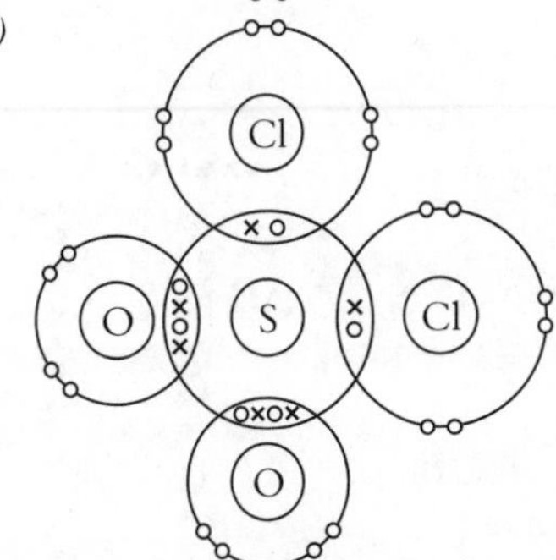

2. *(a)* There are covalent bonds between C and H and between C and Cl. The compound does not readily dissociate: the intramolecular bonds are strong. The compound is volatile: molecules can escape from the intermolecular forces of attraction into the vapour phase.
3. Strong forces of electrostatic attraction between the ions make it difficult to split off ions from the solid structure – to melt the solid. The dipole–dipole interactions between $C^{\delta+}$—$Cl^{\delta-}$ bonds in neighbouring molecules are much weaker.

Checkpoint 4.7: The coordinate bond

1. The electron configuration of Cu^{2+} is (Ar)$3d^9$. Four electron pairs from $4H_2O$ are coordinated into the valence shell. They can be accommodated in four $4sp^3$ hybrid orbitals. The bonding electrons are shown differently from the examples in Checkpoint 4.6. Both representations are correct.
2. The electron configuration of Fe is (Ar)$3d^6 4s^2$, and that of Fe^{3+} is (Ar)$3d^5$. Fe^{3+} in the complex ion has five electrons in the 3d orbitals. These can occupy three of the five d orbitals and leave two empty 3d orbitals to combine with one 4s and three 4p orbitals to form six d^2sp^3 hybrid orbitals. These can accommodate six pairs of electrons from $6H_2O$.

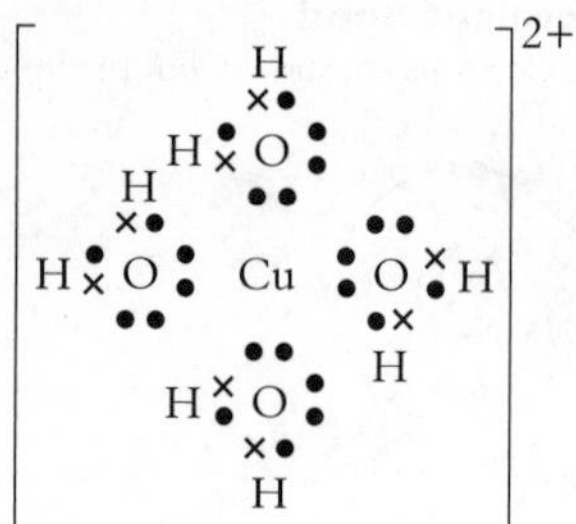

$[Cu(H_2O)_4]^{2+}$

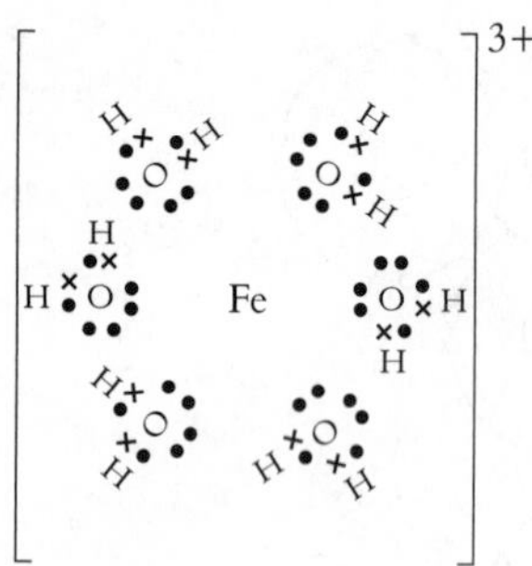

$[Fe(H_2O)_6]^{3+}$

3.

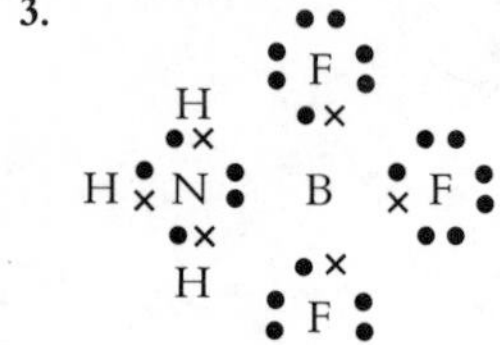

4.

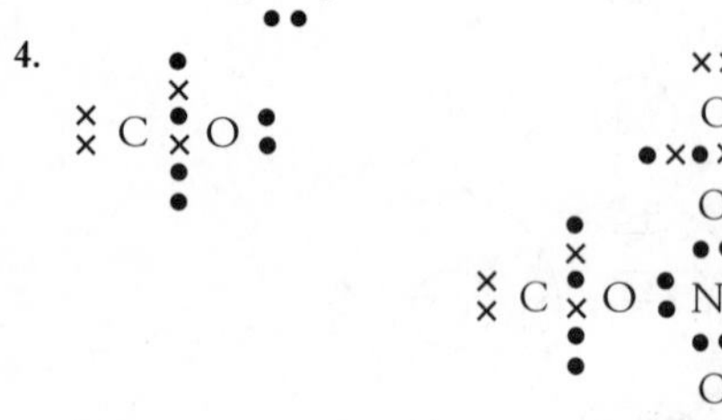

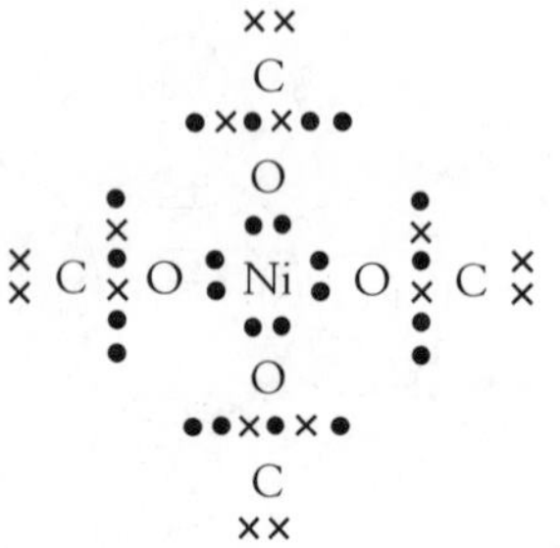

5. The electron configurations are Cu (Ar)$3d^{10}4s$ and Cu^{2+} (Ar)$3d^9$.
N in NH_3 has a lone pair of electrons which it can coordinate to Cu^{2+}. The 4s and the three 4p orbitals of Cu are available to receive the four lone pairs from $4NH_3$.
6. $PbCl_2 + 2Cl^- \longrightarrow [PbCl_4]^{2-}$
Pb has the electron configuration (Xe)$4f^{14}5d^{10}6s^26p^2$, and Pb^{2+} has (Xe)$4f^{14}5d^{10}6s^2$
Four Cl^- can coordinate to occupy 6p orbitals.

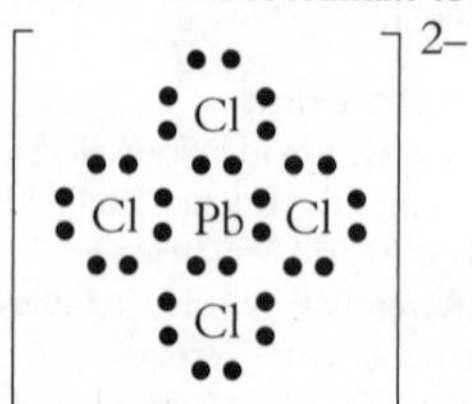

Checkpoint 4.8A: Intermolecular forces I

1. See § 4.8.2.
2. Xenon (atomic number 54) has more electrons than neon (atomic number 10). The more electrons there are in an atom, the further the outermost electrons are removed from the nucleus and the easier they are to polarise; see Figure 4.8B.
3. *(a)* 2, −269 °C (ii) 2, −254 °C
(b) (i) 18, −186 °C (ii) 16, −183 °C
(c) The pair with 18 and 16 electrons have higher boiling temperatures than the pair with 2 electrons. The greater the number of electrons the stronger are the van der Waals forces.

Checkpoint 4.8B: Intermolecular forces II

1. See § 4.8.3.
2. See Figure 4.8J. The evidence is reviewed in §4.8.3, e.g. Figures 4.8E and 4.8F.
3. See §4.8.2.
4. *(a)* dipole–dipole interaction
(b) van der Waals forces
(c) dipole-dipole interaction
(d) hydrogen bonds
5. *(a)*

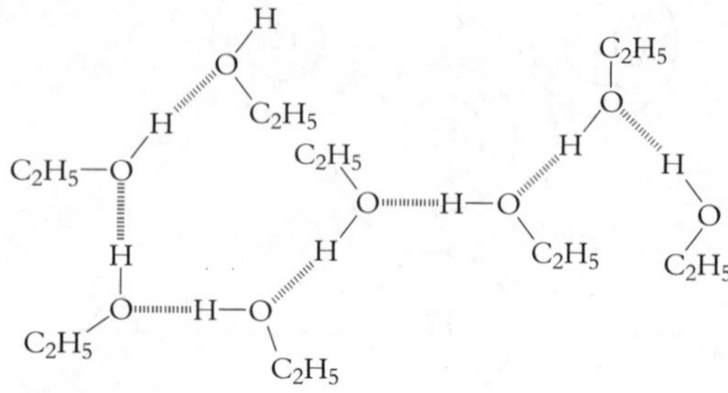

(b) See Figure 4.8I.
(c) See Figure 4.8H.
(d)

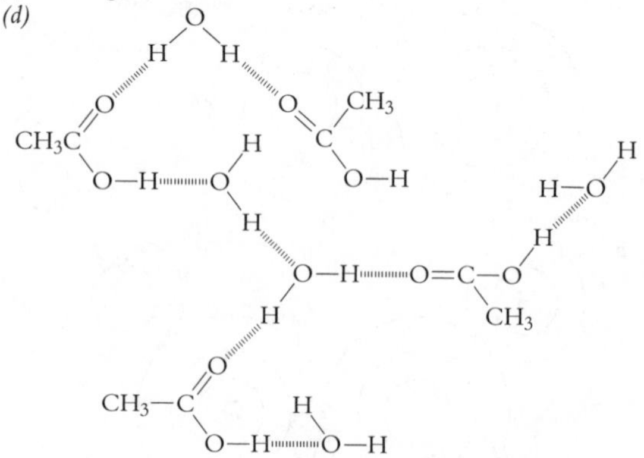

(e) H_2O and NH_3 can both form 4 hydrogen bonds; see Figure 4.8G.
6. Boiling temperature (see Figure 4.8F) about −90°C. Melting temperature [see Figure 4.8E] about −100°C.
The density of water should be slightly less than the density of ice, in the absence of hydrogen bonding.

Questions on Chapter 4

1. The octet theory of valency – the theory that atoms combine in order to achieve an outer octet of electrons – is discussed in § 4.3.1. Successes include NaCl, § 4.3.1, MgF_2, § 4.3.3, MgO, § 4.3.5, and other ionic compounds [see §§ 4.3.6 and 4.3.7], and covalent compounds such as CH_4, § 4.4, CO_2, § 4.4, multiple bonds, e.g. N_2, § 4.4, and coordinate bonds, § 4.7.
Some elements do not have an outer octet of electrons in their compounds, e.g. transition metals.
The octet rule breaks down in a number of cases which include the following.
   1. Compounds with one unpaired electron, e.g. NO_2. The structures

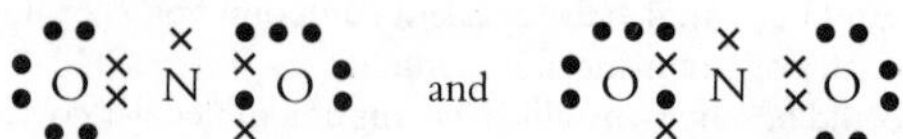

can be represented by the delocalised structure O ═ N ═ O

2. Compounds with atoms which have an incomplete octet, e.g. BF_3 in which B has 6 electrons in its outer shell.

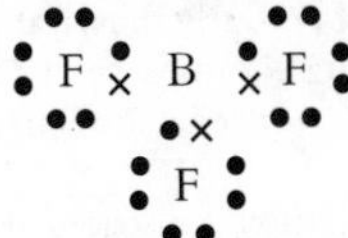

3. Compounds in which atoms have an expanded octet. In the third period the 3d orbitals can be used not only for π–π multiple bonding but also for additional bond formation. Phosphorus ($3s^2 3p^3 3d^0$) can be excited to $3s^1 3p^3 3d^1$ with the intake of a quantity of energy which is small enough to be more than compensated for by the formation of two additional bonds. In PCl_3, P has an octet of electrons; in PCl_5 the octet has expanded to 10 electrons. In SF_6 and SiF_6^{2-} the octet has expanded to 12 electrons.

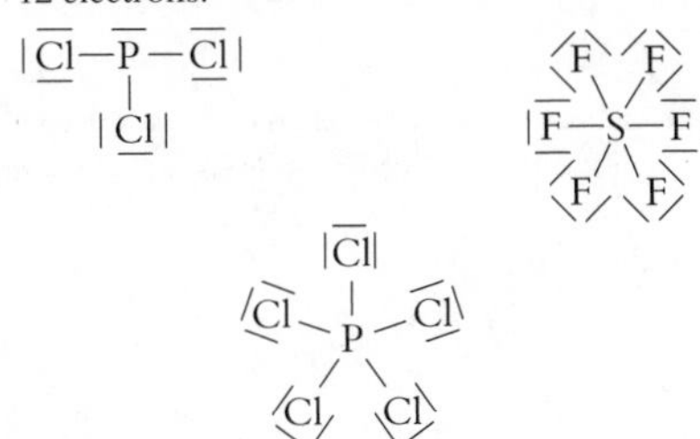

2. *(a)* In NaH, H is an anion.
   $Na(2.8.1) \longrightarrow Na^+(2.8) + e^-$
   $H(1) + e^- \longrightarrow H^-(2)$

   (b) In NH_4^+, N forms 3 covalent bonds to H atoms and a coordinate bond to H^+.

   $NH_3 + H^+ \longrightarrow [NH_4]^+$

   (c) Be in Group 2 has very high first and second ionisation energies because the valence electrons are close to the nucleus. With Cl_2, it forms covalent bonds.

   Cl Be Cl   H F

   (d) HF has covalent bonds.
   Owing to the high electronegativity of fluorine the bond is polar: $H^{\delta+}$—$F^{\delta-}$ and hydrogen bonding occurs (see Figure 4.8D).

   (e) In CCl_4, four covalent bonds are formed.

   The $C^{\delta+}$—$Cl^{\delta-}$ bond is polar, and there is dipole–dipole interaction between molecules, making the compound a liquid at room temperature.

   (f) Copper, like other metals, has metallic bonds; see § 6.3.

3. In N_2, the molecules are non-polar. There are weak van der Waals forces between molecules, and the boiling temperature is very low.
   In $C(CH_3)_4$ van der Waals forces operate between the non-polar covalent molecules, and the boiling temperature is higher than for nitrogen. In the unbranched hydrocarbon $CH_3CH_2CH_2CH_2CH_3$ the van der Waals forces are stronger because the molecules can align themselves with other molecules.
   In C_4H_9OH, hydrogen bonds operate between molecules and this compound therefore has the highest boiling temperature.

4. *(a)* C_3H_8: van der Waals forces are stronger between linear molecules which can align themselves with neighbouring molecules.

   (b) The alcohol: hydrogen bonds are greater in the alcohol than in the amine because oxygen is more electronegative than nitrogen; therefore the $O^{\delta-}$—$H^{\delta+}$ bond is more polar than the $N^{\delta-}$—$H^{\delta+}$ bond.

   (c) The alcohol: its molecules are held together by hydrogen bonds.

   (d) The ketone: the bond $>C^{\delta+}{=}O^{\delta-}$ is polar and gives rise to dipole–dipole interactions between molecules.

5. Water is less dense than ice [see § 4.8.3] and therefore ponds and lakes freeze from the top downwards. Hydrogen bonds maintain the three-dimensional structure of protein molecules and DNA molecules; see § 4.8.

6. *(a)* A

   (b) (i) I The 4s electron in the outermost shell is furthest from the nucleus and easiest to remove. II Electrons closer to the nucleus are progressively more difficult to remove.
   (ii) I The second electron is removed against the attraction of K^+. II 2p III The last electrons are the 1s electrons, close to the nucleus.

   (c) (i) H_2O (ii) CH_4 (iii) H_2O

   (d)

1s	2s	2p	3s	3p	3d	4s
↑↓	↑↓	↑↓ ↑↓ ↑↓	↑↓	↑↓ ↑↓ ↑↓	↑ ↑ ↑ ↑ ↑	

7. *(a)* (i) I. Both A ($1s^2 2s^2 2p^6$) and G ($1s^2 2s^2 2p^6 3s^2 3p^6$) have completed their outer octets, but the outer electrons in G are further from the nucleus and easier to remove than those in A. II. In D the outer electrons are in the 3d shell, further from the nucleus and easier to remove.
   (ii) I. p-orbital; see Figure 2.4 C, II. s-orbital; see Figure 2.4B.
   (iii)

1s	2s	2p	3s	3p	3d	4s
↑↓	↑↓	↑↓ ↑↓ ↑↓	↑↓	↑ ↑		

   (iv) D has a lower ionisation energy than E and forms a cation more easily.

   (b) (i) For mass spectrometry see § 1.9.
   (ii) D: $(^{35}Cl^{37}Cl)^+$, E: $(^{37}Cl^{37}Cl)^+$.

   (c) (i) I see §§ 4.6.3, 4.8.1, 4.8.2 II see § 4.6.3 and Figure 4.6D
   (ii) see §§ 4.6.3, 4.8.1
   (iii) Li—H +0.9, C—O +1.0, B—C + 0.5

8. *(a)* Mg with 2 valence electrons forms a stronger metallic bond than Na, with only one valence electron.

   (b) covalent, macromolecular

   (c) 1000 °C

   (d) Chlorine consists of individual Cl_2 molecules with negligible forces between them. Sulphur consists of S_8 molecules with van der Waals forces between them.

   (e) 400 K. The atoms are larger, with more electrons, and the metallic bond is therefore stronger.

9. *(a)* (i) Let % of B = x.
   Then $[10(x/100)] + [11(100 - x)/100] = 10.81$ and $x = 19\%$
   (ii) One line at $m/z = 10$ and height 19 and one line at $m/z = 11$ and height 81

   (b) X = B, $a = 5$, $b = 12$

   (c) (i)

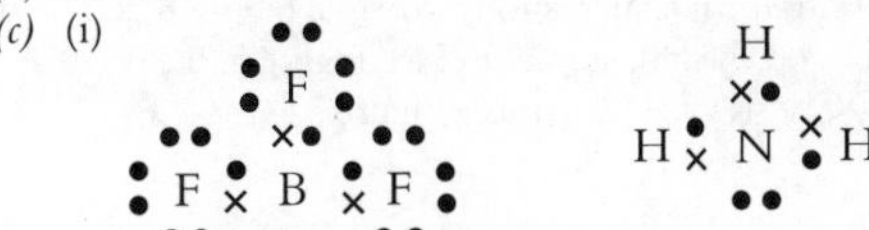

(ii) The lone pair of N forms a coordinate bond to complete the octet of B.

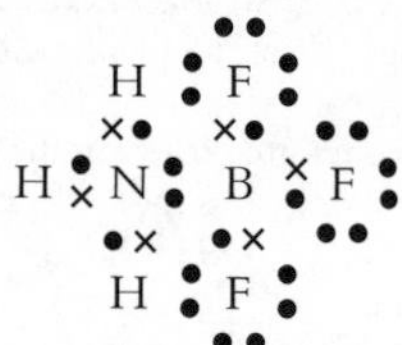

(d) (i) I, II see § 6.6.

(ii)

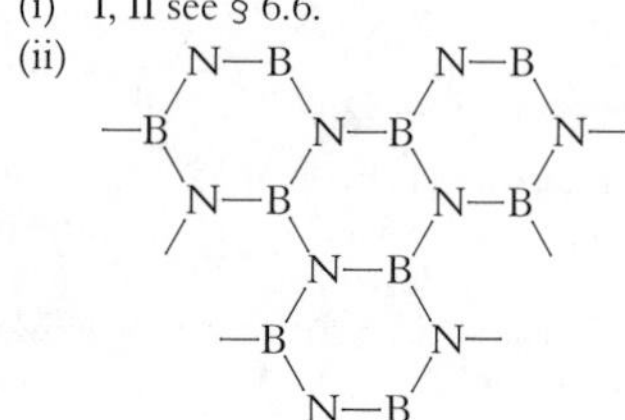

10. *(a)* (i) In NaCl, the electron density is greater round the nucleus of Na^+ than round the nucleus of Cl^-. The electron cloud of Cl^- is not perfectly spherical; it is drawn towards neighbouring Na^+ ions. In H_2^+, the electron density is distributed evenly between the two H nuclei.

(ii) In molecules the electron density is distributed symmetrically – or in some cases only approximately symmetrically – between the bonded atoms. In ions the electron density is greater in the region surrounding the nucleus of the positive ion.

(iii)

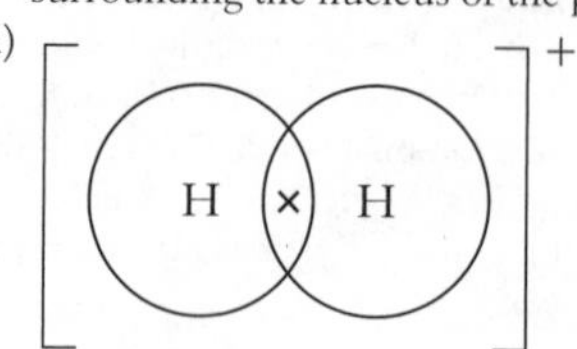

(b) (i) delocalisation; see § 5.4.1

(ii) The electron density between each carbon atom and its neighbour is the same. There is no evidence for the Kekulé formula:

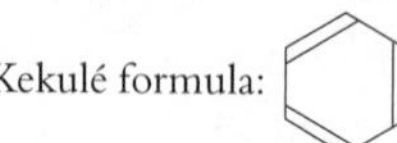

CHAPTER 5: THE SHAPES OF MOLECULES

Checkpoint 5.2: Shapes of molecules

1. *(a)* coplanar *(b)* similar to Figure 5.2G; tetrahedral
2. Three electron pairs give a trigonal planar arrangement similar to BCl_3, Figure 5.2B
3. Br has 7 electrons in the outer shell, three forming covalent bonds in BrF_3, leaving 2 lone pairs. The arrangement of electron pairs is a trigonal bipyramid, as in Figure 5.2L
4. The arrangement of bonds in H—O—Br resembles that in H—O—H, Figure 5.2F. *(a)* The orbitals are as shown in Figure 5.2G. *(b)* The molecule is a bent line.
5. The bonds are tetrahedrally distributed as shown in Figure 5.2J for CHBrClF. The dipoles cancel to give a zero dipole.
6. Xe uses 4 electrons in bond formation and has 2 lone pairs. The arrangement of the 6 electron pairs is octahedral, as in ICl_4, Figure 5.2L, and the molecule is square planar, as in Figure 16.1.
7. *(a)* Sn has 4 electrons in the outer shell and forms four covalent bonds with 4 Cl atoms. To minimise repulsion between the electron clouds, the angle between the bonds is the maximum, 109.5°, the tetrahedral angle; see Figure 5.2F.
   (b) P, with 5 electrons in the outer shell, forms 3 covalent bonds to 3H atoms and has one lone pair of electrons. The arrangement of bonds is tetrahedral, the shape of the molecule similar to NH_3 in Figure 5.2F.
   (c) P in PF_5 forms 5 covalent bonds in a trigonal bipyramidal arrangement similar to IF_5 in Figure 5.2L.
   (d) B has 3 electrons in its outer shell and forms 3 covalent bonds in a trigonal planar arrangement, similar to BCl_3 in Figure 5.2A
   (e) Be with 2 electrons in its outer shell forms 2 covalent bonds. The molecule BeH_2 is linear, similar to $BeCl_2$ in Figure 5.2A.
8. *(a)* F_2O: similar to H_2O, Figure 5.2F
   (b) $SeCl_4$: similar to SF_4, Figure 5.2L
   (c) SO_3: trigonal planar, similar to SO_2, Figure 5.2C
   (d) PF_6^-: octahedral, similar to SF_6, Figure 5.2L
   (e) $COCl_2$: trigonal planar; see Figure 5.2C

Checkpoint 5.3: Bonding

1. AsH_3 – like NH_3; PH_4^+ – like NH_4^+; H_3O^+ – like NH_3; CS_2 – linear; $CH_2{=}C{=}CH_2$, linear, similar to ethene, Figure 5.3G,
   H—C≡N linear
2. CH_4 tetrahedral, BF_3 planar, NF_3 tetrahedral, ICl_4^-, see Figure 5.2L; BrO_3^- tetrahedral, similar to SO_3^{2-}, Figure 5.2H; ClO_4^- tetrahedral; $CHCl_3$ tetrahedral
3. O_2 NO_3^- CO_2 CN^-

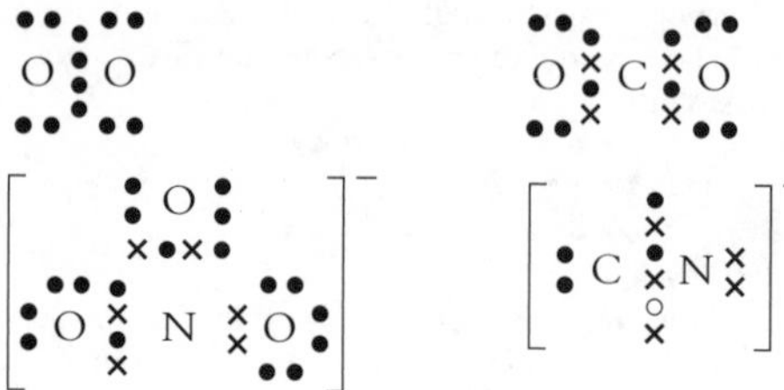

4. The CO_2 molecule is linear so the $\overset{\delta-}{O}{=}\overset{\delta+}{C}{=}\overset{\delta-}{O}$ dipoles cancel.
   In H_2O the $\overset{\delta+}{H}—\overset{\delta-}{O}—H^{\delta+}$ dipoles do not cancel because the molecule is bent.
5. NH_3 NH_4^+ Cl^- H_2O H_2O_2 SiH_4 HOCl

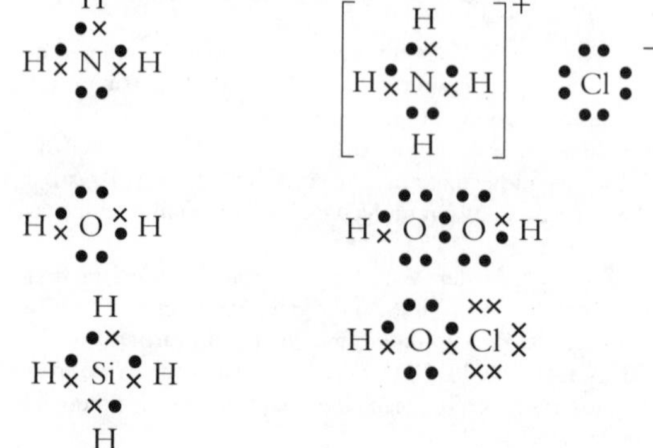

6. CH_4 and NH_4^+ have the same number of electrons. Differences in chemical properties arise from the charge on NH_4^+ and the difference in electronegativity between C and N.
7. Similar to ethene; *cis*- and *trans*-isomers

Checkpoint 5.4: Hybrid bonds

1. Stereochemistry: there are no isomers of CH_2XY, but there are isomers of CHXYZ.
2. See § 5.4 first paragraph.
3. See § 5.3.2 and Figure 5.3E.
4. See § 28.2 for the Kekulé structure. Superseded because of X-ray work [§§ 28.1, 28.2] and thermodynamics – delocalisation energy; see § 5.4.1.

Questions on Chapter 5

1. See § 5.2. These molecules are shown in the section. The distribution of bonding pairs and lone pairs places them as far apart as possible to minimise repulsion between them.
2. See Figures 5.2A, 5.2F and 5.2L. In H_2O the bond angle is 105° because repulsion between the lone pair orbitals is greater than repulsion between bonding orbitals.
3. *(a)* For NH_3 see Figure 5.2 F.
   (b) for H_2O see Figure 5.2F.
   (c) for $CH_2 = CH_2$ see Figures 5.2 C and 5.3G
   (d) I_3^- linear

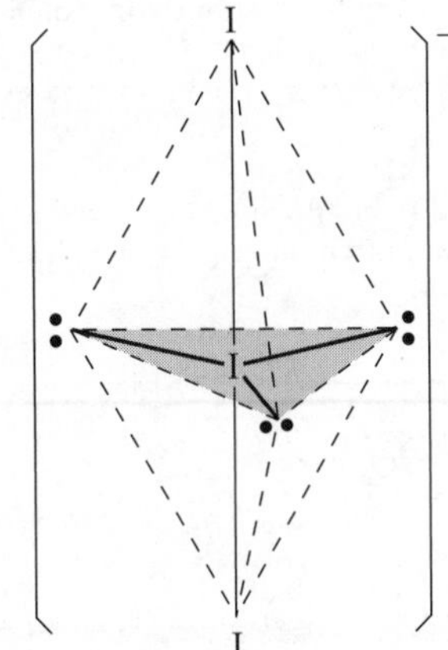

   (e) SF_6, see Figure 5.2L.
4. *(a)* See § 5.2.
   (b) F_2O similar to H_2O, Figure 5.2F; H_3O^+ similar to NH_3, Figure 5.2F; ClF_4^- similar to ICl_4^-, Figure 5.2L.
5. *(a)* For the stereoisomers see Figure 5.2J.
   (b) BF_3: sp^2 hybrid bonds and trigonal planar molecule
   NH_3: sp^3 hybrid bonds are tetrahedrally distributed, and the molecule is a trigonal pyramid.
   (c) XeF_4: 4 bonds and 2 lone pairs give an octahedral distribution of bonds and a planar molecule, similar to ICl_4^- in Figure 5.2L.
   CCl_4: sp^3 hybrid bonds give a tetrahedral molecule.
   (d) Repulsion between lone pairs > repulsion between bonding orbitals. The difference is greater in oxygen than in nitrogen.
6. *(a)* (i) BF_3 planar (like BCl_3 [Figure 5.2B]), CH_4 tetrahedral [Figure 5.2F], SF_6 octahedral [Figure 5.2L]
   (ii) Repulsion between lone pairs > repulsion between bonding pairs; see § 5.2.3.
   (iii) $BeCl_2$ linear [Figure 5.2 A], BF_5 octahedral (like IF_5, Figure 5.2 L)
   (b) (i) T_m increases with the size of the molecules because, with more electrons, there are stronger attractions between temporarily induced dipoles; see § 4.8.1.
   (ii) Hydrogen bonding between H_2O molecules raises T_m.
   (c) There are δ+ H atoms bonded to electronegative N and S atoms. There are δ– O atoms in >C=O groups to bond to δ+ H atoms.
7. *(a)* NaCl, $MgCl_2$, $AlCl_3$, PCl_3, PCl_5, SCl_2, SCl_4, SCl_6
   (b) $SiCl_4$, 16.5%
   (c) (i)

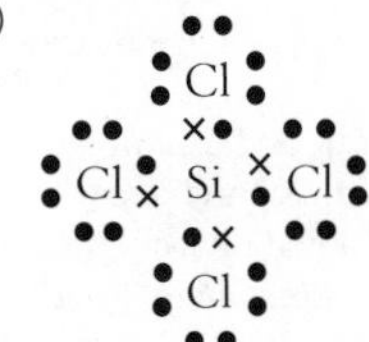

   (ii) tetrahedral; see § 5.2 for valence shell electron pair repulsion theory
   (iii) planar, similar to BCl_3, Figure 5.2B (also exists as the dimer Al_2Cl_6 with a tetrahedral arrangement of bonds round each Al).
   (d) (i) $SiCl_4(l) + H_2O(l) \longrightarrow Si(OH)_4(s) + 4HCl(g)$
   (ii) No reaction because C in CCl_4 has a full octet, and there are no empty orbitals for electron pairs from H_2O to coordinate into; see § 23.5.2.
8. *(a)* Ne: 10p, 10n, 10e
   Na^+: 11p, 12n, 10e
   S^{2-}: 16p, 16n, 18e
   α particle 2p, 2n
   (b) (i) I A is a noble gas with the very stable electron configuration 2.8. II D has one electron more than A and easily loses one electron to acquire a noble gas electron configuration.
   (ii) I p orbital; see Figure 2.4 C; II s orbital: see Figure 2.4B
   (iii)

1s	2s	2p	3s	3p	3d	4s
↑↓	↑↓	↑↓ ↑↓ ↑↓	↑↓	↑ ↑ ☐	☐☐☐☐☐	☐

   (iv) D because D^+ has a noble gas electron configuration
   (c) (i) true (ii) true
   (d) (i) 2 bonding pairs < 1 lone pair + 1 bonding pair < 2 lone pairs
   (ii) Lone pairs are closer to the nucleus and therefore closer to each other and repulsion is stronger.
   (e) (i) I. opposite charges separated by a short distance; see § 4.8
   II. a covalent bond in which the electron density is greater at one end of the bond than at the other, e.g. $—O^{\delta-}—H^{\delta+}$; see § 4.6.3
   (ii) I. The low T_b is due to the weak forces of attraction between molecules.
   II. N is more electronegative than P therefore the $—N^{\delta-}—H^{\delta+}$ bond is more polar and the dipole–dipole attractions between molecules are stronger.
9. *(a)* a covalent bond in which the electron density is greater at one end of the bond than at the other, e.g. $—O^{\delta-}—H^{\delta+}$; see § 4.6.3
   (b) a bond between atoms of different electronegativity
   (c) A large anion can be polarised by a small cation, especially a multiply charged cation; see § 4.6.4
   (d) Electron density is not spherically symmetrical in a polarised anion.
   (e) (i) $BeCl_2$ [see Figure 5.2A]; NCl_3 similar to NH_3 in Figure 5.2F; SF_6 [see Figure 5.2L]
   (ii) NCl_3 because N has a lone pair of electrons which can coordinate to H^+.

CHAPTER 6: CHEMICAL BONDING AND THE STRUCTURE OF SOLIDS

Checkpoint 6.7: Covalent structures

1. *(a)* There are weak bonds between layers of covalently bonded atoms; see Figure 6.7A.
   (b) The sliding of one layer of atoms over another gives a lubricating action.
   (c) All the atoms are covalently bonded in a macromolecular structure; see Figure 6.6A.
   (d) See § 6.6 for diamond (cutting and drilling) and § 6.7 for graphite (lubricant and electrical conductor).
2. Gaseous iodine consists of individual molecules with negligible forces of attraction between them. Solid iodine consists of covalently bonded I_2 molecules held in a molecular structure by van der Waals forces; see Figure 6.5B.
3. *(a)* They are molecular solids which melt or sublime at room temperature. Both are hard solids.
   (b) Solid CO_2 can be used down to a lower temperature and it leaves no residue because it sublimes.
   (c) Water vapour in the air is cooled as solid 'dry ice' takes the enthalpy of vaporisation from the air and condenses.
4. Diamond should have the higher density because the distances between layers of carbon atoms in graphite are greater than the bond length. See §§ 6.6, 6.7 for properties.
5. The electrons in diamond are in bonding orbitals located between the bonded atoms. In graphite 3 electrons from each carbon atom form covalent bonds in localised orbitals, and the fourth is delocalised: it occupies an orbital spread over the layer of bonded carbon atoms. The delocalised electrons are responsible for the electrical conductivity of graphite and for its shine.
6. The structure resembles Figure 6.6A but has alternate Si and C atoms. It is hard, like diamond. In graphite each carbon atom forms two sp^2 hybrid bonds to two other carbon atoms. The fourth electron forms a π-bond between carbon atoms, and electrons in the π-orbitals are delocalised. Silicon cannot form π-bonds; this ability is restricted to the small atoms of carbon, nitrogen and oxygen; see § 5.2.2.
7. Boron forms 3 bonds to N atoms. Each N atom forms 3 bonds to B atoms and has also a lone pair, which becomes delocalised.

Checkpoint 6.8: Metallic structures

1. All the atoms in the piece of metal are bonded together as described in § 6.3.
2. See § 6.3.
3. *(a)* In a close-packed structure the space between atoms is minimal; see § 6.8.
   (b) If each atom in a structure is in contact with 8 others its coordination number is 8.

Questions on Chapter 6

1. *(a)* van der Waals forces
   (b) van der Waals forces
   (c) sp^3 hybrid bonds
   (d) sp^2 hybrid bonds and π-bonds
   (e) Silicon forms four sp^3 hybrid bonds. Oxygen forms two sp^3 hybrid bonds.
2. For the metallic bond see § 6.3 and Figure 6.3A; for ionic solids see § 6.4 and Figure 6.4C.
3. The number of ions with which it is in contact; see also § 6.4.
   (a) 6 *(b)* 8
   The Cs^+ ion is larger than Na^+ and more Cl^- ions can surround it.
4. *(a)* See 6.3.
   (b) See § 6.4: electrolytes, high melting temperature, fracture easily
   (c) § 6.5: gases or liquids or low melting temperature solids, non-electrolytes
   (d) § 6.6: solids, hard, high melting temperature, non-electrolytes
5. NaCl: ionic; see § 6.4
   Na: metallic; see § 6.3
   PCl_5: molecular covalent; see § 6.5
   graphite: macromolecular covalent; see § 6.7
   ice: covalent molecules joined by hydrogen bonds; see § 4.8.3, Figure 4.8J
6. *(a)* See § 6.4 *(b)* See § 6.5 *(c)* See §§ 6.6, 6.7
   A quantity of energy *a* is required to break off ions or molecules from the solid, and a quantity of energy *b* is released when the ions or molecules are hydrated. If $b > a$, the substance will dissolve.
7. NaCl: see § 6.4, Figure 6.4A
   ice: see § 4.8.3, Figure 4.8 J
   poly(ethene); see §§ 4.4.3, Figure 4.4 J and 27.8.10
   aluminium; see § 6.3
   iodine; see § 4.4.3 and Figure 4.4I
8. *(a)* (i) See § 6.6. (ii) See § 6.7. (iii) See § 6.3.
   (b) (i) diamond, see § 6.6 and Figure 6.6A; graphite, see § 6.7, Figure 6.7A
   (ii) Copper has more valence electrons than sodium and can form stronger metallic bonds.
   (iii) All metals are good electrical conductors; see § 6.3.
9. *(a)*, *(b)* See §6. 4.
   (c) The ratio (radius of Cs^+/ radius of Cl^-) is much greater than the ratio (radius of Na^+/ radius of Cl^-) and more Cl^- ions can be accommodated round one Cs^+ ion than round one Na^+ ion; see § 6.4
10. *(a)* (i)

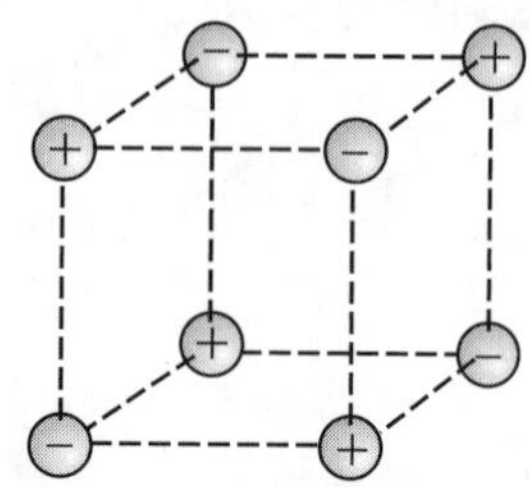

   (ii) 6
   (b) e.g. conducts electricity when in aqueous solution with electrolysis to give $H_2 + Cl_2$
   (c) (i) The bonding pair of electrons come from one of the bonded atoms only; see § 4.8
   (ii)

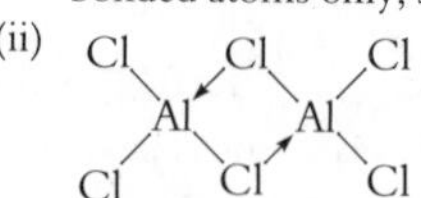

   It is a covalent compound and forces of attraction between molecules are weaker than those between ions in an electrovalent compound.
11. *(a)* Mg, metallic bond; see § 6.3.
   $MgCl_2$: ionic bond; see §§ 6.4, 6.9
   (b) The ionisation energy for $Mg \longrightarrow Mg^{2+} + 2e^-$ is compensated for by the energy given out when $Mg^{2+}(Cl^-)_2$ is formed. The ionisation energy for $Al \longrightarrow Al^{3+} + 3e^-$ is so great that it is not compensated for by the energy given out when $Al^{3+}(Cl^-)_3$ is formed.
   (c) $MgCl_2(s) + aq \longrightarrow Mg^{2+}(aq) + 2Cl^-(aq)$
   H_2O molecules coordinate into the Mg^{2+} ion by means of the lone pairs on the O atom in the H_2O molecule.

PART 2: PHYSICAL CHEMISTRY

CHAPTER 7 GASES

Checkpoint 7.6: Partial pressures

1. 2.5×10^4 N m^{-2}
2. (a) 3.03×10^4 N m^{-2} CO, 5.05×10^4 N m^{-2} O_2, 2.02×10^4 N m^{-2} CO_2
   (b) 3.03×10^4 N m^{-2} CO, 5.05×10^4 N m^{-2} O_2
3. 5.33×10^5 N m^{-2}
4. (a) $p(NH_3) = 1.96 \times 10^4$ N m^{-2}, $p(H_2) = 5.39 \times 10^4$ N m^{-2}; $p(N_2) = 2.45 \times 10^4$ N m^{-2}
   (b) No change

Questions on Chapter 7

1. (a) Molecules of gas are in constant motion and spread out – diffuse – to occupy the whole of a container; see § 7.7.
   (b) Pressure is due to collisions between molecules and the walls of the container; see § 7.7.
   (c) The compressibility of gases is due to the large distances between molecules; see § 7.7.
2. (a) Since PV/T = constant for a fixed mass of an ideal gas [§ 7.5], pressure increases linearly with the temperature in kelvins when the volume is kept constant. As the temperature increases, the kinetic energy of the molecules increases [§ 7.7] and the frequency of collisions with the container – the pressure – increases.
   (b) No, PV is not constant.
3. Since $P = 100 \times 10^3$ Pa, $n = 1$ mol, $T = 300$ K, $R = 8.314$ J K^{-1} mol^{-1} and $PV = nRT$, $V = 24.9$ dm^3 mol^{-1}
4. In a gas, e.g. N_2, the molecules are far apart. In a solid, e.g. NaN_3, the particles are closer together.
5. (a) The volume is halved.
   (b) The volume is increased by a factor of 3.
   (c) The volume increases by a factor of 2.5.
   (d) The volume is decreased by a factor of 4.
6. (a) The pressure doubles.
   (b) The pressure increases by a factor 873/573.
   (c) The pressure increases by a factor of 4.
   (d) The pressure is halved.
7. $V_1 = 60.0$ dm^3, $P_1 = 101$ kPa, $T_1 = 296$ K, $P_2 = 6.70$ kPa, $T_2 = 268$ K
   Since $P_1V_1/T_1 = P_2V_2/T_2$, $V_2 = 819$ dm^3
   No.
8. Amount of $O_2 = \dfrac{1.53 \times 10^{-3}\ \text{dm}^3}{22.4\ \text{dm}^3\,\text{mol}^{-1}} \times \dfrac{273\ \text{K}}{310\ \text{K}} \times \dfrac{0.987}{1.01}$
   $= 5.88 \times 10^{-5}$ mol
   Amount of Hb $= 0.25 \times 5.88 \times 10^{-5}$ mol $= 1.47 \times 10^{-5}$ mol
   Mass of Hb = 1.00 g, therefore M of Hb $= 6.80 \times 10^4$ g mol^{-1}
9. (a) (i) Ratio C 54.5%/12 : H 9.1%/1 : O 36.4%/16 gives C_2H_4O
   (ii) $PV = nRT$
   95.0×10^{-3} Pa $\times 200 \times 10^{-6}$ m^3
   $= (0.539\ \text{g}/M) \times 8.314$ J K^{-1} mol^{-1} $\times 373$ K
   M = 88 g mol^{-1}
   (iii) C_2H_4O has $M = 44$ g mol^{-1}, therefore molecular formula is $C_4H_8O_2$.
   (b) (i) $2C_3H_6O_2 + 7O_2 \longrightarrow 6CO_2 + 6H_2O$
   (ii) 1 mol $C_3H_6O_2$ needs 3.5 mol $O_2 = 3.5 \times 24.0$ dm^3 at rtp = 84.0 dm^3 at rtp

CHAPTER 8 LIQUIDS

Checkpoint 8.2: Liquids

1. (a) The particles in liquids are further apart than in solids but much closer together than in gases.
   (b) Forces of attraction between molecules of a liquid are weaker than in solids but much stronger than those in gases.
2. (a) Heat is absorbed by molecules, giving them enough kinetic energy to break free from the intermolecular forces of attraction between them and other molecules in the liquid and vaporise.
   (b) The change from solid to liquid involves breaking fewer intermolecular bonds than the change from liquid to gas.

Checkpoint 8.3: Vapour pressure

1. (a) See § 8.3.1.
   (b) In order, water < ethanol < ethoxyethane
   (c) (i) Vapour pressure increases with temperature because more molecules have enough energy to break free from the liquid phase.
   (ii) Strong intermolecular forces decrease vapour pressure because they make it difficult for molecules to break free from other molecules in the liquid.
   (iii) The volume of liquid has no effect.
2. A liquid in a beaker can take heat from its surroundings to supply the energy which molecules need to break free of the attraction of other molecules and enter the vapour phase.
   A liquid in an insulated container cannot take heat from its surroundings. As the molecules with highest energy escape from the liquid, the average energy of the remaining molecules falls – the liquid cools.
3. Some substances decompose at their boiling temperatures at atmospheric pressure.

Checkpoint 8.4: Molar mass of volatile liquid

1. See § 8.4. Use the equation
   $pV = nRT = (m/M)RT$
   Don't forget that volume has the unit m^3.
   The value of M obtained is 86 g mol^{-1}. The unit CH_2 has $M = 14$ g mol^{-1}. The multiple of CH_2 that gives a molar mass of approximately 86 g mol^{-1} is $(CH_2)_6$. The value of M is therefore $14 \times 6 = 84$ g mol^{-1}.
2. Use the equation $pV = (m/M)RT$. The value of M obtained is 90 g mol^{-1}.
   The unit CH_2Cl has $M = 49.5$ g mol^{-1}.
   The formula must be $C_2H_4Cl_2$ and the molar mass 99 g mol^{-1}.
3. Use the equation $pV = (m/M)RT$. The value of M obtained is 53 g mol^{-1}. The unit CH_2 has $M = 14$ g mol^{-1}. The formula is $(CH_2)_n$ so $M = 14n = 14 \times 4 = 56$ g mol^{-1}.
4. The same method as above gives 154 g mol^{-1}

Checkpoint 8.5: Raoult's Law

1. Mole fraction of **X** = 1/5
   Mole fraction of **Y** = 4/5
   Partial pressure of **X** = (1/5) × 25 kPa = 5 kPa
   Partial pressure of **Y** = (4/5) × 45 kPa = 36 kPa
   Total = 41 kPa
2. A: $p_A = (2/5) \times 15$ kPa = 6 kPa
   B: $p_B = (3/5) \times 40$ kPa = 24 kPa
   Total = 30 kPa
3. See § 8.5.2, Figures 8.5 C, D and E.
4. svp is > calculated, and T_b is < calculated.

Checkpoint 8.6: Partition

1. See § 8.6.1. If s g is the mass of **S** in ethoxyethane,
$$\frac{s\ \text{g}/100\ \text{cm}^3}{(10.0 - s)\ \text{g}/500\ \text{cm}^3} = 5.0$$
and $s = 5.0$ g.
2. See § 8.6.1. *(a)* 3.57 g *(b)* 4.01 g

Questions on Chapter 8

1. *(a)* The molecules of a liquid are in motion. See § 8.2.
   (b) Molecules of a liquid with kinetic energy above average may break free from the forces of attraction which operate between molecules and escape into the vapour phase; see § 8.3.
2. See your practical work and also §§ 8.7.2–4.
3. *(a)* § 8.6.1.
   (b) §§ 8.7.1, 8.7.2.
4. In an ideal mixture [see § 8.5.1 and Figures 8.5A, B and C] and in a non-ideal mixture which shows small deviation from ideal behaviour, the lower boiling temperature liquid distils over first, and when it has all distilled the second liquid distils.
   In a non-ideal mixture which forms an azeotrope [see § 8.5.4 and Figures 8.5F, and G], one of the components distils until a mixture of a certain composition is reached. This mixture, the azeotropic mixture, distils at a constant boiling temperature until all the liquid mixture has distilled. The liquid which distils first is the one which is in excess of the azeotropic composition.
5. See §§ 8.6, 8.6.1; 3.55 g
6. (a) See § 8.5.1.
   (b) See Figure 8.5A.
   (c) See Figure 8.5B.
7. *(a)* (i) See Figure 8.5 C.
   (ii) See Figure 8.5G(a)
   (b) Intermolecular forces in methanol and ethanol are similar. A positive deviation [see Figure 8.3F(a)] means that the vapour pressure of the mixture is greater than the sum of the partial vapour pressures. Forces of attraction between molecules of cyclohexane and ethanol are smaller than forces of attraction between molecules in the pure components.
8. *(a)* See Figures 8.5F(a) and 8.5G(a).
   (b) A negative deviation means that the vapour pressure of the mixture is less than the sum of the partial vapour pressures of the components. This happens when intermolecular forces of attraction in a mixture of **A** and **B** are greater than those in pure **A** or in pure **B**. When these intermolecular bonds form between molecules of **A** and molecules of **B**, heat is given out and the temperature rises.
9. *(a)* See §§ 8.6, 8.6.1.
   (b) Say that an aqueous solution contains 10 g of a solute. One extraction with an organic solvent dissolves 80% of the solute (8 g). A second extraction will remove 80% of the remainder (1.6 g). A third extraction will remove 80% of the remainder (0.32 g), a total of 9.92 g.
10. Take 25 cm^3 of aqueous ethanoic acid (say 2 M). Add it to 25 cm^3 of 2-methylpropan-1-ol in a separating funnel. Stopper the separating funnel and shake vigorously for 1–2 minutes. Open the tap occasionally to release the pressure. Allow the layers to settle. Separate 20 cm^3 of each layer. Discard the portion near the junction of the two layers. Pipette 10.0 cm^3 of the aqueous layer into a conical flask, and titrate with 0.100 M sodium hydroxide solution, using phenolphthalein as indicator. Pipette 10.0 cm^3 of the alcohol layer and titrate it in the same way.
    Calculate the ratio of [ethanoic acid in alcohol layer]/[ethanoic acid in aqueous layer].
11. *(a)* (i) A horizontal line, since PV = constant.
    (ii) Forces of attraction between molecules become important at high pressure. The volume of the molecules compared with the volume of the container becomes non-negligible at high pressure and low temperature.
    (b) (i) See Figure 8.3B.
    (ii) A liquid boils when svp = atmospheric pressure.
    (iii) At reduced pressure the liquid distils below its T_b and there is less risk of decomposition.
    (c) $PV = nRT$
    $1.01 \times 10^5 \times 153 \times 10^{-6} = n \times 8.314 \times 373$
    $n = 4.98 \times 10^{-3}$
    $M = 0.597/n = 120$
12. *(a)* (i) I. The solid is a structure consisting of individual molecules held together in a regular arrangement by intermolecular forces of attraction.
    II. The intermolecular bonds break. The covalent I-I bonds remain intact.
    (ii) See § 6.2.
    (b) (i) See § 8.2. (ii) See § 8.3.
    (c) 1. $p/4.78\ \text{Pa} = 183/0.3$ therefore $p = 2.92 \times 10^3$ Pa
    2. $PV = nRT$
    $4.78 \times 183 \times 10^{-6} = n \times 8.314 \times 273$
    $n = 3.85 \times 10^{-7}$ mol
13. *(a)* (i) (1) At low pressure the intermolecular forces in the real gas are negligible.
    (2) N_2 is closer to ideal behaviour. In HCl there are dipole-dipole interactions.
    (ii) Partial pressure of $N_2 = 0.20\ \text{Pa} \times 1/4 = 0.05$ Pa
    Partial pressure of $O_2 = 0.40\ \text{Pa} \times 2/4 = 0.20$ Pa
    Total pressure = 0.25 Pa
    (b) dipole–dipole, see § 4.8.1; H bonding, [see § 4.8.3], van der Waals forces, [see § 4.8.2]
    (c) (i) $p_A = 32\ \text{kPa} \times 1/4 = 8$ kPa
    $p_B = 16\ \text{kPa} \times 3/4 = 12$ kPa
    (1) Total vp = 20 kPa
    (2) Mole fraction of A in vapour = 8/20 = 0.4
    (ii) (1) positive. Intermolecular forces of attraction are less than in the individual liquids. Ethanol cannot form hydrogen bonds with methylbenzene.
    (2) positive. Dipole–dipole attractions between the different molecules are weaker than those between molecules of trichloromethane.
14. *(a)* (i) See § 3.8. (ii) See § 3.9.
    (b) Ratio C 38.7%/12: H 9.7%/1: O 51.6%/ 16 gives CH_3O
    (c) (i) $PV = nRT$
    (ii) $1.00 \times 10^5\text{Pa} \times 2.34 \times 10^{-4}\ \text{m}^3$
    $= n \times 8.31\ \text{J K}^{-1}\ \text{mol}^{-1} \times 350\ \text{K}$
    $n = 8.05 \times 10^{-3}$ mol
    (iii) 8.05×10^{-3} mol = $0.500\ \text{g}/M\ \text{g mol}^{-1}$ therefore $M = 62$
    (iv) M of $CH_3O = 31$, therefore molecular formula is $C_2H_6O_2$

CHAPTER 9 SOLUTIONS

Checkpoint 9.3: Solutions

1. Add a crystal of solid to each of the solutions. If the crystal dissolves, the solution is unsaturated. If the crystal does not dissolve the solution is saturated. If a mass of crystals appears, the solution was supersaturated.
2. *(a)* (i) 80 g per 100 g water
   (ii) 50 g (approximately) of solid crystallise
   (b) (i) 105 g per 100 g water
   (ii) 40 g per 100 g water
   (c) 2 g sodium chloride and 75 g potassium nitrate.
3. The solution is in a state of dynamic equilibrium. Calcium sulphate is constantly crystallising from solution and solid calcium sulphate is constantly dissolving.

CHAPTER 10 THERMOCHEMISTRY

Checkpoint 10.8: Combustion

1. 983 kJ; $\Delta H_c^\ominus$ at 37 °C, rather than at 25 °C
2. 12.0 g Calculate the heat required $(mc\Delta T)$ to heat 2.00 kg of water from 20 °C to 100 °C. What amount of methane must be burnt to liberate this quantity of heat?
   What mass of methane is this?
3. *(a)* See § 10.6.
   (b) ΔH positive – process is endothermic; ΔH negative – process is exothermic
   (c) exothermic
   $mc\Delta T = 20.0\text{ g} \times 4.18\text{ J K}^{-1}\text{ g}^{-1} \times 10.0\text{ K} = 836\text{ J}$
   (d) $mc\Delta T = 50.0\text{ g} \times 0.38\text{ J K}^{-1}\text{ g}^{-1} \times 90\text{ K} = 1.71\text{ kJ}$
4. Heat = $6.00\text{ kJ K}^{-1} \times 2.12\text{ K} = 12.72\text{ kJ}$
   Amount of Mg = $2.00\text{ g}/24\text{ g mol}^{-1} = 0.0833\text{ mol}$
   Molar enthalpy change = $-12.72\text{ kJ}/0.0833\text{ mol}$
   $= -153\text{ kJ mol}^{-1}$
5. Heat = $100\text{ g} \times 4.18\text{ J K}^{-1}\text{ g}^{-1} \times 3.2\text{ K} = 1338\text{ J}$
   Amount of $H_2O = 50.0 \times 10^{-3}\text{ dm}^3 \times 0.500\text{ mol dm}^{-3}$
   $= 0.025\text{ mol}$
   Molar enthalpy of neutralisation = $-1338/0.025$
   $= -53.5\text{ kJ mol}^{-1}$

Checkpoint 10.10: Enthalpy changes

1. *(a)* – *(b)* – *(c)* – *(d)* + *(e)* –
2. The enthalpy content of a substance changes with conditions. One mole of bromine vapour contains more enthalpy than one mole of liquid bromine because enthalpy has been taken in to convert $Br_2(l)$ into $Br_2(g)$. The enthalpy content of one mole of water is greater at 5 °C than at 0 °C because enthalpy has been taken in to convert $H_2O(s)$ into $H_2O(l)$.

Checkpoint 10.11: Standard enthalpy changes

1. *(a)* See § 10.6.1.
   (b) See § 10.7.1; for methods see §§ 10.8.3, 10.8.4
2. 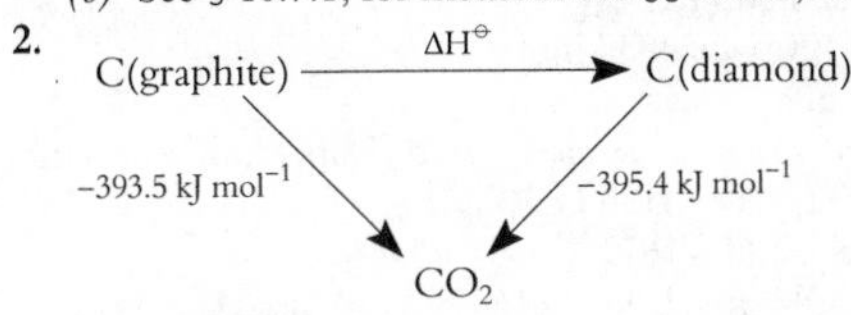

   $-393.5 = \Delta H^\ominus - 395.4$ and $\Delta H^\ominus = +1.9\text{ kJ mol}^{-1}$
3. 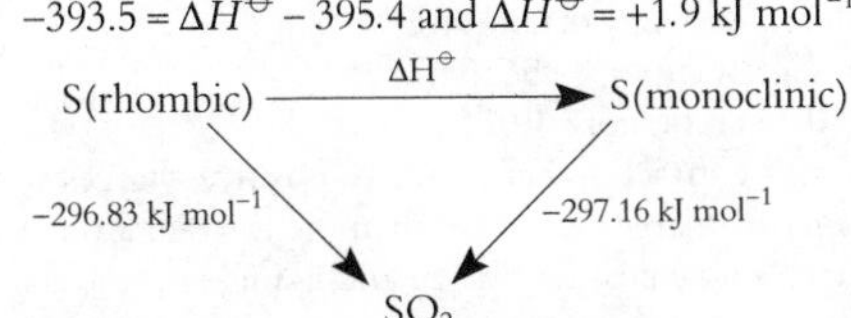

   $-296.83 = \Delta H^\ominus - 395.4$
   $\Delta H^\ominus = +0.33\text{ kJ mol}^{-1}$
4. $N_2H_4(l) + H_2(g) \longrightarrow 2NH_3(g); \Delta H_r^\ominus$
   $+50.63 \quad 0 \quad -92.22 \quad \Delta H^\ominus_{\text{formation}}/\text{kJ mol}^{-1}$
   $\Delta H_r^\ominus = -92.22 - 50.63 = -142.9\text{ kJ mol}^{-1}$
5. *(a)* Oxidation produces CO_2 as well as CO.
   (b) 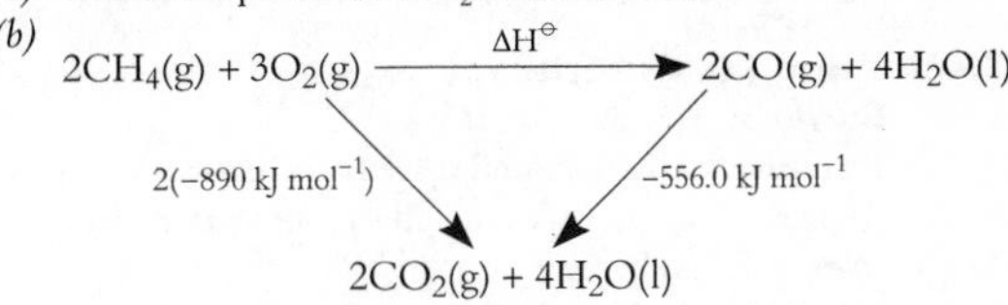

   $-1780 = \Delta H^\ominus - 566.0 \Rightarrow \Delta H^\ominus = -1214\text{ kJ mol}^{-1}$
6. *(a)* $C(s) + O_2(g) \longrightarrow CO_2(g); \Delta H^\ominus = \Delta H_f^\ominus(CO_2)$
   (b) $K(s) + \frac{1}{2}Cl_2(g) + \frac{3}{2}O_2(g) \longrightarrow KClO_3(s); \Delta H^\ominus = \Delta H_f^\ominus(KClO_3)$
   (c) $2C(s) + 3H_2(g) + \frac{1}{2}O_2(g) \longrightarrow C_2H_5OH(l); \Delta H^\ominus = \Delta H_f^\ominus(C_2H_5OH)$
   (d) $2Al(s) + \frac{3}{2}O_2(g) \longrightarrow Al_2O_3(s); \Delta H^\ominus = \Delta H_f^\ominus(Al_2O_3)$
   (e) $2C(s) + 2H_2(g) + O_2(g) \longrightarrow CH_3CO_2H(l); \Delta H^\ominus = \Delta H_f^\ominus(CH_3CO_2H)$
7. $3Mg(s) + N_2(g) \longrightarrow Mg_3N_2(s); \Delta H_f^\ominus$
   3 mol of Mg = 3 × 24 g
   $\Delta H_f^\ominus = -12.7\text{ kJ} \times 3 \times 24/2 = -457\text{ kJ mol}^{-1}$
8. *(a)* Bonds broken:
   (C=C) + (H—H) = 612 + 436 = 1048 kJ mol⁻¹
   Bonds made:
   (C—C) + 2(C—H) = −(348 + 826) = −1174 kJ mol⁻¹
   $\Delta H^\ominus = -1174 + 1048 = -126\text{ kJ mol}^{-1}$
   (b) Bonds broken: 2(C=C) = 1224 kJ mol⁻¹
   Bonds made: 4(C—C) = −1392 kJ mol⁻¹
   $\Delta H^\ominus = -1392 + 1224 = -168\text{ kJ mol}^{-1}$ of reaction
   (c) Bonds broken:
   $4C_{at} + 4(H—H) = (4 \times 715) + (4 \times 436) = 4604\text{ kJ mol}^{-1}$
   Bonds made: 4(C—C) + 8(C—H) =
   $(4 \times 348) + (8 \times 413) = -4696\text{ kJ mol}^{-1}$
   $\Rightarrow \Delta H^\ominus = -92\text{ kJ mol}^{-1}$
   (d) prefer exothermic reaction (ii)
   (e) The bond angles of carbon are strained in the 4-membered ring.

Checkpoint 10.13: Lattice enthalpy

1. *(a)* Na^+ (2.8) is much smaller than Cs^+ (2.8.8.18.18) and can approach more closely to the F^- ion.
   (b) Cl^- (2.8.8) has a smaller radius than I^- (2.8.8.18) and can approach more closely to Na^+.
   (c) In NaCl the ions are singly charged. In MgO the ions are doubly charged, and the forces of attraction between them are therefore stronger than in NaCl.
2. Sodium iodide has a high degree of ionic character in its bonds, and the model of two point charges applies. In zinc sulphide, the S^{2-} ion is polarised by the Zn^{2+} ion, and the bonds have some covalent character (see §§ 4.6.3, 4.6.4).

Checkpoint 10.14: Standard enthalpy of reaction and average standard bond enthalpies

1. $\Delta H_1^\ominus$ = standard enthalpy of sublimation (or vaporisation or atomisation) of magnesium.
   $\Delta H_2^\ominus$ = standard bond dissociation enthalpy of oxygen.
   $\Delta H_3^\ominus$ = standard ionisation enthalpy of magnesium.
   $\Delta H_4^\ominus$ = electron affinity of oxygen.
   $\Delta H_5^\ominus$ = standard lattice enthalpy of magnesium oxide.

An arrow pointing upwards indicates a process in which the enthalpy change is positive (enthalpy is taken in).

$\Delta H_6^\ominus = \Delta H_1^\ominus + \Delta H_2^\ominus + \Delta H_3^\ominus + \Delta H_4^\ominus + \Delta H_5^\ominus = -604\ \text{kJ mol}^{-1}$

2. The method is simply
$\Delta H^\ominus_{\text{reaction}} = \Delta H_f^\ominus$ (products) $- \Delta H_f^\ominus$ (reactants) [see § 10.4.2].
(a) -1560 kJ mol^{-1} *(b)* -1370 kJ mol^{-1}
(c) -286 kJ mol^{-1} *(d)* -5520 kJ mol^{-1}
3. **A** standard enthalpy of formation of rubidium chloride
B standard enthalpy of vaporisation of rubidium
C standard bond dissociation enthalpy of chlorine
D standard ionisation enthalpy of rubidium
E electron affinity of chlorine
F standard lattice enthalpy of rubidium chloride
E = −**D** − **C** − **B** + **A** − **F** = −372 kJ mol^{-1}

Checkpoint 10.15: Entropy

1. *(a)* **B** *(b)* **B** *(c)* **A** *(d)* **B** *(e)* **A**
(f) Extensive hydrogen bonding persists in the liquid phase.
2. *(a)* decrease *(b)* increase *(c)* decrease *(d)* decrease
3. $b < c < e < a < d < f$
4. *(a)* − *(b)* + *(c)* − *(d)* − *(e)* +
5. In a solid the atoms or molecules or ions are arranged in an ordered structure. In a gas the particles are free to move: it is a more disordered state; see § 10.15.

Checkpoint 10.16: Free energy

1. *(a)* Exothermic: dissolution of many ionic compounds, reactions of sodium with oxygen and water, neutralisation of e.g. NaOH(aq) with HCl(aq)
(b) Endothermic: dissolution of KCl in water, melting of ice, vaporisation of water, dissolution of ammonium carbonate.
(c) All the examples in (b) involve an increase in entropy.
(d) e.g. photosynthesis
2. *(a)* + *(b)* + *(c)* + *(d)* − *(e)* −
3. *(a)* Negative because both ΔH and $(-T\Delta S)$ are −ive.
(b) Could be +ive or −ive because ΔH is +ive and $(-T\Delta S)$ is −ive
(c) Could be +ive or −ive because ΔH is −ive and $(-T\Delta S)$ is +ive
(d) Positive because both ΔH and $(-T\Delta S)$ are +ive.
(e) In *(a)*, no: ΔH and $(-T\Delta S)$ are both −ive at all temperatures.
In (b) yes: at high T, $(-T\Delta S)$ has a higher −ive value and may outweigh +ive ΔH.
In (c) yes, −ive ΔH could be outweighed by a +ive $(-T\Delta S)$ at high T.
In (d), no, ΔH and $(-T\Delta S)$ are both +ive at all temperatures.
4. $\Delta H^\ominus = 96$ kJ mol^{-1}; $\Delta S^\ominus = 0.138$ kJ mol^{-1} and
$\Delta G^\ominus = \Delta H^\ominus - T\Delta S^\ominus$
At 300 K, $\Delta G^\ominus = 96 - (300 \times 0.138) = +54.6$ kJ mol^{-1}; reaction is not feasible.
At 800 K, $\Delta G^\ominus = 96 - (800 \times 0.138) = -14.4$ kJ mol^{-1}; reaction is feasible.

Questions on Chapter 10

1. Take, say 50.0 cm^3 of 0.100 mol dm^{-3} sodium hydroxide. Note the temperature, T_0. Titrate with, say 0.100 mol dm^{-3}

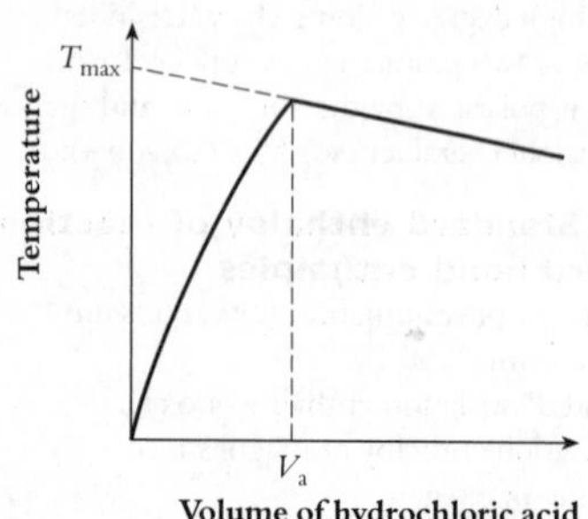

hydrochloric acid at the same temperature. Have a stirrer and a thermometer in the titration flask. Record the temperature after the addition of, say each 5.00 cm^3 of acid. Plot the temperature against the volume of acid added.
Note the volume of acid, V_a, corresponding to the maximum temperature recorded. Extrapolate to find the maximum temperature, T_{max}.
Then heat evolved = $(50.0 + V_a) \times 4.18 \times (T_{max} - T_0)$ J
Amount of H$^+$ neutralised = $50.0 \times 10^{-3} \times 0.100$ mol
Standard enthalpy of neutralisation = Heat evolved/Amount of H$^+$ neutralised.
The standard enthalpy of neutralisation refers to the enthalpy absorbed in the reaction.

$H^+(aq) + OH^-(aq) \longrightarrow H_2O(l)$

This is the same whether the H$^+$(aq) comes from nitric, hydrochloric or sulphuric acids. In the case of the weak acid, ethanoic acid, the salt is partially hydrolysed:

$CH_3CO_2^-(aq) + H_2O(l) \longrightarrow CH_3CO_2H(aq) + OH^-(aq)$

with the result that the hydrogen ion in ethanoic acid is incompletely neutralised and the standard enthalpy of neutralisation is lower than for strong acids.
2. $\Delta H^\ominus = 90 + 418 + 122 - 348 - 718 = -436$ kJ mol^{-1}; see Figure 10.12A
3. *(a)* (C—H) average standard bond enthalpy
$= 1664/4 = 416$ kJ mol^{-1}
Bonds in C_2H_6 = (C—C) + 6(C—H) = 2827 kJ mol^{-1}
(C—C) = 2827 − (6 × 416) = 331 kJ mol^{-1}
(b) C_3H_8 bonds = 2(C—C) + 8(C—H) = 3990 kJ mol^{-1}; see § 10.11
4. −201 = 113 + 2490 + 19.4 + 151 − 628 + LE [see Figure 10.12A]
LE = −2346 kJ mol^{-1}
5. *(a)* See § 10.9
(b)

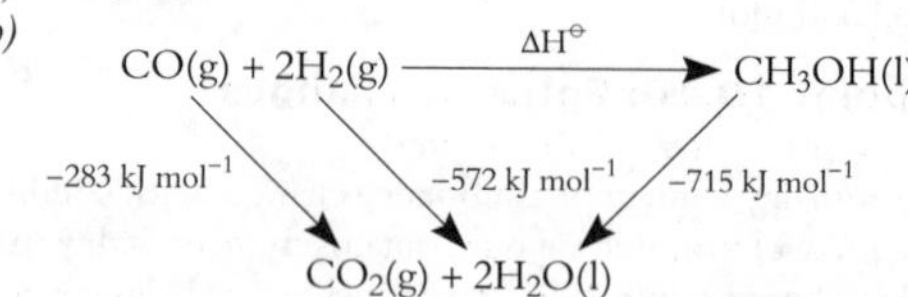

$-283 - 572 = \Delta H^\ominus - 715 \Rightarrow \Delta H^\ominus = -140$ kJ mol^{-1}
(c) Whether the route is CO + 2H$_2$ ⟶ products of combustion or CO + 2H$_2$ ⟶ CH$_3$OH ⟶ products of combustion the standard enthalpy change is the same by either route.
6. *(a)* Benzene is stabilised by delocalisation of π-electrons, see §§ 5.4.1 and 10.11.2.
(b) Both 2(−120) = −240 kJ mol^{-1}
7. See § 10.8.3 for a similar problem.
Heat liberated = mass of water × rise in temperature × specific heat capacity of water, 4180 J kg^{-1} K^{-1}.
= 50.0 × 0.8 × 4.18 J = 167 J
Amount of KOH dissolved = 0.166/56 mol
Molar standard enthalpy of solution
= −167 J × 56/0.166 mol = −56 kJ mol^{-1}
8. *(a)* See § 10.14 and Figure 10.14A.
(b) The force of attraction between two positive charges and two negative charges is greater than the force of attraction between a single positive charge and a single negative charge.
(c) (i) The ions in LiF are smaller, closer together and the lattice enthalpy is greater.
(ii) Li$^+$ is a very small cation and the enthalpy of hydration has a higher negative value than that of Na$^+$.
(iii) The sum (+lattice enthalpy − hydration enthalpy) has values/kJ mol^{-1} of LiCl −40, LiF +6, NaCl −3, NaF +3. The salt with a negative value or the lowest positive value of this sum is the more soluble.

9. (a) See § 10.15.
(b) (i) Decrease. There is a decrease in the number of moles of gas.
(ii) Decrease. The number of moles of gas has decreased. There is one type of molecule instead of two.
(iii) Increase. One mole of solid has formed three moles of gas. A gas is a more disordered state of matter than a solid.
(iv) No change. Two moles of gas have formed two moles of different gases.

10. See § 10.8.4.

11. (a) -2250 kJ mol^{-1}
(b) Ionisation energies are larger for the smaller Mg atom than for Ca. The lattice enthalpy of MgO is greater than that of CaO because Mg^{2+} and O^{2-} approach more closely than Ca^{2+} and O^{2-}.

12. (a) The third ionisation energy for Ca is very high; therefore $CaCl_3$ is not formed.
(b) To form Ca^{2+} is more endothermic than the formation of Ca^+. However, the formation of $CaCl_2$ includes the term (2 × electron affinity of Cl) which is highly exothermic. The sum of the terms makes the formation of $CaCl_2$ more exothermic than that of CaCl and therefore preferred.

13. (a) By definition, for an element in its normal state, $\Delta H^\ominus_f = 0$; see § 10.6.1.
(b) coal -394 kJ mol^{-1}, gas -891 kJ mol^{-1}
(c) (i) natural gas (ii) natural gas
(d) Natural gas produces more energy per mole of CO_2.

14. (a) lattice enthalpy: see §§ 10.12, 10.13, Born–Haber cycle: see § 10.12.
A high lattice enthalpy shows strong bonding; see § 10.13.
The Born-Haber cycle of KCl is similar to Figure 10.12A for NaCl.
$\Delta H^\ominus_F = \Delta H^\ominus_S + \frac{1}{2}\Delta H^\ominus_D + \Delta H^\ominus_I + \Delta H^\ominus_E + \Delta H^\ominus_L$
$-437 = +89 + 121 + 419 - 349 + \Delta H^\ominus_L$
$\Delta H^\ominus_L = -717$ kJ mol^{-1}
(b) See § 10.14. Hydration is solvation by water.
$KI(s) + aq \longrightarrow K^+(aq) + I^-(aq)$; $\Delta H^\ominus_{solution}$
$\Delta H^\ominus_{solution} = -296 - 321 + 649 = +32$ kJ mol^{-1}
There is an increase in entropy.
(c) See § 10.11 for average standard bond enthalpy (mean bond enthalpy).
$H_2C{=}CH_2 + H_2 \longrightarrow H_3C{-}CH_3$
Bonds broken: C=C (612) + H—H (436)
$= +1048$ kJ mol^{-1}
Bonds made: 2(C—H) (826) + C—C (348)
$= -1174$ kJ mol^{-1}
$\Delta H^\ominus = -126$ kJ mol^{-1}
Delocalisation of electrons in the benzene ring stabilises the molecule; see § 10.11.2.

15. (a) standard conditions
(b) (i) $Cl_2(g) \longrightarrow 2Cl(g)$
(ii) The standard bond enthalpies of C—C and C—H differ in different compounds.
(iii) A C—C bond breaks. The average standard bond enthalpy of C—C is less than that of C—H.
$C_3H_8(g) + 5O_2(g) \longrightarrow 3CO_2(g) + 4H_2O(l)$
$\Delta H^\ominus_F$ 0   3(−394)   4(−286)
$-2220 = 3(-394) + 4(-286) - \Delta H^\ominus_F$
$\Delta H^\ominus_F = -106$ kJ mol^{-1}

16. (a) See § 10.11.
Bonds broken: 4(C—H) + 2(O=O)
Bonds made: 2(C=O) + 4(O—H)
Enthalpy change = Enthalpy of bonds broken − Enthalpy of bonds made
(b) (i) $\Delta G^\ominus = \Delta H^\ominus - T\Delta S$
$= -519 - (298 \times 81.7 \times 10^{-3})$
$= -519 - 24.3 = -543$ kJ mol^{-1}
(ii) $\Delta S^\ominus$ is negative, $-T\Delta S^\ominus$ is positive
$\Delta G^\ominus = -802 - T\Delta S^\ominus$
$-T\Delta S^\ominus$ is a positive quantity which increases with T, therefore $\Delta G^\ominus$ becomes less negative with increasing T.
(iii) Reactions I and III do not involve a change in the number of moles of gas. In II, 2.5 moles of gas form 3 moles of gas, and $\Delta S^\ominus$ is positive.
(c) (i) The reaction will take place left to right [see § 10.16]. $\Delta G^\ominus$ is negative. $K_c > 1$
(ii) For all the reactions $\Delta G^\ominus$ is negative. The activation energy must be supplied before methane is oxidised. At 3000 K reaction I is feasible. In reaction III combustion is incomplete. The supply of oxygen is insufficient to allow reaction I to occur.
(d) (i) $K_c\text{I} = [CO_2]\,[H_2O]^2/([CH_4]\,[O_2]^2)$
$K_c\text{II} = [CO]\,[H_2O]^2/([CH_4]\,[O_2]^{3/2})$
$K_c\text{IV} = [CO_2]/([CO]\,[O_2]^{1/2})$
Dividing the expression for K_cI by that for K_cII gives the expression for K_cIV unit = (mol dm^{-3})$^{1/2}$
(ii) 3200 K when $K_c\text{I} = K_c\text{II}$, $K_c\text{IV} = 1$

17. (a) $S^\ominus$ increases very slowly from 200 K to 273 K, then increases as ice forms water, then increases gradually from 273 K to 373 K, when there is a big increase as water forms steam, a bigger increase than for the change from ice to water.
(b) $H_2O(g) \longrightarrow H_2O(l)$
189 J K^{-1} mol^{-1} ⟶ 70 kJ mol^{-1}
From $H_2O(g)$ to $H_2O(l)$ $\Delta S^\ominus = 119$ J K^{-1} mol^{-1}:
condensation is exothermic. With $\Delta H^\ominus$ negative and $\Delta S^\ominus$ positive $\Delta G^\ominus$ has a negative value.
At equilibrium $\Delta G^\ominus = 0$
$T\Delta S^\ominus = \Delta H^\ominus$
$T = 373$ K
$\Delta S^\ominus = S^\ominus(g) - S^\ominus(l) = 189 - 70 = 119$ J K^{-1} mol^{-1}
$\Delta H^\ominus = 0.119 \times 373 = 44.4$ kJ mol^{-1}
(c) $CH_4(g) + H_2O(g) \longrightarrow CO(g) + H_2(g)$;
$\Delta H^\ominus = 210$ kJ mol^{-1}
The reaction is endothermic; $\Delta H^\ominus$ is positive.
$\Delta S^\ominus = 198 + 131 - 186 - 189 = -46$ J K^{-1} mol^{-1}
$\Delta G^\ominus = \Delta H^\ominus - T\Delta S^\ominus$
Since $\Delta S^\ominus$ is negative, $T\Delta S^\ominus$ is positive therefore $\Delta G^\ominus$ can become negative when the positive value of $\Delta H^\ominus$ is compensated by the negative value of $-T\Delta S^\ominus$.
(d) The energy of activation is high.
(e) $CaO(s) + CO_2(g) \longrightarrow CaCO_3(s)$; $\Delta H^\ominus = -178$ kJ mol^{-1}
$\Delta S^\ominus = 90 - 40 - 214 = -164$ J K^{-1} mol^{-1}
$\Delta G^\ominus = -178 - T\Delta S$
$0 = -178 - T_s(-0.164)$
$T_s = 1085$ K

18. (a) See §§ 10.6, 10.12.
(b) $\Delta H^\ominus_{solution}$ refers to $AgF(s) \longrightarrow Ag^+(aq)F^-(aq)$
$AgF(s) \longrightarrow Ag^+(g) + F^-(g)$; $\Delta H^\ominus = +969$ kJ mol^{-1}
$Ag^+(g) + F^-(g) \longrightarrow Ag^+(aq)\ F^-(aq)$;
$\Delta H^\ominus = -991$ kJ mol^{-1}
$\Delta H^\ominus_{solution} = +969 - 991 = -22$ kJ mol^{-1}
(c) (i) See NaCl, Figure 10.12A for help.
(ii) $-203 = +278 + 79 + 731 + EA - 969$
$\Rightarrow EA = -322$ kJ mol^{-1}

19. (a) See NaCl, Figure 10.12A for help. Add another step; vaporisation of $Br_2(l) \longrightarrow Br_2(g)$; $\Delta H^\ominus_{vap}$
(b) Add all the steps to obtain $\Delta H^\ominus_F = -361$ kJ mol^{-1}
Include the step $\frac{1}{2}Br_2(l) \longrightarrow \frac{1}{2}Br_2(g)$; $\frac{1}{2}\Delta H^\ominus_{vap}$
$\frac{1}{2}\Delta H^\ominus_{vap} + 97 - 325 + 107 + 498 - 753 = -361$
$\frac{1}{2}\Delta H^\ominus_{vap} = 15$ kJ mol^{-1} and $\Delta H^\ominus_{vap} = 30$ kJ mol^{-1}

CHAPTER 11 CHEMICAL EQUILIBRIUM

Checkpoint 11.5: Le Chatelier's Principle

1. An increase in pressure increases the percentage conversion into ammonia by changing the position of equilibrium; see § 11.5.3.

   A rise in temperature decreases the percentage conversion into ammonia by decreasing the equilibrium constant; see § 11.5.4. Iron and molybdenum catalyse the reaction, speeding up the attainment of equilibrium without changing the position of equilibrium.
2. *(a)* An increase in temperature decreases the equilibrium constant of this exothermic reaction and therefore decreases the extent of conversion of NO_2 into N_2O_4; see § 11.5.4.
   (b) An increase in pressure does not change the equilibrium constant, but it moves the position of equilibrium towards the N_2O_4 side; see § 11.5.3.
   (c) An increase in volume decreases the pressure and moves the position of equilibrium towards the NO_2 side.
3. *(a)* The position of equilibrium:
   (i) moves towards the RHS when the temperature increases;
   (ii) moves towards the LHS when the volume increases and pressure therefore decreases;
   (iii) does not change when a catalyst is added (but is reached more rapidly);
   (iv) moves towards the LHS when chlorine is added, in order to maintain the constant value of the equilibrium constant;
   $$K_p = \frac{p(Cl_2(g)) \times p(PCl_3(g))}{p(PCl_5(g))}$$
   (v) moves towards the LHS when a noble gas is added because the pressure on the system has increased. In an attempt to reduce the increased pressure, the equilibrium moves to reduce the number of moles of gas present, that is $PCl_3(g)$ and $Cl_2(g)$ combine to form $PCl_5(g)$.

   (b) The equilibrium constant:
   (i) increases with temperature because the decomposition is endothermic;
   (ii) is independent of pressure and therefore the volume of the container;
   (iii) is independent of the catalyst or
   (iv) of the addition of chlorine or
   (v) of a noble gas.
4. Ice at 0 °C can cancel a part of the increase in pressure by a decrease in volume; that is by melting. Most other solids increase in density as the temperature falls.

Checkpoint 11.6: Equilibrium constants

1. *(a)* $K_p = p(CH_4(g)) \times p^2(H_2S(g))/(p(CS_2(g)) \times p^4(H_2(g)))$
   (b) $K_p = p^4(NO(g)) \times p^6(H_2O(g))/(p^4(NH_3(g)) \times p^5(O_2(g)))$
   (c) $K_p = p^2(NH_3(g)) \times p^4(H_2O(g))/(p^2(NO_2(g)) \times p^7(H_2(g)))$
2. *(a)* $K_c = [Sn^{4+}(aq)]\,[Fe^{2+}(aq)]^2/([Sn^{2+}(aq)]\,[Fe^{3+}(aq)]^2)$
   (b) $K_c = [Fe^{3+}(aq)]/([Fe^{2+}(aq)]\,[Ag^+(aq)])$
   (c) $K_c = [Cr^{2+}(aq)]^2\,[Fe^{2+}(aq)]/[Cr^{3+}(aq)]^2$
3. $K_c = [C]^2/[A]\,[B] = (0.50)^2/(0.25 \times 0.40) = 2.5$
4.

	2D +	E ⇌	F
Initial amounts	1.00	0.75	0
Equilibrium amounts	0.70	0.60	0.15

   $K_c = 0.15/(0.70^2 \times 0.60) = 0.510\ dm^6\ mol^{-2}$
5. $K_p = p(SO_3)/(p(SO_2) \times p(O_2)^{1/2})$
   $= 1.00/(0.050 \times 0.025^{1/2}) = 126\ atm^{-1/2}$
   $K_p = p^2(SO_3)/(p^2(SO_2) \times p(O_2))$
   $= 1.00/(0.050^2 \times 0.025) = 1.60 \times 10^4\ atm^{-1}$
6. $CH_3CO_2H(l) + C_2H_5OH(l) \rightleftharpoons CH_3CO_2C_2H_5(l) + H_2O(l)$

	$CH_3CO_2H(l)$	$C_2H_5OH(l)$	$CH_3CO_2C_2H_5(l)$	$H_2O(l)$
Initial amounts	1.00 mol	5.00 mol	0	0

   Amount of acid $= 289 \times 10^{-3} \times 0.200$ mol $= 0.0578$ mol

   Equilibrium amounts
   0.0578 mol 4.0578 mol 0.9422 mol 0.9422 mol
   $K_c = (0.9422)^2/(0.0578 \times 4.0578) = 3.79$

Checkpoint 11.8: Phase equilibria

1. *(a)* The areas S, L, G are similar to the areas ice, liquid and vapour in Figure 11.3.
   (b) A is the triple point.
   (c) The freezing temperature (shown by the line between S and L) rises with increasing pressure. This is because the transition from liquid to solid involves a decrease in volume and is favoured by an increase in pressure, in accordance with Le Chatelier's Principle.
2. *(a)* transition from solid to gas
   (b) the line between solid and gas
   (c) The line between solid and liquid slopes from left to right. In water the line slopes from right to left because water expands on freezing.

Questions on Chapter 11

1. *(a)* $K_p = p^2(NO_2(g))/p(N_2O_4(g))$
   (b) See § 11.5; equilibrium moves towards LHS with an increase in pressure and towards the RHS with an increase in temperature.
2. *(a)* $K_p = p^2(SO_3(g))/(p^2(SO_2(g)) \times p(O_2(g)))$
   (b) It follows from the composition of the equilibrium mixture that partial pressures are
   $p(SO_2) = 0.27P$, $p(O_2) = 0.40P$, $p(SO_3) = 0.33P$
   These values are inserted into the expression for K_p.
   $K_p = 3.73\ atm^{-1}$
   (c) Rearranging the expression for K_p gives
   $p(SO_3)/p(SO_2) = \sqrt{K_p p(O_2)}$
   (d) The reaction involves a decrease in volume; therefore an increase in pressure moves the position of equilibrium towards the formation of SO_3. However, SO_2 is easily liquefied above a pressure of 2 atm.
3. *(a)* $K_p = p(H_2(g)) \times p(CO_2(s))/(p(H_2O(g)) \times p(CO(g)))$
   (b) From the composition of the equilibrium mixtures, partial pressures are:
   $p(H_2(g)) = p(CO_2(g)) = 0.333P$;
   $p(H_2O(g)) = p(CO(g)) = 0.167P$
   Inserting these values into the expression for K_p gives $K_p = 4.00$; it is dimensionless.
   (c) No; the total pressure does not appear in the equilibrium constant.
4. $K_c = [Fe^{3+}(aq)]/([Ag^+(aq)]\,[Fe^{2+}(aq)])$
   $= 0.56/(0.44)^2 = 2.89\ mol^{-1}\ dm^3$.
5. $K_c = [Cr^{2+}(aq)]^2[Fe^{2+}(aq)]/[Cr^{3+}(aq)]^2$
   $= (0.27)^2 \times 0.11/(0.030)^2$
   $= 8.91\ mol\ dm^{-3}$
6. *(a)* Since $K_c = [R]^2/([P]^2[Q])$
   the unit of K_c is concentration^{-1}.
   (b) The value of $[R]^2/([P]^2\,[Q]) = 0.33$
   which is not the equilibrium value.
   (c) From $K_c = (3/V)^2/[(3/V)^2(3/V)] = 6.0$,
   $V = 18.0\ dm^3$.
7. *(a)* The value of $[SO_3]^2/([SO_2]^2\,[O_2]) = 19.6$ which is not the equilibrium value.
   (b) The reaction will proceed from left to right to increase $[SO_3]$.
8. *(a)* Rapid cooling slows down the forward and reverse reactions and keeps the mixture in its equilibrium concentrations. Ethanoic acid can be titrated.
   (b) See § 11.5.1. Addition of ethanol will move the position of equilibrium towards the RHS.
   (c) $K_c = [CH_3CO_2C_2H_5]\,[H_2O]/[CH_3CO_2H]\,[C_2H_5OH]$
   $= 3.98$

The amount of ethanoic acid in the mixture is equal to amount of NaOH added minus the amount of NaOH that remained for back-titration.
The amount of ester is equal to the initial amount of ethanoic acid minus the amount that remains to be neutralised by NaOH.

9. *(a)* air and water or natural gas; see § 22.4
(b) $K_p = p^2(NH_3(g))/(p(N_2(g)) \times p^3(H_2(g))$; atm^{-2}
(c) See § 11.5.1.
(d) I. increase in yield; see § 11.5.3
II. More N_2 and H_2 combine in order to keep the ratio $p^2(NH_3(g))/(p(N_2(g)) \times p^3(H_2(g)))$ constant.
(e) I. decrease in yield; see § 11.5.4,
II. Equilibrium is reached very slowly at low temperatures.
(f) Iron; see § 22.4.
(g) I. Provides an alternative reaction route of lower activation energy; see § 14.4.
II. The position of equilibrium is unchanged. Equilibrium is reached more rapidly.

10. *(a)* (i) High temperature reduces the yield because the reaction is exothermic. However, at a low temperature the reaction proceeds slowly. A compromise of 450 °C is used, with a catalyst.
High pressure increases the yield because the reaction involves a decrease in volume. However sulphur dioxide liquefies at high pressure and a plant that can withstand high pressure is costly. Therefore a moderate 2 atm is used.
(ii) 1 $SO_3(s) + H_2O(l) \longrightarrow H_2SO_4(aq)$
2 The reaction is strongly exothermic. SO_3 reacts with water vapour in the air above the absorber to form a mist of sulphuric acid. In the Contact process, $SO_3(s)$ reacts with concentrated sulphuric acid to form oleum, $H_2S_2O_7$. This reacts with water to form sulphuric acid.
(b) (i)

	$2SO_2(g)$	$+ O_2(g)$	$\rightleftharpoons 2SO_3(g)$	Total
Initial amount	10 mol	5.0 mol	0	15 mol
Equilibrium amount	1 mol	0.5 mol	9 mol	10.5 mol
(ii) Mole fraction	1/10.5	0.5/10.5	9/10.5	
(iii) Partial pressure	200/10.5	100/10.5	1800/10.5	

(iv) $K_p = p^2(SO_3)/(p^2(SO_2) \times p(O_2))$
(v) $= (1800/10.5)^2/[(10.5/200)^2 \times (10.5/100)] = 8.5\ kPa^{-1}$
(c) See Figure 21.9D.

11. *(a)* See § 11.2. (Both forward and backward reactions are occurring.)
(b) See § 11.5. (A catalyst speeds up both forward and backward reactions.)
(c) B: $K_c = [NO_2(g)]^2/[N_2O_4(g)]$
(d) (i) $x =$ **B**, $y =$ **D** or **A**, $z =$ **C**
(ii) The rate of reaching equilibrium will be slow.
(iii) Plant that will withstand high pressure is costly.
(iv) The reaction is exothermic therefore higher temperature reduces the percentage of product in the equilibrium mixture. The new maximum will be reached more rapidly at the higher temperature.

12. *(a)* 5.52 g $NO_2 = 5.52/(14 + 32) = 0.12$ mol NO_2 and 5.52 g $N_2O_4 = 0.060$ mol N_2O_4.
(b) (i) $K_c = [NO_2(g)]^2/[N_2O_4(g)]$
(ii) $K_c = (0.12/4.80)^2/(0.060/4.80) = 0.05\ mol\ dm^{-3}$.
(c) (i) $K_p = p^2(NO_2(g))/p(N_2O_4(g))$
(ii) $x(NO_2) = 0.12/0.18 = 0.667$
(iii) $K_p = (0.667P)^2/0.333P = 66\ kPa^2/33\ kPa = 133\ kPa$
(d) decrease: The system responds to an increase in P by a decrease in volume. This is achieved when the position of equilibrium moves from R to L and 2 volumes of gas form one volume of gas.

13. *(a)* See § 11.2.
(b) The reaction involves a decrease in volume as 4 moles of gas form 2 moles of gas.
(c) (i)

	NH_3	H_2	N_2	Total
	24.0 g	13.5 g	60.3 g	
Amount	1.41 mol	6.75 mol	2.15 mol	10.3 mol
Mole fraction	0.137	0.655	0.209	
Partial pressure	1.37 atm	6.55 atm	2.09 atm	10.0 atm

(ii) $K_p = p^2(NH_3)/(p(N_2) \times p^3(H_2))$
$= (1.37)^2/[2.09 \times (6.55)^3] = 3.20 \times 10^{-3}\ atm^{-2}$
(iii) The reaction is exothermic therefore K_p decreases with rising temperature.
(d) See discussion in § 10.17 and activation energy in § 14.3.

14. *(a)* Amount of $Cl_2 = 11.1/71 = 0.156$ mol
Amount of $PCl_5 = 83.4/208.5 = 0.400$ mol
Amount of PCl_5 at equilibrium
$= 0.400 - 0.156 = 0.244$ mol
(b) $K_c = [PCl_3]\ [Cl_2]/[PCl_5]$
$= (0.156/9.23)^2/(9.23/0.244) = 1.08 \times 10^{-2}\ mol\ dm^{-3}$
(c) (i) $K_p = p(PCl_3) \times p(Cl_2)/p(PCl_5)$
(ii) Mole fraction of $Cl_2 = 0.156/0.556 = 0.281$
$p(Cl_2) = 250 \times 0.156/0.556 = 70.14$ kPa
(iii) $p(PCl_5) = 250\ kPa \times 0.244/0.556 = 109.7$ kPa
(iv) $K_p = (70.14)^2/109.7 = 44.9$ kPa

CHAPTER 12 ELECTROCHEMISTRY

Checkpoint 12.5: Electrolysis

1. 1.8 g. Remember that $3Na^+$ are liberated for every one Al^{3+}.
2. *(a)* 2.40 g *(b)* 7.10 g *(c)* 6.35 g *(d)* 20.7 g *(e)* 0.200 g
Remember that 1 mole of electrons liberates 1 mol M^+, $\frac{1}{2}$ mol M^{2+}, 1 mol A^-, $\frac{1}{2}$ mol A^{2-}, etc.
3. *(a)* double *(b)* no change *(c)* no change *(d)* double
Remember: Quantity of electricity = Current × Time.
Assume that there is enough copper(II) sulphate in the solution for the supply of copper(II) ions not to run out.
4. 1.23×10^{-3} mol metal, 2.46×10^{-3} mol electrons, +2

Checkpoint 12.6 A: Acids and bases

1. See § 12.6.1.
2. *(a)* $[Al(H_2O)_6]^{3+}$ is a proton donor; see § 19.4.1.
(b) The Cl atom attracts electrons in the Cl – C bond because chlorine is a more electronegative element than carbon and it therefore facilitates the ionisation of H^+.
(c) Since $AlCl_3 + Cl^- \longrightarrow AlCl_4^-$ [see § 28.8.7], an unshared electron pair in Cl^- is accepted by the Lewis acid $AlCl_3$, with the formation of a covalent bond.
3. See § 12.6.1.
(a) No hydrogen ions are produced. H_2O produces OH^- ions and is therefore a base.
(b) The proton donor, the acid, is H_2O. The proton acceptor, the base, is NH_3.
4. As an acid, a proton donor, e.g.
$H_2O(l) + CH_3NH_2(g) \rightleftharpoons CH_3NH_3^+(aq) + OH^-(aq)$
As a base, a proton acceptor, e.g.
$CH_3CO_2H(aq) + H_2O(l) \rightleftharpoons CH_3CO_2^-aq) + H_3O^+(aq)$
5. *(a)* $pK_w = 15$ *(b)* pH = 13
6. *(a)* RCOBr base, $FeBr_3$ acid.
(b) NH_3 base, Ag^+ acid.
(c) $CH_3CO_2^-$ base, HF acid.

Checkpoint 12.6B: pH and dissociation constants

1. If $K_w > 10^{-14}\ mol^2\ dm^{-6}$, $[H^+] > 10^{-7}$, and pH < 7.
2. HCl(aq) is completely ionised, but CH_3CO_2H is incompletely ionised.

3. See § 12.6.4. The acid with the higher value of pK_a is the weaker.
4. See § 12.6.1; e.g. CH_3CO_2H and $CH_3CO_2^-$, e.g. $C_2H_5NH_2$ and $C_2H_5NH_3^+$.
5. In *(a)*, *(b)* and *(c)* $[H^+(aq)] = [acid]$ and $pH = -lg[H^+(aq)]$
In *(d)* $[OH^-(aq)] = [NaOH(aq)]$;
in *(e)* $[OH^-(aq) = 2[Ca(OH)_2(aq)]$
$pOH = -lg [OH^-(aq)]$ and $pH = 14 - pOH$
(a) 3.0 *(b)* 1.6 *(c)* 4.4 *(d)* 12.4 *(e)* 11.8
6. $K_a = [H^+(aq)] [A^-(aq)]/[HA(aq)]$; see § 12.7.6
(a) $K_a = [H^+(aq)]^2/1.00 \times 10^{-2} = 1.74 \times 10^{-5} \Rightarrow pH = 3.38$
(b) $K_a = [H^+(aq)]^2/0.100 = 1.78 \times 10^{-4} \Rightarrow pH = 2.37$
7. *(a)* $[H^+(aq)] = antilg(-pH) = 2.18 \times 10^{-5}\ mol\ dm^{-3}$
$K_a = [H^+(aq)]^2/2.00 = 3.97 \times 10^{-10}\ mol\ dm^{-3}$
(b) $[H^+(aq)] = antilg(-pH) = 5.50 \times 10^{-6}\ mol\ dm^{-3}$
$K_a = [H^+(aq)]^2/1.00 = 3.02 \times 10^{-11}\ mol\ dm^{-3}$

Checkpoint 12.7: Titration

1. See §§ 12.7, 12.7.1. The indicator can be used [see Figure 12.7A in § 12.7] for titration of a strong base into a strong acid, e.g., NaOH + HCl, and a strong base into a weak acid, e.g., $NaOH + CH_3CO_2H$. The indicator is unsuitable for the titration of a weak base [see Figure 12.7A(c) and (d)], e.g., Na_2CO_3 or $NaHCO_3$.
2. An indicator changes colour very rapidly over a range of about 2 pH units. Many titrations have an equivalence point at which the pH changes rapidly by up to 8 pH units for the addition of a small volume of titrant [see Figure 12.7 A(a)]. The range of pH must include the pH range over which the indicator changes colour.
Phenolphthalein changes colour at pH 8–10 [see Figure 12.7C]. A weak base titrated into a strong acid has an equivalence point at pH 3–7, which is outside the range for phenolphthalein. Methyl orange and methyl red could be used.
3. See Figure 12.7A(c). For an equivalence point of pH 3–7, the indicators methyl orange and methyl red could be used [see Figure 12.7C], while thymol blue and phenolphthalein should be avoided.
4. *(a)* $0.50\ cm^3$ of HCl(aq) is un-neutralised; volume of solution = $49.5\ cm^3$
$[H^+(aq)] = 0.5 \times 10^{-3} \times 0.100/49.5\ mol\ dm^{-3} \Rightarrow pH = 3.00$
(b) $0.30\ cm^3$ of HCl(aq) un-neutralised; volume of solution = $49.7\ cm^3$
$[H^+(aq)] = 0.3 \times 10^{-3} \times 0.100/49.7\ mol\ dm^{-3} \Rightarrow pH = 3.22$
(c) $0.10\ cm^3$ of HCl(aq) un-neutralised; volume of solution = $49.9\ cm^3$
$[H^+(aq)] = 0.10 \times 10^{-3} \times 0.100/49.9\ mol\ dm^{-3}$
$\Rightarrow pH = 3.70$
(d) $0.10\ cm^3$ of NaOH(aq) remains un-neutralised; volume = $50.1\ cm^3$
$[OH^-(aq)] = 0.10 \times 10^{-3} \times 0.100/50.1\ mol\ dm^{-3}$
$\Rightarrow pOH = 3.70 \Rightarrow pH = 10.3$
(e) $0.50\ cm^3$ of NaOH(aq) remains un-neutralised; volume = $50.5\ cm^3$
$[OH^-(aq)] = 0.50 \times 10^{-3} \times 0.100/50.5\ mol\ dm^{-3}$
$\Rightarrow pOH = 3.00 \Rightarrow pH = 11.0$

Checkpoint 12.8: Buffers

1. See § 12.8.
2. *(a)* Amount of $H^+(aq) = 1.00 \times 10^{-3}$ mol
Volume of solution = $1.00\ dm^3$
$[H^+(aq)] = 1.00 \times 10^{-3}\ mol\ dm^{-3}$, and pH = 3
(b) When $H^+(aq)$ is added to a solution of $NH_4^+CH_3CO_2^-$ an equilibrium is established:
$CH_3CO_2^-(aq) + H^+(aq) \rightleftharpoons CH_3CO_2H(aq)$
The position of equilibrium lies over to the RHS because ethanoic acid is a weak acid; therefore hydrogen ions are removed from solution and the pH change is small.
3. a salt of this weak base with a strong acid, e.g. $(CH_3)_2NH_2^+Cl^-$
(a) $H^+(aq) + (CH_3)_2NH(aq) \rightleftharpoons (CH_3)_2NH_2^+(aq)$
(b) $OH^-(aq) + (CH_3)_2NH_2^+(aq) \rightleftharpoons (CH_3)_2NH(aq) + H_2O(l)$
4. pH = 4.76. Since amount of NaOH = 10.0×10^{-3} mol, and amount of $CH_3CO_2H = 20.0 \times 10^{-3}$ mol, the solution contains 10.0×10^{-3} mol CH_3CO_2Na + 10.0×10^{-3} mol CH_3CO_2H. pH = pK_a, [see § 12.8] = 4.76.
5. $RCO_2H(aq) + H_2O(l) \rightleftharpoons RCO_2^-(aq) + H_3O^+(aq)$
(i) H_3O^+ ions combine with RCO_2^- ions $\longrightarrow RCO_2H$
(ii) OH^- ions combine with H_3O^+ ions $\longrightarrow H_2O$
6. $RNH_2(aq) + H_2O(l) \rightleftharpoons RNH_3^+(aq) + OH^-(aq)$
(i) H_3O^+ ions combine with OH^- ions $\longrightarrow H_2O$
(ii) OH^- ions combine with RNH_3^+ ions $\longrightarrow RNH_2 + H_2O$
7. *(a)* (i) $H_2NCH_2CO_2H(aq) + H_2O(l) \rightleftharpoons H_3N^+CH_2CO_2H(aq) + OH^-(aq)$
(ii) $H_2NCH_2CO_2H(aq) + H_2O(l) \rightleftharpoons H_2NCH_2CO_2^-(aq) + H_3O^+(aq)$
(b) H_3O^+: reverse of *(a)*(i)
(c) OH^- reverse of *(a)*(ii)
8. See § 12.8.2 on enzymes and pH.

Checkpoint 12.9: Salt hydrolysis

1. The salts of weak bases *(a)* and *(b)* have pH < 7. The salts of weak acids *(c)* and *(d)* have pH > 7.
2. *(a)* 8.7 *(b)* $0.167\ mol\ dm^{-3}$. Phenolphthalein could be used.
3. In both cases $\Delta H^\ominus$ refers to the reaction between 1 mol $H^+(aq)$ and 1 mol $OH^-(aq)$.
4. The products are water and ammonium chloride, which is partially hydrolysed:
$NH_4^+(aq) + H_2O(l) \rightleftharpoons NH_3(aq) + H_3O^+(aq)$
Thus not all the hydrogen ions have been removed in neutralisation, and $\Delta H^\ominus$ is lower than that for a strong acid and a strong base.

Checkpoint 12.10: Complex ions

1. *(a)* A soluble complex ion, $PbCl_4^{2-}(aq)$ is formed.
(b) The alkaline solution precipitates $Mg(OH)_2(s)$, which dissolves in $NH_3(aq)$ to form $[Mg(NH_3)_2]^{2+}(aq)$.
(c) Nickel hydroxide dissolves to form soluble complex ions:
(i) in an excess of aqueous ammonia to form $[Ni(NH_3)_6]^{2+}(aq)$, deep blue
(ii) in aqueous potassium cyanide to form $[Ni(CN)_4]^{2-}(aq)$, orange
(iii) in concentrated hydrochloric acid to form $[NiCl_4]^{2-}(aq)$, blue

Questions on Chapter 12

1. *(a)* $HCl(g) + H_2O(l) \longrightarrow H_3O^+(aq) + Cl^-(aq)$
(b) $NH_3(g) + H_2O(l) \longrightarrow NH_4^+(aq) + OH^-(aq)$
(c) $CH_3CO_2H(l) + H_2O(l) \longrightarrow CH_3CO_2^-(aq) + H_3O^+(aq)$
(d) $C_2H_5NH_2(s) + H_2O(l) \longrightarrow C_2H_5NH_3^+(aq) + OH^-(aq)$
(e) $H_2NCH_2CO_2H(s) + H_2O(l) \longrightarrow {}^+H_3NCH_2CO_2H(aq) + OH^-(aq)$
$H_2NCH_2CO_2H(s) + H_2O(l) \longrightarrow H_2NCH_2CO_2^-(aq) + H_3O^+(aq)$
2. *(a)* Brönsted base:
$NH_3(aq) + H_2O(l) \rightleftharpoons NH_4^+(aq) + OH^-(aq)$
(b) Brönsted acid:
$NH_4^+(aq) + OH^-(aq) \rightleftharpoons NH_3(aq) + H_2O(l)$
(c) Brönsted acid:
$HSO_3^-(aq) + OH^-(aq) \longrightarrow SO_3^{2-}(aq) + H_2O(l)$
Brönsted base:
$HSO_3^-(aq) + H^+(aq) \longrightarrow SO_2(g) + H_2O(l)$
Reducing agent:
$5HSO_3^-(aq) + 2MnO_4^-(aq) + H^+(aq) \longrightarrow 5SO_4^{2-}(aq) + 2Mn^{2+}(aq) + 3H_2O(l)$
(d) Reducing agent:
$5C_2O_4^{2-}(aq) + 2MnO_4^-(aq) + 16H^+(aq) \longrightarrow 10CO_2(g) + 2Mn^{2+}(aq) + 8H_2O$

Brönsted acid:
$H_2C_2O_4(aq) + H_2O(l) \rightleftharpoons H_3O^+(aq) + HC_2O_4^-(aq)$

(*e*) Brönsted acid: $[Fe(H_2O)_6]^{3+}(aq) + H_2O(l) \rightleftharpoons$
$[Fe(H_2O)_5(OH)]^{2+}(aq) + H_3O^+(aq)$
Oxidising agent:
$2[Fe(H_2O)_6]^{3+}(aq) + [Sn(H_2O)_6]^{2+}(aq) \longrightarrow$
$2[Fe(H_2O)_6]^{2+}(aq) + [Sn(H_2O)_6]^{4+}(aq)$

3. See § 12.2.1.
$4OH^-(aq) \longrightarrow O_2(s) + 2H_2O(l) + 4e^-$
Amount of $O_2 = 0.500\ dm^3/22.4\ dm^3$
Charge needed $= 4 \times 0.500/22.4 = 0.0893$ Faradays
Current × Time = 0.500 A × Time = 0.0893 × 96 500 C
Time = 172 345 s = 287 min

4. (*a*) See Figure 12.7A(a).
(*b*) The shape of the curve is similar to Figure 12.8(a) but the rapid change in pH occurs after the addition of 50.0 cm^3 of 1 M sodium hydroxide to 25.0 cm^3 of 1 M sulphuric acid.
(*c*) As in Figure 12.7A(b).
At the end-point in (*c*) sodium ethanoate is partially hydrolysed:
$CH_3CO_2^-(aq) + H_2O(l) \rightleftharpoons$
$CH_3CO_2H(aq) + OH^-(aq)$
and the solution is therefore alkaline.

5. (*a*) The ammonium ion reacts with water:
$NH_4^+(aq) + H_2O(l) \rightleftharpoons H_3O^+(aq) + NH_3(aq)$
making the solution acidic.
(*b*) Ammonia reacts with hydrogen ions:
$NH_3(aq) + H^+(aq) \rightleftharpoons NH_4^+(aq)$
Ammonium ions react with hydroxide ions.
$NH_4^+(aq) + OH^-(aq) \rightleftharpoons NH_3(aq) + H_2O(l)$
Thus both hydrogen ion and hydroxide ion can be absorbed by the solution without a change in pH.

6. See § 12.2.1 and Figure 12.2A. Using copper electrodes and copper(II) sulphate as electrolyte, one can find the quantity of electricity needed to deposit a weighed quantity of copper. The ratio moles of electrons/moles of Cu atoms gives the charge on a copper ion.

7. Quantity of electricity = 0.200 A × 2.00 × 60 × 60 s = 1440 C
No. of moles of electrons = 1440/96 500 = 0.0149 Faradays
No. of moles of silver ion in solution =
$200 \times 10^{-3} \times 0.0500$ mol = 0.0100 mol
No. of moles of electrons used to discharge all the silver ions = 0.0100 mol
No. of moles of electrons flow in excess of this amount = 0.0049 mol
Amount of H_2 liberated by the excess of electrons = 0.00 245 mol
Volume, at stp, of $H_2 = 0.002\ 45 \times 22.4\ dm^3 = 0.0549\ dm^3$ = 55 cm^3

8.

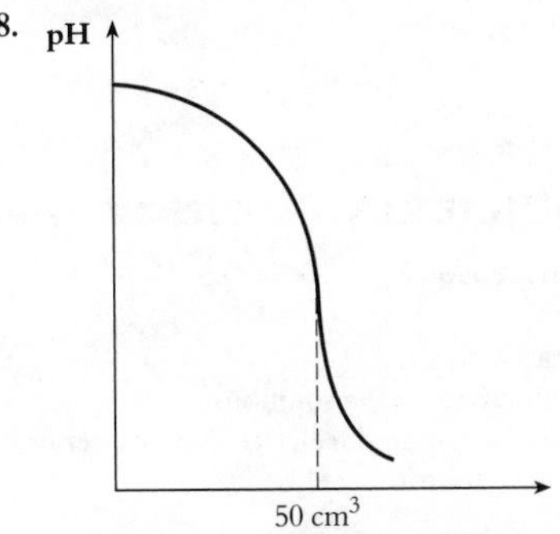

e.g., methyl red or methyl orange

9. (*a*) See 12.6.1. (*b*) See § 12.6.4. (*c*) See §§ 12.6.4 –5.
(*d*) (i) pH = 2
(ii) $[H^+(aq)]^2/[CH_3CO_2H(aq)] = K_a$
$[H^+(aq)]^2/0.010 = 1.8 \times 10^{-5} \Rightarrow pH = 3.37$
(iii) $pH = pK_a + \lg \{[Salt]/[Acid]\}$
$= 4.74 + \log 1 = 4.74$

10. (*a*) $K_a = [H^+(aq)]\ [CH_3CO_2^-(aq)]/[CH_3CO_2H(aq)]$
(*b*) Increase. The system can take in heat through ionisation.
(*c*) See § 13.3.5.
(*d*)

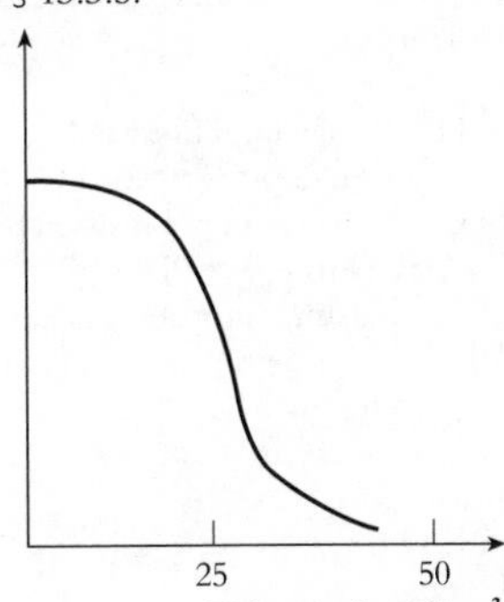

(*e*) $pH = pK_a + \lg \{[Salt]/[Acid]\} = 4.74 + \lg 2 = 5.04$
(*f*) See § 12.8.

11. (*a*) (i) A: $K_a = [H^+]^2/[HA]$
$1.38 \times 10^{-4} = [H^+]^2/0.15 \Rightarrow pH = 2.34$
B: 0.02 mol dm^{-3} lactic acid + 0.1 mol dm^{-3} sodium lactate
$pH = pK + \lg([salt]/[acid]) = pK + \lg(0.1/0.2) = 3.50$
(ii) To *A* the pH falls; to *B* the fall in pH is very small because H^+ ions are absorbed by combining with lactate ions to form lactic acid molecules.
(iii) 0.15 mol dm^{-3} lactic acid $\longrightarrow$ 0.15 mol dm^{-3} sodium lactate. This is the salt of a weak acid and a strong base, so pH > 7.
0.20 mol dm^{-3} lactic acid + 0.10 mol dm^{-3} sodium lactate $\longrightarrow$ 0.30 mol dm^{-3} sodium lactate. The concentration of the salt is higher, so the pH is higher.
(*b*) $PV = (m/M)RT$
$\rho = 1.15\ g\ dm^{-3} = m/V$
$m/V = \rho M/RT$
$1.15 \times 10^3 = 95.3 \times 10^3 \times M/(8.314 \times 298)$
$M = 29.9$
M of hydrocarbon = 30, therefore formula is C_2H_6.
(*c*) (i) trigonal planar, similar to Figure 5.2B
(ii) A lone pair of electrons on N of NH_3 coordinates into the outer shell of B, giving a tetrahedral arrangement of electron pairs round B.

12. (*a*) H_2O is a proton donor.
(*b*) Na^+ and Cl^- do not react with water, but $CH_3CO_2^-$ ions do because ethanoic acid is a weak acid. The OH^- ions formed make the solution alkaline.
$CH_3CO_2^-(aq) + H_2O(l) \rightleftharpoons$
$CH_3CO_2H(aq) + OH^-(aq)$
(*c*) $[H^+] = 0.01 = 1 \times 10^{-1}$, and pH = 1
(*d*) As *c* increases, $[H^+(aq)]$ increases, and pH decreases. If *c* doubles, $[H^+(aq)]$ doubles and pH decreases by lg 2, that is by 0.301.

13. (*a*) (i) proton-donor (ii) proton-acceptor
(*b*) conjugate acid–base pair; see § 12.8
(*c*)(i) $K_a = [H^+(aq)]\ [CH_3CO_2^-(aq)]/[CH_3CO_2H(aq)]$
(ii) $[H^+(aq)]^2 = 1.74 \times 10^{-5}\ M \times 0.1\ M$; pH = 2.88
(*d*) (i) HCO_2H is the stronger acid with the higher K_a
(ii) The pH of methanoic acid solution is lower than that of ethanoic acid even though the concentration of methanoic acid is half that of ethanoic acid. The pH of ethanoic acid at 0.050 M would be 2.88 + lg 2 = 3.18
(*e*) (i) See Figure 12.7A.
(ii) Phenol red. The pH changes rapidly over the pH range 7–9.

14. (a) (i) $C_3H_7CO_2H(l) + H_2O(l) \rightleftharpoons CH_3CO_2^-(aq) + H_3O^+(aq)$
(ii) $pK_a = 4.91$
(b) (i) $C_3H_7CO_2H(aq) + NaOH(aq) \longrightarrow CH_3CO_2Na(aq) + H_2O(l)$
(ii) phenolphthalein
(c) (i) See § 12.8.
(ii) Addition of H^+: change in pH resisted by $C_3H_7CO_2^-(aq) + H^+(aq) \rightleftharpoons C_3H_7CO_2H(aq)$
Addition of OH^-: change in pH resisted by $H_3O^+(aq) + OH^-(aq) \rightleftharpoons 2H_2O(l)$
(iii) 15.0 cm^3 of 0.1 mol dm^{-3} propanoic acid + 15.0 cm^3 of 0.1 mol dm^{-3} sodium propanoate
$pH = pK_a + lg$ ([Salt/[Acid])
$= 4.91 + lg\ 1 = 4.91$
(iv) e.g., amino acids § 12.8.2
15. (a) (i) See §§ 12.6.1, 12.6.4.
(ii) See § 12.8.
(b) (i) 0.05 mol $dm^{-3} \times 2 = 0.10$ mol dm^{-3} of $H^+ \Rightarrow pH = 1$
(ii) 0.01 mol dm^{-3} $OH^- \Rightarrow pOH = 2 \Rightarrow pH = 12$
(c) (i) $K_a = [H^+(aq)]^2/[HA(aq)]$
$6.3 \times 10^{-5} = [H^+(aq)]^2/0.020$
$[H^+(aq)] = 1.12 \times 10^{-3}$ mol dm^{-3}; pH = 2.95
(ii) See Figure 12.7A(b).
(iii) Thymolphthalein changes over the vertical section of the titration curve.
16. (a) (i) See 12.6.1.
(ii) H_2O, $C_6H_5CO_2^-$
(b) (i) $K_a = \dfrac{[CH_3CO_2^-(aq)][H^+(aq)]}{[CH_3CO_2H(aq)]}$
(ii) 2.87
(iii) 1.0
(iv) HCl is completely ionised. Ethanoic acid is chiefly in the form of molecules.
(c) (i) Sodium ethanoate is the salt of a weak acid and is hydrolysed with the production of OH^- ions.
$CH_3CO_2^-(aq) + H_2O(l) \rightleftharpoons CH_3CO_2H(aq) + OH^-(aq)$
(ii) Sodium chloride dissolves without hydrolysis.
(d) Amount of HCl = $25.00 \times 10^{-3} \times 0.1000 = 2.500 \times 10^{-3}$ mol
Amount of $Na_2CO_3 = 1.250 \times 10^{-3}$ mol
$[Na_2CO_3] = 1.250 \times 10^{-3}/20.0 \times 10^{-3}$
$= 6.25 \times 10^{-2}$ mol dm^{-3}
17. (a) Both curves show a rapid increase in pH when 50 cm^3 of NaOH(aq) have been added. Both show a very slow rise in pH after the endpoint. The curve for ethanoic acid starts at a higher pH than that for hydrochloric acid. The increase in pH is more gradual and the part of the curve where the pH rises very rapidly is shorter than for HCl(aq); see Figure 12.8A and B. The pH at the endpoint is higher for the weak acid.
(b) Change colour when the pH changes. Phenolphthalein changes colour at pH 9 which is on the steep part of the titration curve in both cases; see Figure 12.8B.
(c) pH = 4.30; $[H^+(aq)] = 5.01 \times 10^{-5}$ M
$[H^+(aq)]\,[A^-(aq)]/[HA(aq)] = K_a$,
therefore $K_a = 5.01 \times 10^{-5}$ mol dm^{-3}
At pH = 2.5, $[H^+(aq)] = 3.16 \times 10^{-3}$ mol dm^{-3} and
$[H^+(aq)]^2 = K_a c$
therefore $c = 0.200$ mol dm^{-3}
18. (a See § 12.8.
(b) (i) maximum buffering capacity
(ii) pH = pKa + lg{[sodium ethanoate]/[ethanoic acid]}
5.5 = 4.74 + lg{[salt]/[acid]} therefore
[salt]/[acid] = 5.75
[salt] = 5.75 × 0.10 M = 0.575 M
Mass of $CH_3CO_2Na = 0.575 \times 92 = 52.9$ g
(c) (i) Phenolphthalein changes pH at the pH of the endpoint, pH 9.
(ii) <7. The salt of a weak base and a strong acid is hydrolysed to give an acidic solution.
$NH_4^+(aq) + H_2O(l) \rightleftharpoons NH_3(aq) + H_3O^+(aq)$
(d) (i) $HCO_3^-(aq) + H^+(aq) \rightleftharpoons H_2CO_3(aq) \rightleftharpoons CO_2(aq) + H_2O(l)$
(ii) $HCO_3^-(aq) + OH^-(aq) \rightleftharpoons CO_3^{2-}(aq) + H_2O(l)$
19. (a) (i) The ionic product for water; § 12.6.2.
(ii) 1.00×10^{-14} mol^2 dm^{-6}
(iii) K_w increases with temperature ⟹ dissociation is endothermic.
(b) (i) 13.4/106 = 0.126 mol Na_2CO_3
(ii) Amount of $H^+ = 0.252$ mol;
$[H^+(aq)] = 0.252/4.00$ mol $dm^{-3} = 0.063$ mol dm^{-3}
pH = −lg 0.063 = 1.20
(iii) Amount of NaOH = 13.4/40 = 0.335 mol
Amount of $H^+ = 0.252$ mol
Amount of OH^- after neutralisation = 0.083 mol
pOH = −lg[0.083/4.00] = 1.68 ⟹ pH = 12.3
20. (a) (i) and (ii) See § 12.6.2.
(iii) K_w is higher at the higher temperature; dissociation is endothermic and ΔH is positive
(b) (i) $[OH^-] = 0.300$ M
pOH = 0.523 and pH = 13.5
(ii) $[OH^-] = 0.300$ M × 25/250 = 0.0300 M
pOH = 1.52 and pH = 12.5
(iii) Amount of OH^- added
$= 25.0 \times 10^{-3} \times 0.300$ mol $= 7.5 \times 10^{-3}$ mol
Amount of H^+ added
$= 75.0 \times 10^{-3} \times 0.200$ mol $= 15.0 \times 10^{-3}$ mol
Solution contains 7.5×10^{-3} mol H^+ in
100 $cm^3 = 7.5 \times 10^{-2}$ M H^+, pH = 1.12

CHAPTER 13 OXIDATION–REDUCTION EQUILIBRIA

Checkpoint 13.3: Electrode potentials

1. oxidising agent: See Table 13.3
2. (a) See § 13.2, (b) §§ 13.2.1, 13.2.2.
3. (a) emf = $E^\ominus$ (RHS) − $E^\ominus$ (LHS) = −0.46 V.
(b) For a reaction to happen spontaneously, $E^\ominus$ must be positive [see § 13.3.3].
$Cu(s) + 2Ag^+(aq) \longrightarrow Cu^{2+}(aq) + 2Ag(s)$; $E^\ominus = +0.46$ V
(c) from Cu to Ag
4. Oxidation takes place at the anode.
5. Find emf = $E^\ominus_{\text{RHS electrode}} - E^\ominus_{\text{LHS electrode}}$
The reactions for which this emf is positive are (b), (e), (h).
6. $MnO_4^-(aq) + 8H^+(aq) + 5e^- \rightleftharpoons Mn^{2+}(aq) + 4H_2O(l)$
Addition of H^+ (aq) drives the equilibrium from left to right and makes MnO_4^- a stronger oxidising agent.

Checkpoint 13.4: Rusting

1. (a), (b) See § 13.4.
(c) Parts not in contact with air.
(d) Increases the conductivity of the solution.
(e) Zn, Mg. Metals above iron in the electrochemical series corrode in preference to iron.

Questions on Chapter 13

1. All of them because all have more negative values of $E^\ominus$.
2. Those with more positive values of $E^\ominus$: I_2, Cu^{2+}.
3. See § 13.4 Sacrificial protection means connecting a metal with a more negative value of $E^\ominus$ to iron so that this metal becomes the anode in a cell and is oxidised while iron becomes the cathode and is protected from oxidation.

4. *(a)* A high negative value of $E^\ominus$ makes potassium a powerful reducing agent – a very reactive metal.
(b), (c) Calcium and magnesium have highly negative values of $E^\ominus$ and are powerful reducing agents with a strong tendency to form cations – very reactive metals. One would expect calcium to be more reactive than magnesium; see Table18.8 and less reactive than potassium.
(d) Iron has a less negative value of $E^\ominus$ than the previous metals and is less reactive. Since $E^\ominus$ is more negative than that for hydrogen, iron liberates hydrogen from acids.
(e) Copper has a positive value of $E^\ominus$: compared with hydrogen it is an oxidising agent and does not liberate hydrogen from dilute acids.
(f) With its high positive value of $E^\ominus$, chlorine is a powerful oxidising agent. The tendency is for chlorine to be reduced to chloride ion by oxidising one of the elements above it in Table 13.3.

5. Since emf is positive, chlorine is acting as an oxidising agent, with $E^\ominus = 1.36$ V.
$\text{emf} = 1.63 = 1.36 - E^\ominus_{Co^{2+}(aq)/Co(s)} \Rightarrow E^\ominus_{Co^{2+}(aq)/Co(s)} = -0.27$ V
$Cl_2(aq) + Co(s) \longrightarrow 2Cl^-(aq) + Co^{2+}(aq)$
The Co/Co^{2+} electrode is the negative electrode; this is where electrons are released.

6. $\text{emf} = E^\ominus_{\text{RHS electrode}} - E^\ominus_{\text{LHS electrode}}$
(a) +0.40 V *(b)* +0.26 V *(c)* −0.29 V *(d)* +0.94 V
(e) −0.46 V *(f)* +0.78 V *(g)* +0.63 V

7. *(a)* The species with a value of $E^\ominus$ more positive than that of Cl_2/Cl^- (+1.36 V) are MnO_4^-, Ce^{4+} and BrO_3^-.
(b) $VO_2^+ + 2H^+ + e^- \longrightarrow VO^{2+} + H_2O$
$MnO_4^- + 18H^+ + 5VO_2^+ \longrightarrow Mn^{2+} + 5VO^{2+} + 9H_2O$
(c) −0.40 − (−0.76) = +0.36 V
(d) $MnO_4^- = BrO_3^- > Cl_2 > Cr_2O_7^{2-} > I_2 > S_4O_6^{2-}$

8. *(a)* See § 3.15.1.
(b) (i) +7 (ii) +1 (iii) +2
(c) (i) $5Fe^{2+}(aq) + MnO_4^-(aq) + 8H^+(aq) \longrightarrow 5Fe^{3+}(aq) + Mn^{2+}(aq) + 4H_2O(l)$
(ii) Amount of $KMnO_4 = 27.2 \times 10^{-3} \times 0.0200$ mol $= 5.44 \times 10^{-4}$ mol
Amount of $Fe^{2+} = 5 \times 5.44 \times 10^{-4}$ mol
$[Fe^{2+}] = 5 \times 5.44 \times 10^{-4} \times (1000/25.0)$ mol dm^{-3} $= 0.109$ mol dm^{-3}.
(iii) Amount of $Fe^{2+} = 5 \times 29.0 \times 10^{-3} \times 0.0200$ mol
$[Fe^{2+}] = 5 \times 29.0 \times 10^{-3} \times 0.0200 \times (1000/25.0)$ mol dm^{-3}
$\Rightarrow [Fe^{3+}] = 0.116$ mol dm^{-3}
Iron converted into $Fe^{2+} = 0.109$ mol
Rust converted into $Fe^{3+} = 0.116$ mol
Total = 0.225 mol
% Fe^{3+} in total = (0.116/0.225) × 100% = 51.6%
(d) (i) There was no rust in the solution so the solution contained no Fe^{3+} and the addition of Zn had no effect.
(ii) e.g. in fencing and many other uses
(e) Combining two electrodes,
$Fe^{3+} + e^- \longrightarrow Fe^{2+}$; $E^\ominus = +0.77$ V
$Zn \longrightarrow Zn^{2+} + 2e^-$; $E^\ominus = +0.76$ V
$E^\ominus = +1.53$ V
Combining two electrodes
$Zn \longrightarrow Zn^{2+} + 2e^-$; $E^\ominus = +0.76$ V
$Fe^{2+} + 2e^- \longrightarrow Fe$; $E^\ominus = -0.04$ V
$E^\ominus = +0.72$ V
The reaction that happens is that with the higher value of $E^\ominus$; that is
$2Fe^{3+} + Zn \longrightarrow 2Fe^{2+} + Zn^{2+}$

9. *(a)* e.g. hydrochloric acid, 1.000 mol dm^{-3}
(b) e.g. KCl(aq)
(c) H_2(g, 1 atm) | H^+(aq), 1 mol dm^{-3} ¦¦ Sn^{2+}(aq) | Sn(s)
(d) (i) $E^\ominus = -0.44 - (-0.14) = -0.30$ V
(ii) Electrons flow from Fe^{2+} | Fe to Sn^{2+} | Sn therefore Fe is a better reducing agent than Sn.
(e) Tin and iron will form a cell. Of the alternatives,
$Fe^{2+} + Sn \longrightarrow Sn^{2+} + Fe$; $E^\ominus = -0.44 + 0.14 = -0.30$ V
$Fe + Sn^{2+} \longrightarrow Fe^{2+} + Sn$; $E^\ominus = +0.44 - 0.14 = +0.30$ V
the reaction with the positive value of $E^\ominus$ takes place: Fe is oxidised to Fe^{2+}, and Sn^{2+} is reduced to Sn.

10. *(a)* (i) $H_2(g) \longrightarrow 2H^+(aq) + 2e^-$, anode, $E^\ominus = 0.838$ V
$2H^+(aq) + 2e^- \longrightarrow H_2(g)$, cathode, $E^\ominus = 0$ V
(ii) $H^+(aq) + OH^-(aq) \longrightarrow H_2O(l)$
H_2(g, 1 atm) | H^+(aq, 1 mol dm^{-3}) ¦¦ OH^-(aq, 1 mol dm^{-3}) | H_2(g, 1 atm)
(b) See § 13.4
(i) $Zn \longrightarrow Zn^{2+} + 2e^-$
(ii) $Fe \longrightarrow Fe^{2+} + 2e^-$
(c) (i) CH_3CO_2H acid, $CH_3CO_2^-$ base, H_3O^+ acid, OH^- base, H_2O acid/base
(ii) $K_a = 1.76 \times 10^{-5}$ mol dm^{-3} = $[H^+][CH_3CO_2^-]/[CH_3CO_2H]$
$CH_3CO_2^-$ suppresses ionisation of CH_3CO_2H so $[CH_3CO_2H] = 0.20$ mol dm^{-3}
$CH_3CO_2^-$ from ionisation of CH_3CO_2H is negligible in comparison with $CH_3CO_2^-$ from CH_3CO_2Na.
So $[CH_3CO_2^-] = 0.20$ mol dm^{-3}
1.76×10^{-5} mol dm^{-3} = $[H^+] \times 0.20/0.20$
$[H^+] = 1.76 \times 10^{-5}$ mol dm^{-3},
$[CH_3CO_2H] = 0.20$ mol dm^{-3},
$[CH_3CO_2^-] = 0.20$ mol dm^{-3}

11. *(a)* (i) The value of $E^\ominus$ for $Cl_2 \longrightarrow 2Cl^-$ is lower than that for $MnO_4^- \longrightarrow Mn^{2+}$ therefore MnO_4^-, H^+(aq) oxidises Cl^- to Cl_2.
(ii) This makes it easier to see the endpoint, when the last drop of potassium manganate(VII) remains pink.
(b) (i) $5BiO_3^- + 30H^+ + 10e^- \longrightarrow 5Bi^{3+} + 15H_2O$
$2Mn^{2+} + 8H_2O \longrightarrow 2MnO_4^- + 16H^+ + 10e^-$
$2Mn^{2+} + 5BiO_3^- + 14H^+ \longrightarrow 2MnO_4^- + 5Bi^{3+} + 7H_2O$
(ii) $E^\ominus$ of BiO_3^-/Bi^{3+} has a larger positive value.
(c) (i) $MnO_4^-(aq) + 8H^+(aq) + 5Fe^{2+}(aq) \longrightarrow Mn^{2+}(aq) + 4H_2O(l) + 5Fe^{3+}(aq)$
(ii) Amount of $FeSO_4 = 25.0 \times 10^{-3} \times 0.100$ $= 2.50 \times 10^{-3}$ mol
Amount of MnO_4^- in 25.0 cm^3 = 0.50×10^{-3} mol
Amount of Mn in alloy = $0.50 \times 10^{-3} \times 10$ $= 5.00 \times 10^{-3}$ mol
Mass of Mn = 0.275 g and % = (0.275/2.30) × 100 = 11.9%

12. *(a)* See § 13.3.2.
(b) $3ClO^- \longrightarrow 2Cl^- + ClO_3^-$
+5
(c) $E^\ominus$ positive
(d) Cu(s)
$2Cu^+(aq) \longrightarrow Cu^{2+}(aq) + Cu(s)$; $E^\ominus = 0.37$ V
(e) $2MnO_4^{2-} \longrightarrow MnO_4^- + 2MnO_2$
$E^\ominus = +0.95$ V

13. *(a)* standard hydrogen electrode; 0 V; § 13.2.2
(b) hydrogen at 1 atm, solutions of ions at 1 mol dm^{-3}, temperature stated (usually 25°C)
(c) connects half-cells; see § 13.2.2, e.g. KCl(aq)
(d) See § 13.3.2
(e) The highest value of $E^\ominus$ is obtained from
$Fe^{2+}(aq) + 2e^- \longrightarrow Fe(s)$; $E^\ominus = -0.44$ V
$Zn(s) \longrightarrow Zn^{2+}(aq) + 2e^-$; $E^\ominus = +0.76$ V
Therefore Fe^{2+} is reduced.

CHAPTER 14 REACTION KINETICS

Checkpoint 14.2: Reaction rates

1. See effect of particle size on rate of reaction, § 14.2.1.
2. See effect of particle size on rate of reaction, § 14.2.1.
3. *(a)* (i) $6a^2$ (ii) a^3 (iii) $6/a$
   (b) Increases. Rate increases as ratio of surface area to volume increases: there is more surface area for acid to attack in a certain mass of chips.
4. *(b)* 5.0×10^{-3} mol *(c)* 0.34 g *(d)* 1.75 min
   (e) The curve would be steeper and the volume of 120 cm^3 would be reached more rapidly.
   (f) A different catalyst could be used.
   A more concentrated solution of hydrogen peroxide could be used; this would give a steeper graph.

Checkpoint 14.3: Collision theory

1. *(a)* See § 10.7.1.
   (b) See § 14.3 and Figure 14.3A.
2. *(a)* Fraction of molecules with energy $\geqslant E$ at T_1
   (b) T_2
   (c) The average kinetic energy of the molecules increases. The fraction of the molecules with energy above average increases.
3. **A** and **B** must have energy $\geqslant$ activation energy for the reaction. Also they must collide in an orientation which favours reaction; see Figures 14.3A and B.

Checkpoint 14.8: Catalysis

1. (i) saves on fuel costs (ii) saves the cost of constructing plant that will withstand high pressure
2. *(a)* See § 14.3, Figure 14.3C.
   (i) e.g. hydrogenation of liquid oils $\longrightarrow$ solid fats, e.g. margarine
   (ii) e.g. manufacture of ammonia in the Haber process catalysed by Fe/V
   (iii) e.g. cracking of hydrocarbons catalysed by SiO_2/Al_2O_3
3. See § 14.3 and Figure 14.3A.
4. See § 14.5.2, the lock and key theory.
5. See § 14.5.2.
6. *(a)* A substance which increases the rate of a chemical reaction without being consumed in the reaction
   (b) platinum; $2CO(g) + 2NO(g) \longrightarrow 2CO_2(g) + N_2(g)$
   (c) CO is poisonous, NO is an irritant; they are converted into harmless products.
7. *(a)* The products are not released.
   (b) The surface area over which the catalyst is in contact with reactants is increased.
   (c) adsorption of a substance which makes it unable to adsorb the reactants

Checkpoint 14.9: Thermodynamics

1. A spontaneous reaction takes place of its own accord once the reactants are mixed. $\Delta G^\ominus$ is negative; see § 10.16. The rate of reaction depends on the energy of activation. The presence of a catalyst lowers the activation energy.
2. The rate depends on the activation energy; see §§ 14.3, 14.12.1.

Checkpoint 14.14A: Initial rates

1. See §§ 3.10, 14.11, 14.13.2.
2. See § 14.12.2. None of the reacting mixture is used up for analysis.
3. *(a)* When $[\mathbf{B}]_0$ remains constant and $[\mathbf{A}]_0$ is doubled, the rate is quadrupled, therefore rate $\propto [\mathbf{A}]^2$. When $[\mathbf{A}]_0$ remains constant and $[\mathbf{B}]_0$ is doubled the rate remains constant, therefore rate is independent of $[\mathbf{B}]$. Rate $= k[\mathbf{A}]^2$.
   (b) $k = 5.0\ dm^3\ mol^{-1}\ s^{-1}$
   (c) $1.8\ mol\ dm^{-3}\ s^{-1}$
4. *(a)* When $[\mathbf{B}]$ is constant and $[\mathbf{A}]$ is doubled, the rate doubles: the reaction is first order in $[\mathbf{A}]$. When $[\mathbf{A}]$ is constant and $[\mathbf{B}]$ is doubled the rate quadruples: the reaction is second order in $[\mathbf{B}]$; overall order = 3
   (b) $k = 1.5 \times 10^{-3}\ mol^{-2}\ dm^6\ min^{-1}$
   (c) $8.7 \times 10^{-6}\ mol\ dm^{-3}\ min^{-1}$

Checkpoint 14.14B: First-order reactions

1. From 120 to 15 cpm = 3 half-lives $\Rightarrow t_{1/2} = 1$ hour
2. Four half-lives elapse; therefore the isotope decreases from 100% to 6.25%.
3. A comparison of the time taken for $[\mathbf{A}]$ to fall from 0.800 M to 0.400 M and the time for $[\mathbf{A}]$ to fall from 0.400 M to 0.200 M shows that the reaction is first order in $[\mathbf{A}]$.
   (b) $6.3 \times 10^{-4}\ mol\ dm^{-3}\ s^{-1}$
   (c) The rate constant is calculated from: Rate $= k[\mathbf{A}]$.
   $7.9 \times 10^{-4}\ s^{-1}$
4. *(b)* Amount of benzene diazonium chloride $= 5.50 \times 10^{-4}$ mol.
   Volume of nitrogen at stp $= 5.50 \times 10^{-4} \times 22\,400\ cm^3$.
   Volume of nitrogen at 50 °C = 14.6 cm^3.
   (c) 10.3 min = 618 s
   (d) $t_{1/2}$ is the same for different concentrations.
   (e) Use the graph; $1.06 \times 10^{-6}\ mol\ dm^{-3}\ s^{-1}$
   (f) Use: Rate $= k[\mathbf{A}]_0$; $9.7 \times 10^{-4}\ s^{-1}$

Checkpoint 14.14C: Order of reaction

1. 1st order because rate $\propto [N_2O]$
2. 2nd order because when [NO] is halved rate is reduced by a factor 4
3. Compare 1 and 3; then Rate $\propto [BrO_3^-]$
   Compare 1 and 2; then Rate $\propto [Br^-]$
   Compare 3 and 4; then Rate $\propto [H^+]^2$
   Rate $= k[BrO_3^-]\,[Br^-]\,[H^+]^2$, 4th order overall,
   $k = 12\ mol^{-3}\ dm^9\ s^{-1}$
4. From 1 and 2, Rate $\propto [S_2O_8^{2-}]$
   From 2 and 3, Rate $\propto [I^-]$
   Rate $= [S_2O_8^{2-}(aq)]\,[I^-(aq)]$; $k = 36\ dm^3\ mol^{-1}\ s^{-1}$.
5. Titrate the ethanoic acid formed against standard sodium hydroxide solution at measured intervals of time after the start of the reaction. Allow for the amount of sulphuric acid present. Convert titres into amounts of ester. Plot [ester] against time. Obtain the initial rate from the gradient at time = 0. Do a number of runs at different [ester]. Plot initial rate against [ester].
6. 1st order. Time for concentration to fall from $40 \times 10^{-4}\ mol\ dm^{-3}$ to $20 \times 10^{-4}\ mol\ dm^{-3}$ = 38 minutes = time for concentration to fall from $20 \times 10^{-4}\ mol\ dm^{-3}$ to $10 \times 10^{-4}\ mol\ dm^{-6}$.
7. *(a)* (i) 1 (ii) 1
   (b) From 2 and 3, Rate $\propto [CH_3CO_2C_2H_5]$
   From 2 and 1, Rate $\propto [OH^-]$
   Rate $= k[CH_3CO_2C_2H_5]\,[OH^-]$
   (c) $0.195\ dm^3\ mol^{-1}\ s^{-1}$
8. *(a)* $1.7 \times 10^{-4}\ mol\ dm^{-3}\ s^{-1}$
   (b) $5.1 \times 10^{-4}\ mol\ dm^{-3}\ s^{-1}$
   (c) $15.3 \times 10^{-4}\ mol\ dm^{-3}\ s^{-1}$
9. Plot the amount of *trans*-isomer against time. Draw tangents to the graph at $t = 0$ and other times. Plot the gradient of each tangent against the amount of *trans*-isomer that remains. Is the gradient $\propto$ amount remaining? If it is, the reaction is first order. 1st order; $k = 1.75 \times 10^{-4}\ s^{-1}$

Checkpoint 14.17: Reaction kinetics

1. *(a)* See §§ 14.3, 14.17.1 for activation energy.
   (b) See § 14.3 for the change in the distribution of values of molecular energy with temperature change. At higher temperatures, the average energy of the molecules increases and also the fraction of molecules with very high energies increases.
   (c) See § 14.4 for the decrease in activation energy which a catalyst brings.

2. See §§ 14.3, 14.17.1.
3. See §§ 1.10.6, 14.15, 26.4.7, 27.8.11.
4. See § 14.17.2. An approach $H^{\delta+}—I^{\delta-} \longrightarrow \longleftarrow H^{\delta+}—I^{\delta-}$ will minimise repulsion between like charges. An approach $I^- \longrightarrow CH_3—Br$ will minimise repulsion between I^- and the $\delta-$ charge on Br, and the electrons of I^- will be well placed to bond to CH_3. An approach
$(CH_3)_3N \longrightarrow C_2H_5—I$
will minimise repulsion between the lone pair of electrons on the nitrogen atom and the $\delta-$ charge on I, and the lone pair of nitrogen will be well placed to bond to the alkyl group.

Questions on Chapter 14

1. See § 14.13.2.
2. *(a)* 1 *(b)* $[H_2O]$ remains constant.
3. *(a)* concentration time^{-1}.
   (b) time $^{-1}$
   (c) concentration^{-1} time^{-1}; see § 14.13.2.
4. 30 hr (2 half-lives)
5. 9 days: drops from 160 to 20 in 3 half-lives
6. Compare runs 1 and 2: Rate $\propto [S_2O_8^{2-}]$.
   Compare runs 2 and 3: Rate $\propto [I^-]$.
   Initial rate = Rate constant $[S_2O_8^{2-}]$ $[I^-]$ and the rate constant can be found.
   (a) 1 *(b)* 1
   (c) 6.0×10^{-3} dm^3 mol^{-1} s^{-1}; 1.08×10^{-5} dm^3 mol^{-1} s^{-1}
7. RDS see § 14.18. Mechanisms are discussed in §§ 14.18.1, 14.18.2, 26.4.7, 27.8.2, 28.8.5, 28.8.7, 29.8.3, 29.9.4, 29.9.5, 31.8, 33.8.2, 33.10.2, 33.13.1, 34.4.
8. *(a)* See § 14.12.2.
   (b) (i) See § 14.12.2.
   (ii) At intervals of time, withdraw samples with a pipette. Titrate against a standard solution of potassium manganate(VII); see §§ 3.15.1, 21.6.3.
   (d) order = 1, $k = 6.0 \times 10^{-4}$ s^{-1}
9. *(a)* (i) see Figure 14.3C
   (ii) equal
   (iii) The fraction of molecules with energy $\geq E_A$ increases with temperature.
   (b) (i) $d[N_2O_5]/dt = k[N_2O_5]$
   (ii) I
   (iii) k = Gradient = Rate (Pa s^{-1})/$p(N_2O_5$ (Pa))
   $= 0.86/1000 = 8.6 \times 10^{-4}$ s^{-1}
10. *(a)* (i) $CH_3COCH_3 + I_2 \longrightarrow CH_3COCH_2I + HI$
    (ii) Rate = $k[CH_3COCH_3]$ $[H^+(aq)]$
    (iii) **A** because in **B** H^+ is involved in a fast step and would not enter into the rate equation.
    (iv) I_2 reactant, $H^+(aq)$ catalyst
    (v) Faster: Br_2 is a stronger electrophile than I_2.
    (b) One possibility is
    $SO_2(g) + NO_2(g) \longrightarrow SO_3(g) + NO(g)$
    $2NO\cdot + O_2 \longrightarrow 2NO_2$
11. *(a)* (i) Then the rate will depend only on $[I^-]$.
    (ii) Reaction would start slowly in the absence of $H^+(aq)$ if H_2O_2 were added before $H^+(aq)$.
    (iii) Then $[H(aq)]^+$ will be constant and $[H_2O_2]$ will be constant.
    (b) (ii) Linear plot shows Rate $\propto [I^-]$
    (c) (i) The $H^+(aq)$ ions take part in a fast step which is not rate-determining.
    (ii) mol dm^{-3} s^{-1}/(mol^n dm^{-3n} × mol dm^{-3}) = mol^{-n} dm^{3n} s^{-1}
12. *(a)* (i) mol dm^{-3} s^{-1}/mol^3 dm^{-9} = mol^{-2} dm^6 s^{-1}
    (ii) double: reaction is 1st order in $[O_2]$
    (iii) decrease by a factor 4: reaction is 2nd order in [NO]
    (b) (i) 3
    (ii) Collisions between 3 particles are relatively infrequent.
    (c) (i) NO has an unpaired electron
    [dot-and-cross diagrams of NO and N_2O_2]
    (ii) Energy is required to break the N—N bond. Energy is given out when the N—N bond in N_2O_2 is formed.
    (iii) This is a fast step.
    $N_2O_2 + O_2 \longrightarrow 2NO_2$
    (d) (i) The reaction is exothermic, therefore a rise in temperature drives the position of equilibrium from right to left.
    (ii) Equilibrium would be attained faster, but the yield of NO_2 would be lower. The process could operate at a moderate temperature and remove NO_2 as formed to drive the position of equilibrium from left to right
    (e) (i) disproportionation: ox. no. of N in $NO_2 = +4$, in $NO_2^- = +3$, in $NO_3^- = +5$
    (ii) $NO_2 + e^- \longrightarrow NO_2^-$
    $NO_2 + H_2O \longrightarrow NO_3^- + 2H^+ + e^-$
13. *(a)* The reaction mixture must be placed in a thermostatted bath. The progress of the reaction can be followed by measuring the intensity of the colour of $MnO_4^-(aq)$ ions in a spectrophotometer; see §§ 14.12.2, 35.7. Alternatively a 25.0 cm^3 portion of the reaction mixture can be taken, the reaction stopped by making the solution alkaline and the concentration of Mn^{2+} ions obtained by titration against H_2O_2. Another option is to titrate the remaining MnO_4^- against a reductant, e.g. $FeSO_4$. Runs are done at different temperatures.
    (b) The reaction starts slowly and the rate increases as more Mn^{2+} ions are formed. This indicates autocatalysis; see § 14.8.
    (c) $MnO_4^-(aq) + 8H^+(aq) + 5e^- \longrightarrow Mn^{2+}(aq) + 4H_2O(l)$
    $C_2O_4^{2-}(aq) \longrightarrow 2CO_2(g) + 2e^-$
    $2MnO_4^-(aq) + 16H^+(aq) + 5C_2O_4^{2-}(aq) \longrightarrow 2Mn^{2+}(aq) + 8H_2O(l) + 10CO_2(g)$
    (d) Amount of
    NaOH = $12.5 \times 10^{-3} \times 0.0800$ mol = 1.00×10^{-3} mol
    Amount of $H_2SO_4 + H_2C_2O_4 = 0.500 \times 10^{-3}$ mol
    $[H_2SO_4] + [H_2C_2O_4] = 0.0500$ mol dm^{-3}.
14. *(a)* A powder has more surface area/mass to react with the acid; see § 14.2.1.
    (b) The particles may not have sufficient energy to overcome repulsion between the electron clouds.
    (c) (i) in mol dm^{-3} (2): 6.4×10^{-5} (3) 16.0×10^{-2} (4) 1.5×10^{-2}
    (ii) $k = 0.444$ mol^{-2} dm^6 s^{-1}
    (iii) increase
    (iv) no effect
15. *(a)* (i) 3 (ii) mol^{-2} dm^6 s^{-1} (iv) double (v) decrease
    (ii) Follow the concentration of H_2O_2 by titration against $KMnO_4$; see § 3.16.1.
    (iv) double
    (v) Raising the pH decreases $[H^+]$ and decreases the rate.
    (b) (i) change from purple to pale pink
    (ii) $5O_2^{2-}(aq) + 2MnO_4^-(aq) + 16H^+(aq) \longrightarrow 2Mn^{2+}(aq) + 5O_2(g) + 8H_2O(l)$
    (c) H_2O_2 oxidises $Mn^{2+}(aq)$ (pale pink) to $MnO_4^-(aq)$ (purple).
    (d) (i) H:O:O:H
    (ii) See Figure 21.6A.
16. *(a)* See § 14.4, first paragraph.
    (i) See § 14.5.1, esterification [§ 33.8.2] and hydrolysis of esters [§ 33.8.2], amides [§ 3.15] and nitriles [§ 33.16].
    (ii) See § 24.8.
    (iii) See §§ 14.7, 26.6.
    (iv) See § 14.5.2.

(b) (i) See § 14.6.
(ii) See §§ 14.5.2, 14.7.
(iii) See § 14.7.
(iv) See § 14.7, poisoning.

17. (a) (i) Compare expts 1 and 2: rate doubles when $[(CH_3)_3CBr]$ doubles. Compare expts 2 and 3; rate does not change when $[OH^-]$ doubles.
(ii) 6.0×10^{-3} mol dm^{-3} s^{-1} = $k \times 2.0 \times 10^{-3}$ mol dm^{-2}
$k = 3.0$ s^{-1}
(iii) Rate = 3.0 s^{-1} × 4.0×10^{-3} mol dm^{-3}
= 1.2×10^{-2} mol dm^{-3} s^{-1}
(b) nucleophilic substitution, S_N2; see § 29.9.1
(c) Lucas test for 1° and 3° alcohols; see § 30.7.2, Table 30.7

PART 3: INORGANIC CHEMISTRY

CHAPTER 15 PATTERNS OF CHANGE IN THE PERIODIC TABLE

Checkpoint 15.4: The elements of Period 3

1. (a) Na $1s^22s^22p^63s$
Ca $1s^22s^22p^63s^23p^64s^2$
V $1s^22s^22p^63s^23p^64s^23d^{10}$
N $1s^22s^22p^3$
(b) Na_2O electrovalent solid, ionic structure, strong base; V_2O_5 covalent molecular solid, amphoteric; oxides of N gases, covalent, molecular, some neutral (N_2O, NO) and some acidic (NO_2, N_2O_3, N_2O_5). See Figures 15.7D and E.
2. (a) (i) See Figure 15.2F: a gradual increase from left to right, and § 15.4.
(ii) See § 15.4.
(b) See § 15.3: Na electrovalent, crystalline structure, basic, N covalent, simple molecular, acidic or neutral, V ionic with covalent character, macromolecular or layered, basic.
3. (a) covalent; see Figure 4.4C.
(b) Cl is more electronegative than H and attracts the electrons of the covalent bond more than H does: $H^{\delta+}$—$Cl^{\delta-}$
(c) $HCl(aq) + H_2O(l) \longrightarrow H_3O^+(aq) + Cl^-(aq)$
(d) ionic; see Figure 4.3D

Checkpoint 15.5: Compounds of Period 3

1. (a) Ar, Cl_2, P_4, S_8
(b) (i) Na, Mg (ii) none (iii) Al, Si, P, S, Cl, Ar
2. $MgCl_2$ consists of a three-dimensional ionic structure of Mg^{2+} ions and Cl^- ions with strong electrostatic forces of attraction between them. $SiCl_4$ consists of individual covalent molecules with only weak forces of attraction between molecules.
3. NaCl: see Figure 4.3D
MgS: similar to Figure 4.3I

H:P:H (dot-and-cross, with H below P)   :Cl:Si:Cl: (dot-and-cross, with Cl above and below Si)

4. (a) Na, Mg (b) Si,P, S, Cl
(c) Na_2O, MgO, Al_2O_3, SiO_2, P_2O_5, SO_3, Cl_2O_7
NaOH, $Mg(OH)_2$, $Al(OH)_3$, AlO_2^{2-}, $Si(OH)_4$, SiO_3^{2-}, H_3PO_4, H_2SO_4, $HClO_4$
5. See § 15.5.2, Table 15.5B.

Checkpoint 15.7: Blocks of the Periodic Table

1. (a) (i) ionic (ii) basic
(b) (i) ionic (ii) basic
(c) (i) covalent macromolecular (ii) weakly acidic
(d) (i) ionic (ii) basic
(e) (i) covalent macromolecular (ii) acidic
(f) (i) covalent macromolecular (ii) acidic
2. (a) CO (b) Mn_2O_7 (c) N_2O_5 (d) CrO_3 (e) Al_2O_3 (f) SO_2
3. (a) O^{2-} is smaller than S^{2-} therefore O^{2-} is less easily polarised by a cation, and MO is more ionic than MS.
(b) Hydrogen bonding; see § 4.8, Figure 4.8F
(c) The valence electrons of S are more easily promoted than those of O.
O, $1s^22s^22p^22p2p$, uses two 2p orbitals for bonding. In S, $1s^22s^22p^63s^23p^23p3p$, there are 3d orbitals available, and one 3s electron and one 3p electron can be promoted into 3d orbitals making 6 bonding orbitals. The energy required for electron promotion is compensated for by the formation of strong S—F bonds. For oxygen, promotion from 2p to 3d orbitals requires too much energy.
4. (a) See § 4.3.4, Figure 4.3I.
(b) (i) SiO_2 (ii) Na_2O (iii) MgO (iv) SO_3 (v) SO_3
(c) $Na_2O(s) + H_2O(l) \longrightarrow 2NaOH(aq)$
$SO_3(g) + H_2O(l) \longrightarrow H_2SO_4(aq)$
5. (a) (i) $SnCl_2$ is likely to be a crystalline solid which dissolves without being hydrolysed, while $SnCl_4$ is likely to be hydrolysed by water. (ii) SnO_2 is likely to have more acidic character than SnO.
(b) acid strength (i) $SO_3 > SO_2$ (ii) $P_2O_5 > P_2O_3$
6. (a) He or Ne or Ar (b) He (c) Li, Na, K (d) $SiCl_4$
(e) P (f) B, Si (g) S
7. (a) Increase in size down the group as the additional electrons occupy shells further away from the nucleus.
(b) Be. The electrons removed when Be $\longrightarrow$ Be^{2+} are in the 2s subshell close to the nucleus.
(c) (i) Be^{2+} is small in size with a double charge and can polarise Cl^- more than Ba^{2+} can.
(ii) low T_m, solubility in organic solvents, hydrolysed in aqueous solution.

Questions on Chapter 15

1. (a) Al^{3+} has the larger ratio of charge/surface area
(b) $AlCl_3$, $AlCl_3$
2. (a) $Be^{2+} > Ba^{2+}$ because the ratio of charge/ surface area is greater.
(b) $BeCl_2$ should be more covalent and more susceptible to hydrolysis.
3. Sn^{4+} is more polarising than Sn^{2+}; therefore $SnCl_4$ has more covalent character than $SnCl_2$. $SnCl_2$ is a crystalline solid, and $SnCl_4$ is a fuming liquid.
4. (a) See § 10.12.
(b) As the size of atoms increases down a group the electrons to be removed become more distant from the nuclear charge, and the first ionisation energy decreases; see §15.2, Figure 15.2E.
(c) 8: $1s^2\,2s^2\,2p^4$ 10: $1s^2\,2s^2\,2p^6$ 11: $1s^2\,2s^2\,2p^6\,3s$
(d) element 11 < element 8 < element 10
The 3s electron is shielded from the nucleus by a full $2p^6$ shell and is relatively easily removed. There is stability associated with a full p^6 shell, as in the element of atomic no. 10.
(e) (i) In B, a p-electron is removed, which is further from the nucleus than the s-electron in Be.
(ii) From Be to Ca, as the electron to be removed becomes further from the nucleus, the ionisation energy decreases.

5. (i) F (ii) Na (iii) F (iv) Cl (v) F (vi) Al (vii) Al (viii) C (ix) C

6. *(a)* The atomic radii decrease as the charges on the nuclei increase.

(b) The strength of the metallic bond increases Na < Mg < Al as the number of valence electrons increases. Si is a covalent macromolecular structure. P_4 molecules are held together by weak van der Waals forces; in S_8 the van der Waals forces are greater; in Cl_2 very weak forces of attraction operate between molecules.

(c) See § 15.6, Figure 15.6D.

(d) See § 15.6, Figure 15.6E.

7. *(a)* See § 15.2.

(b) e.g. T_m, T_b, atomic radius, first ionisation energy, electronegativity; see § 15.2, Figures 15.2A, B, C, E, F

(c) e.g. acid–base nature of oxides, bond character of chlorides, acid–base character of hydrides, vigour of reaction of elements with oxygen, dilute acids and water; see §§ 15.4–6, Tables 15.4, 15.5A, 15.5B Figures 15.6A–G

(d) See § 15.5.3, Figures 15.6A and F

8. *(a)* (i) Al_2O_3, CaO, MgO, Na_2O

(ii) P_2O_5, SO_2, SiO_2, Al_2O_3

(iii) none

(iv) Al_2O_3, MgO (chiefly basic)

(b) (i) Is the oxide acidic? Take the oxide with bench sodium hydroxide solution, warm, and notice whether the mass of oxide decreases. On addition of acid to a sample of the solution, does a precipitate appear? Evaporate to dryness. Is a salt obtained ?

Is the oxide basic? Take the oxide with bench hydrochloric acid, warm, evaporate to dryness. Is a salt obtained or the original oxide?

Is the oxide neutral? Warm a sample with sodium hydroxide solution and another with hydrochloric acid. Evaporate to dryness. Is the oxide obtained?
Is the oxide amphoteric? On warming with acid, does the amount of oxide decrease? Add sodium hydroxide solution to this solution. Is a precipitate obtained, and does the precipitate dissolve in excess of sodium hydroxide solution?

(c) (i) $MgCl_2$, NaCl, $PbCl_2$

(ii) CCl_4, HCl, $PbCl_4$, $SiCl_4$

(iii) HCl(g) is covalent but HCl(aq) is ionic; see § 12.6.1.

(d) See § 15.5.2.

9. *(a)* See § 10.12.

(b) There is stability associated with a half-full p subshell; therefore energy is given out when C accepts an electron.

(c) Li has the stability associated with a full $2s^2$ subshell. To make Li accept an electron energy must be supplied, and Li therefore has a positive electron affinity, EA.
Be will be more ready to accept electrons to form Be^-; the value of EA will be positive but less positive than that for Li.

(d) To add a second electron to O^- against the repulsion between e^- and O^- requires a large input of energy; therefore the second EA is positive.

10. *(a)* (i) See § 10.12.

(ii) decrease because the electron removed is further from the nucleus

(b) (i) See Figure 15.6D and Table 15.5A.

(ii) Na_2O, P_2O_3, P_2O_5, SO_2, SO_3

$Na_2O(s) + H_2O(l) \longrightarrow 2NaOH(aq)$

$P_2O_5(s) + 3H_2O(l) \longrightarrow 2H_3PO_4(aq)$

$SO_3(s) + H_2O(l) \longrightarrow H_2SO_4(aq)$

(c) +7 and +1

11. *(a)* (i) Cl_2 (ii) Na, Mg, Al, Si

(b) NaCl, MgS

(c)

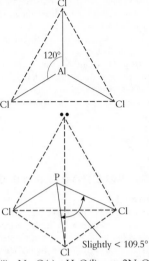

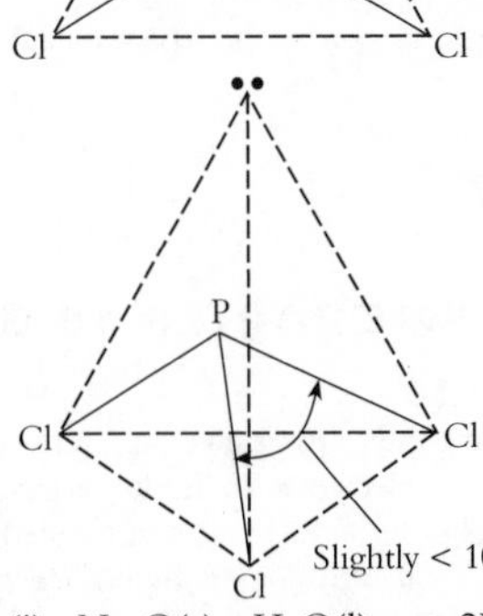

(d) (i) $Na_2O(s) + H_2O(l) \longrightarrow 2NaOH(aq)$

(ii) $SO_2(g) + H_2O(l) \longrightarrow H_2SO_3(aq)$

12. *(a)* (i) I. Large cations and small anions

II. A singly charged cation tends to polarise anions less and give bonds with more ionic character than a multiply charged cation. A singly charged anion is less easily polarised than an anion with a multiple charge.

III. Ions with a full outer shell of electrons are favoured.

(ii) I true, II false, III true, IV false, V true, VI false

(b) (i) Na_2O and NaCl ionic, Al_2O_3 ionic with covalent character, Al_2Cl_6 covalent

(ii) I. It could have a covalent macromolecular structure, e.g. SiO_2, or an ionic structure, e.g. MgO.

II. The T_m is too high to try to electrolyse the solid. If the oxide is ionic, it will be basic. Test to find out whether it will react with acids.

13. (a) See § 4.6.3.

(b) (i) ionic (ii) polar covalent (iii) covalent

(c) (i) The electron pairs of the bonds and the lone pairs spread out to distance themselves as far as possible in order to minimise repulsion between them.

(ii) See Figure 5.2F.

(iii) Repulsion between lone pair–bonding pair is greater than between two bonding pairs.

(iv) N is more electronegative than H so in the bond $N^{\delta-}$—$H^{\delta+}$ the electron density is greater towards the N end than towards the H end of the bond.

(d) (i) sodium, e.g.

$4Na(s) + O_2(g) \longrightarrow 2Na_2O(s)$

$Na_2O(s) + H_2O(l) \longrightarrow 2NaOH(aq)$

(ii) aluminium

$Al_2O_3(s) + 3H_2SO_4(aq) \longrightarrow Al_2(SO_4)_3(aq) + 3H_2O(l)$

$Al_2O_3(s) + 2NaOH(aq) + 3H_2O(l) \longrightarrow 2NaAl(OH)_4(aq)$

(iii) SiO_2 is macromolecular with very strong Si—O bonds. CO_2 is molecular.
Melted with solid NaOH, SiO_2 forms sodium silicate, Na_2SiO_3.

14. *(a)* See § 10.12.
(b) (i) The nuclear charge increases, the atomic radius decreases, the valence electrons are harder to remove.
(ii) The 3p electron of Al is further from the nucleus than the 3s electrons of Mg.
(iii) There is stability associated with a half-full subshell, e.g. the $3p^3$ subshell of P.
(c) The valence electrons of Na and Mg can be removed from the nuclei to form the metallic bond; see § 6.3. The outer electrons of S and Cl are not removed.
(d) (i) the metallic bond; see § 6.3 (ii) the ionic bond; see §§ 3.1, 4.3.3

15. *(a)* a property which is repeated a number of times, each time after a certain number of elements; see § 15.2
(b) The atomic number increases: the charge on the nucleus increases and therefore holds the electrons closer to the nucleus.
(c) (i) Mg with two valence electrons forms a stronger metallic bond than Na with one valence electron.
(ii) Si has a macromolecular structure with each Si atom bonded to four others.
(iii) S_8 molecules are held in a structure by intermolecular forces of attraction. P_4 molecules are loosely bonded to other P_4 molecules.
(iv) Argon is a gas in which very weak van der Waals forces act between the atoms.

CHAPTER 16 GROUP 0 THE NOBLE GASES

Questions on Chapter 16

1. In the formation of ionic bonds, atoms give or accept electrons to attain a full outer shell of electrons – a noble gas electron configuration [see § 4.3.1]. In the formation of covalent bonds, atoms share electrons to attain a full outer shell of electrons [see § 4.4].
2. See § 2.6. Mendeleev had predicted that new elements would be discovered and found to fit the Periodic Table. When the noble gases were discovered they fitted in between Groups 1 and 7 [see § 16.1].
3. See § 16.2: helium balloons (low density), argon (inert atmosphere), neon and krypton (lights).
4. Moving down a group, the outer shell electrons are more distant from the nucleus and easier to remove than electrons in shells closer to the nucleus. Ar < Kr because the Ar atom is smaller than the Kr atom.

CHAPTER 17 HYDROGEN

Checkpoint 17.4: Water

1. *(a)* Water has maximum density at 4 °C so ice is less dense than water and rises to the top of the pond.
(b) There are very strong hydrogen bonds between water molecules and weak van der Waals forces between oil molecules. Both these forces are stronger than the very weak forces of attraction between water molecules and oil molecules.
(c) Ethanol, C_2H_5OH, can form hydrogen bonds with water molecules; see § 4.8.3, Figure 4.8 G.
(d) See § 17.5, Figure 17.5A.
(e) Organic compounds which can form hydrogen bonds with water molecules include alcohols, aldehydes, ketones, carboxylic acids and nitriles.
(f) Hydrolysis occurs because Na_2S is the salt of a weak acid.
$S^{2-}(aq) + 2H_2O(l) \rightleftharpoons H_2S(aq) + 2OH^-(aq)$
The hydrogen sulphide produced smells unpleasant.
(g) KCN is the salt of a weak acid. Hydrolysis occurs with the production of poisonous HCN.
$CN^-(aq) + H_2O(l) \rightleftharpoons HCN(g) + OH^-(aq)$
(h) Aluminium sulphate is the salt of a weak base and is hydrolysed:
$[Al(H_2O)_6]^{3+}(aq) + H_2O(l) \rightleftharpoons [Al(H_2O)_5OH]^{2+}(aq) + H_3O^+(aq)$
The acidic solution will liberate CO_2 from the carbonate solution in a fire extinguisher.

Questions on Chapter 17

1. *(a)* *(b)* See Figure 17.2A.
2. *(a)* e.g. Mg, Zn, Fe *(b)* e.g. Na, K, Ca, Mg *(c)* e.g. Al, Zn *(d)* e.g. Fe, Zn *(e)* e.g. W, Mo; see Figure 17.3A
3. *(a)* $H_2(g) + RCH{=}CHR'(l) \longrightarrow RCH_2CH_2R'(s)$
(b) $3H_2(g) + W_2O_3(s) \longrightarrow 2W(s) + 3H_2O(l)$
(c) $2H_2(g) + O_2(g) \longrightarrow 2H_2O(l)$
(d) $H_2(g) + S(s) \longrightarrow H_2S(g)$
(e) $H_2(g) + Cl_2(g) \longrightarrow 2HCl(g)$
(f) $3H_2(g) + N_2(g) \longrightarrow 2NH_3(g)$
(a) is used in the hydrogenation of unsaturated oils to form fats, *(b)* is used to extract tungsten from its ores, *(c)* is used to propel rockets, *(e)* is used in the manufacture of HCl, *(f)* is used in the manufacture of ammonia for the fertiliser industry.
4. *(a)* $2H_2(g) + O_2(g) \longrightarrow 2H_2O(l)$
(ii) 0.25 mol
(iii) $0.25\ \text{mol} \times 18\ \text{g mol}^{-1} = 4.5\ \text{g}$
(b) (i) See Figure 4.8G.
(ii) High T_b, high T_m compared with hydrides in the same period. Ability to dissolve compounds with which it can form hydrogen bonds, e.g. alcohols and carboxylic acids.
(c) (i) $Na_2O(s) + H_2O(l) \longrightarrow 2NaOH(aq)$
(ii) 13–14

CHAPTER 18 THE s BLOCK METALS: GROUPS 1 AND 2

Checkpoint 18.4: The metals

1. *(a)* The ion has one electron less than the atom. In the ion the number of protons is one less than the number of electrons: the electrons are held closer to the nucleus than in the atom.
(b) The additional protons all go into the nucleus. The additional p electrons occupy orbitals which are further away from the nucleus in Cs^+ than in Li^+.
(c) Na^+ has 11 p and 10 e, Mg^{2+} has 12 p and 10 e. The nucleus of Mg^{2+} with 12 p can hold the 10 e closer to the nucleus than the nucleus of Na^+ with 11 p and 10 e.
(d) Be^{2+} is the ion with the highest ratio of charge/radius. The electron pairs from H_2O coordinate into the outer shell of Be^{2+}. The bond is formed closer to the nucleus in Be^{2+} than in the other ions.

2. Group 2 metals have a stronger metallic bond because they have 2 valence electrons whereas Group 1 metals have only one. The atomic radii and ionic radii of Group 2 metals are smaller than those of Group 2 elements in the same period. The first ionisation energies of Group 2 metals are higher than those of Group 1 elements of the same period.
3. For atomisation, first ionisation energy, etc., see § 10.12.

Checkpoint 18.7: Group 1

1. The electron removed is in the outermost s-subshell. The larger the atom, the further is this electron from the nucleus and the easier it is to remove it against the attraction of the nucleus. See Table 18.5.
2. *(a)* The ion Na^+ does not have great polarising power; see §§ 4.6.3, 4.6.4.
   (b) Na^+ and Cl^- do not react with H_2O.
   (c) CO_3^{2-} reacts with water because it is the anion of a weak acid:

   $$CO_3^{2-}(aq) + H_2O(l) \rightleftharpoons HCO_3^-(aq) + OH^-(aq)$$

   The solution contains a higher $[OH^-]$ than water and is alkaline.
   (d) H_2SO_4 is diprotic $\longrightarrow NaHSO_4$ and Na_2SO_4.
3. *(a)*, *(b)* See § 18.6.3.
   (c) The hydroxides are strong alkalis.
4. (i) $NaOH(aq) + HCl(aq) \longrightarrow NaCl(aq) + H_2O(l)$
   (ii) $2NaOH(aq) + H_2SO_4(aq) \longrightarrow Na_2SO_4(aq) + 2H_2O(l)$
   (iii) $2NaOH(aq) + MgSO_4(aq) \longrightarrow Mg(OH)_2(s) + Na_2SO_4(aq)$
   (iv) $NaOH(aq) + NH_4Cl(s) \longrightarrow NH_3(g) + NaCl(aq) + H_2O(l)$
5. *(a)* to allow ions to pass from the anode compartment into the cathode compartment
   (b) hydrogen, chlorine, sodium chlorate(I), sodium chlorate(V)
   (c) (i) $NaOH(aq) + HCl(aq) \longrightarrow NaCl(aq) + H_2O(l)$
   (ii) $2NaOH(aq) + H_2SO_4(aq) \longrightarrow Na_2SO_4(aq) + 2H_2O(l)$
   (iii) $2NaOH(aq) + MgSO_4(aq) \longrightarrow Mg(OH)_2(s) + Na_2SO_4(aq)$
   (iv) $NaOH(aq) + NH_4Cl(s) \longrightarrow NH_3(g) + NaCl(aq) + H_2O(l)$
6. The solid deliquesces – takes water vapour from the air and dissolves in it to form NaOH(aq). This reacts with CO_2 in the air to give $Na_2CO_3.10H_2O(s)$. The crystals effloresce to form $Na_2CO_3.H_2O$, a white solid.
   40 g NaOH $\longrightarrow$ 62 g $Na_2CO_3.H_2O$,
   and 0.254 g NaOH $\longrightarrow$ 0.394 g $Na_2CO_3.H_2O$.
7. See §§ 18.1, 18.6.7.
   (a) Sodium carbonate, used as $Na_2CO_3.10H_2O$ as a water softener in detergents and used as Na_2CO_3 as a primary standard in titrimetric analysis and in the glass industry, the paper industry and the manufacture of soaps and detergents.
   (b) Coke: coal is mined in Lancashire. Limestone is quarried in Derbyshire. Salt is mined in Cheshire. All these sites are close to the ICI plant in Cheshire. Ammonia is made by the Haber process. The process runs continuously.
   (c) The by-product is $CaCl_2$; see § 18.1 for use and disposal.

Checkpoint 18.9: Group 2

1. The metals react: $M \longrightarrow M^{2+} + e^-$. The ease of removing the electrons increases down the group because the valence electrons are in shells further away from the nucleus. See Table 18.8 for reactions with water.
2. *(a)* lattice enthalpy and enthalpy of hydration; see § 18.9.2
   (b) *(c)* See § 18.9.2, Table 18.9A.
3. See § 18.9.3.
4. See § 18.9.5 for uses.
5. *(a)* See § 18.9.6, Table 18.9B for uses.
   (b) Be^{2+} is small in size and multiply charged and able to polarise Cl^-, so $BeCl_2$ is covalent; see §§ 4.6.3, 4.6.4. In solution Be^{2+} is stabilised by hydration as $Be^{2+}(aq)$.
   (c) O^{2-} is smaller than CO_3^{2-} so Ca^{2+} and O^{2-} can approach more closely than Ca^{2+} and CO_3^{2-}.
   (d) $Mg^{2+}O^{2-}$ has a higher standard lattice enthalpy than $Ba^{2+}O^{2-}$ because Mg^{2+} is smaller than Ba^{2+}. The change $MgCO_3 \longrightarrow MgO + CO_2$ is therefore less endothermic than the change $BaCO_3 \longrightarrow BaO + CO_2$.
6. For diagonal relationships see § 15.3 and Figure 15.3B; e.g. covalent chlorides and acidic solutions of salts due to salt hydrolysis.

Questions on Chapter 18

Questions on Group 1 and Group 2

1. *(a)* Ionic Fr^+H^- reacting with water to give $H_2 + FrOH(aq)$.
   (b) Will combine readily $\longrightarrow$ FrCl etc.
   (c) Will react even when cold $\longrightarrow Fr_2O$. Fr, being the last member of the group, is the most reactive.
   (d) See § 18.6.3.
   (e) See § 18.6.2.
2. Similarity: see physical properties § 18.2 and chemical reactions Table 18.5.
3. *(a)* Hydroxide is sparingly soluble therefore **A** is in Group 2, not Group 1. The speed of the reaction with water suggests calcium.
   (b) $A_r = 40$, **A** is Ca *(c)* red
   (d) $2Ca(s) + O_2(g) \longrightarrow 2CaO(s)$
   $Ca(s) + 2H_2O(l) \longrightarrow Ca(OH)_2(aq) + H_2(g)$
   $CaO(s) + H_2O(l) \longrightarrow Ca(OH)_2(aq)$
4. *(a)* Evidence that **Y** is in Group 2: The first two electrons are easier to remove than the third. The carbonate is insoluble (not in Group 1) and the hydroxide is basic (not amphoteric). Evidence that **Y** is magnesium: It does not colour a flame, and the sulphate is soluble, unlike those of Ca, Sr and Ba.
   (b) $Mg^{2+}(aq) + CO_3^{2-}(aq) \longrightarrow MgCO_3(s)$
   $Mg^{2+}(aq) + 2OH^-(aq) \longrightarrow Mg(OH)_2(s)$
   (c) The carbonate and hydroxide decompose on heating to give magnesium oxide. The small and doubly charged ions $Mg^{2+}O^{2-}$ give magnesium oxide a high lattice enthalpy.
5. *(a)* (i) Strong forces of attraction exist between the oppositely charged ions. Enough energy must be supplied to give the ions the kinetic energy which they need to break free of the lattice.
   (ii) Coordinate bonds form from the lone pairs on O of H_2O to the metal ions. Bond-making is exothermic.
   (iii) The sums (lattice enthalpy + hydration enthalpy) /kJ mol^{-1} are LiF −3, NaF −10, KF −27, RbF −40. Thus, dissolution becomes more exothermic and solubility increases from LiF to RbF.
   (b) The oxides react with water to form hydroxides, e.g. $Na_2O(s) + H_2O(l) \longrightarrow 2NaOH(aq)$
   (c) The first ionisation energy is low.
6. *(a)* For NaCl, see Figure 6.4A; for I_2 see Figure 6.5B, for diamond see Figure 6.6A, for graphite see Figure 6.7A. NaCl conducts electricity when aqueous or molten, I_2 sublimes, diamond is hard and brilliant, graphite is soft and used as a lubricant.
   (b) $Na_2O(s) + H_2O(l) \longrightarrow 2NaOH(aq)$
   $P_2O_5(s) + 3H_2O(l) \longrightarrow 2H_3PO_4(aq)$

   Na_2O is ionic, and O^{2-} ions react with water to give OH^- ions, so the solution is alkaline:

   $O^{2-}(s) + H_2O(l) \longrightarrow 2OH^-(aq)$
   P_2O_5 is covalent, and a lone pair on O of H_2O can coordinate into the d subshell of P as a first step in the formation of PO_4^{3-} and H^+
   $P_2O_5(s) + 3H_2O(l) \longrightarrow 2PO_4^{3-}(aq) + 6H^+(aq)$

(c) (i) First ionisation energy decreases down the group because the electron removed is further from the nucleus.
(ii) See § 18.7.

7. *(a)* (i) $Ca(s) + 2H_2O(l) \longrightarrow Ca(OH)_2(aq) + H_2(g)$
$2Ca(s) + O_2(g) \longrightarrow 2CaO(s)$

Zinc reacts with steam, but not with cold water as calcium does. Zinc burns in oxygen to form ZnO.

(ii) See § 18.9.3. Stability decreases down the group as the distance between M^{2+} and OH^- or M^{2+} and CO_3^{2-} increases. Heat to 100 °C and test for the evolution of CO_2 with limewater.

(b) 4.48 dm^3 CO_2 at stp = 0.200 mol therefore 0.200 mol of $\mathbf{Z}_2CO_3$ or $\mathbf{Z}CO_3$ was used.
Therefore 14.78 g = 0.200 mol, and M = 14.78/ 0.200 = 74.
M of CO_3 = 60 therefore either $2A_r(\mathbf{Z}) + 60 = 74$ and $A_r(\mathbf{Z}) = 7$ or $Z + 60 = 74$ and $A_r(\mathbf{Z}) = 14$. Values of A_r show that **Z** is Li.

(c) Ba^{2+} gives a white precipitate with dilute sulphuric acid. The brown solution suggests iodine. I^- is oxidised by Cu^{2+} to I_2. MX_2 is BaI_2.
$2Cu^{2+}(aq) + 2I^-(aq) \longrightarrow 2Cu^+(aq) + I_2(aq)$

(d) Putting values of $\Delta H_f^\ominus$ under each species,
$Fe_2O_3(s) + 3CO(g) \longrightarrow 2Fe(s) + 3CO_2(g)$
−824 3(−110) 0 3(−394)
$\Delta H_r^\ominus = 3(-394) + 824 + 330 = -28$ kJ mol^{-1}
For 0.1 mol, $\Delta H^\ominus = -2.8$ kJ

8. *(a)* (i) Molten anhydrous NaCl. Aqueous NaCl.
(b) (i) Chlorine: $2Cl^-(aq) \longrightarrow Cl_2(g) + 2e^-$
(ii) Oxygen: $4OH^-(aq) \longrightarrow O_2(g) + 2H_2O(l)$
(c) In a concentrated solution of NaCl, $[Cl^-]$ is high and Cl^- is discharged to form Cl_2. In a very dilute solution of NaCl, OH^- is discharged in preference to Cl^-.
(d) See § 19.4.1. The solution contains $[Al(H_2O)_6]^{3+}(aq)$. A gelatinous ppt forms; this is hydrated $Al(OH)_3(s)$. It dissolves as more NaOH(aq) is added to form a solution of sodium aluminate, $NaAl(OH)_4(aq)$.
$[Al(H_2O)_6]^{3+}(aq) + 3OH^-(aq) \longrightarrow Al(OH)_3(H_2O)_3(s) + 3H_2O(l)$
$Al(OH)_3(H_2O)_3(s) + OH^-(aq) \longrightarrow [Al(OH)_4(H_2O)_3]^-(aq)$

9. *(a)* (i) See § 10.7.1.
(ii) $2Li(s) + C(s) + 1.5\,O_2(g) \longrightarrow Li_2CO_3(s); \Delta H_f^\ominus$
(b) (i) $Li_2CO_3(s) \longrightarrow Li_2O(s) + CO_2(g)$
−1216 −596 −394; $\Delta H = +226$ kJ mol^{-1}
$Na_2CO_3(s) \longrightarrow Na_2O(s) + CO_2(g)$
−1131 −416 −394; $\Delta H = +321$ kJ mol^{-1}
(ii) Thermal stability increases down the group: the value of $\Delta H^\ominus$ for the decomposition of the carbonate becomes more endothermic as the group is descended. The force of attraction between the smaller ions, Li^+, Na^+, and the doubly charged anion CO_3^{2-} is greater than that for the larger cations.
(c) See § 10.12. Down Group 1, the first ionisation energy decreases because the electron removed is in a shell further from the nucleus as the group is descended. The T_m increases down the group because the atoms with more electrons form stronger metallic bonds.
(d) Amount of HCl = $21.2 \times 10^{-3} \times 0.113 = 2.396 \times 10^{-3}$ mol
Amount of $Na_2CO_3 = 0.5 \times 2.396 \times 10^{-3}$ in 25.0 cm^3
= 0.01198 mol in 250 cm^3
Mass of Na_2CO_3 = 1.269 g.
Mass of H_2O = 2.995 − 1.269 = 1.725 g
Molar ratio = 1 : 8, and $x = 8$

Questions on Group 2

1. *(a)* Reacts vigorously; see § 18.8, Table 18.8.
(b) Soluble; see § 18.9.2, Table 18.9A. The solution is alkaline with pH ≈ 13.
(c) Insoluble; see § 18.9.2, Table 18.9A.
(d) Nitrate decomposes $\longrightarrow RaO + O_2 + NO_2$. Carbonate decomposes $\longrightarrow RaO + CO_2$; see § 18.9.3.

2. All are metals and form cations M^{2+}. For reactions see § 18.8, Table 18.8. Compounds MO and $M(OH)_2$ are strong bases. All form carbonates, nitrates and sulphates, and hydrogencarbonates exist in solution.
The differences between Be, Mg and Ca, Sr, Ba are:

- Be and Mg compounds have some covalent character and salts are partially hydrolysed in solution. Compounds of Ca, Sr, Ba are completely electrovalent.
- Reaction with cold water: Be, none; Mg, slow; Ca, Sr, Ba react readily.
- With dilute HNO_3, Be and Mg $\longrightarrow H_2$, whereas others $\longrightarrow NO_2$.
- With NH_3, Be, Mg $\longrightarrow M_3N_2$, whereas others $\longrightarrow MH_2$.
- With N_2, Be does not react, but others form nitrides.

3. *(a)* (i) Mg reacts slowly with cold water, fairly rapidly with steam, while Ca reacts steadily with cold water.
$Mg(s) + H_2O(g) \longrightarrow MgO(s) + H_2(g)$
$Ca(s) + 2H_2O(l) \longrightarrow Ca(OH)_2(aq) + H_2(g)$
(ii) Ca ionises more readily $\longrightarrow Ca^{2+}$ than does Mg because the valence electrons in Ca are further from the nucleus. $Ca(OH)_2$ is more soluble than $Mg(OH)_2$ and this helps the reaction.
(b) (i) See § 18.9.2. (ii) See § 18.9.3.
(iii) MgO reacts more slowly with water than CaO because $Mg(OH)_2$ is less soluble than $Ca(OH)_2$. This is because the decrease in lattice dissociation enthalpy Mg $\longrightarrow$ Ca outweighs the decrease in enthalpy of hydration from $Mg^{2+} \longrightarrow Ca^{2+}$.

4. *(a)* Ba. Ba has the highest negative value of $E^\ominus$, which measures the tendency $M \longrightarrow M^{2+} + 2e^-$.
(b) $Mg(s) + H_2(g) \longrightarrow MgH_2(s)$
(c) $E^\ominus$ values are too highly negative to allow reduction by C or H_2. Electrolysis of the molten anhydrous chlorides can be used.
(d) In hydration, a lone pair of electrons on O of H_2O coordinates into the valence shell of the metal cation. In Mg^{2+} this bond forms closer to the nucleus than in the later elements of the group and more energy is given out.
(e) (i) Ba; see § 18.9.2, Table 18.9 (ii) Mg; see § 18.9.3

5. *(a)* 1. Metal oxide + coke + limestone; high temperature, through draft of air. Used in extraction of iron, § 24.17.1.
2. Oxide; electrolysis of molten anhydrous oxide. Used for Al, § 19.3.2.
3. Metal oxide + chlorine + magnesium. Used for Ti, § 24.12.2.
Other methods are mentioned in § 18.10, including the concept map.
(b) (i) Oxygen converts carbon into CO which escapes. A jet of O_2 is directed onto molten iron, see § 24.17.3.
(ii) The raw materials, iron ore, coke and limestone are not costly. The blast furnace runs continuously. Ti extraction uses Mg, which is costly and is a batch process.
(iii) Ti retains its strength at high temperature.

6. *(a)* (i) Ca (Ar) $4s^2$ ionises to form Ca^{2+} which combines with $2F^-$ or $2Cl^-$ to form CaF_2 or $CaCl_2$.
(ii) CaF_2 is a compound of an electropositive metal and F, the most electronegative element. The lattice enthalpy of CaF_2 is very high and favours the formation of an ionic compound. Similarly, the enthalpy of formation of $CaCl_2$ is exothermic because the lattice enthalpy of the ionic structure is high.

(iii) The lattice enthalpy of CaF_2 is higher than that of $CaCl_2$ because the smaller F^- ion approaches more closely to Ca^{2+} than Cl^- can.

(b) $-1214 = 193 + 590 + 1150 + 158 - 796 + \text{L.E.}$
L.E. = -2509 kJ mol^{-1}

(c) (i) Calcium is too reactive; it reacts even with cold water. This reaction would be too exothermic for safety.
(ii) I. **A** = H_2, **B** = $Ca(OH)_2(s)$
$Ca(s) + 2H_2O(l) \longrightarrow Ca(OH)_2(s) + H_2(g)$
II. $Ca(OH)_2(s) + 2HCl(aq) \longrightarrow CaCl_2(aq) + 2H_2O(l)$
Evaporate to the point of crystallisation.

(d) red; formed from the shells of sea creatures

7. *(a)* (i) $Ba(s) + 2H_2O(l) \longrightarrow Ba(OH)_2(aq) + H_2(g)$
(ii) More vigorously. The metals become more reactive as atomic number increases because the electrons to be removed in ionisation are further from the nucleus.
(iii) $BaCO_3(s) \longrightarrow BaO(s) + CO_2(g)$
(iv) $CaCO_3$. Lattice enthalpy of $CaCO_3$ > LE of $BaCO_3$, and LE of CaO > LE of BaO. The effect of increase in size of the cation is greater in **M**O than in **M**CO_3 because O^{2-} is smaller than CO_3^{2-}. Enthalpy considerations therefore favour
$CaCO_3 \longrightarrow CaO + CO_2$.
(v) Add dilute sulphuric acid. $BaCl_2$ gives a white precipitate of $BaSO_4(s)$, but there is no precipitate with $CaCl_2$.

(b) (i) Ratio Ba, 1.71/137 : O, 0.40/ 16 = 0.0125 : 0.025 = 1 : 2. The formula is BaO_2.
(ii) O^{2-} (iii) -1 (iv) Na_2O_2

(c) (i) $Na_2O_2(s) + H_2SO_4(aq) \longrightarrow H_2O_2(aq) + Na_2SO_4(aq)$
(ii) $BaSO_4$ is sparingly soluble and can be filtered off. Na_2SO_4 is very soluble and difficult to separate from the hydrogen peroxide.

8. *(a)* (i) $2Ca(s) + O_2(g) \longrightarrow 2CaO(s)$
$CaCO_3(s) \longrightarrow CaO(s) + CO_2(g)$
(ii) Mg^{2+} is smaller than Ca^{2+} therefore the lattice enthalpy of $MgCO_3$ > LE of $CaCO_3$. Also LE of MgO > LE of CaO. The effect of increase in size of the cation is greater in **M**O than in **M**CO_3 because O^{2-} is smaller than CO_3^{2-}, therefore
$MgCO_3 \longrightarrow MgO$ is less endothermic than
$CaCO_3 \longrightarrow CaO$.

(b) (i) $Ca(OH)_2(s)$ (ii) 12–13

(c) CaO is basic and SiO_2 is acidic.

(d) (i) Amount of $CaCl_2$ = 6.41/64 = 0.100 mol
Volume of C_2H_2 = 0.100 × 24.0 dm^3 = 2.40 dm^3
(ii) The molecules are much closer together at high P; see § 7.8.

9. *(a)* (i) A white precipitate forms.
$Mg^{2+}(aq) + 2OH^-(aq) \longrightarrow Mg(OH)_2(s)$
(ii) Add dilute nitric acid and aqueous silver nitrate. A white ppt indicates AgCl.
$Ag^+(aq) + Cl^-(aq) \longrightarrow AgCl(s)$

(b) (i) Energy is required to dissociate the ionic lattice. Energy is given out when ions are hydrated. For the small ion Mg^{2+} the enthalpy of hydration is large and compensates the lattice dissociation enthalpy and therefore $MgSO_4$ dissolves. For Ba^{2+} the enthalpy of hydration is smaller and does not outweigh the lattice dissociation enthalpy.
(ii) Electrolysed in aqueous solution. Crystalline. Mg^{2+} and SO_4^{2-} show their individual reactions.

(c) Essential for photosynthesis.

CHAPTER 19 GROUP 3

Questions on Chapter 19

1. See § 19.3.2.

2. *(a)* The chassis needs the strength of steel. The engine block is cast and needs to be made from cast iron. Other parts, bodywork, etc., can be made from Al alloys. The resistance to rust is an advantage, and they do not need the strength of steel. The lower density reduces fuel consumption.
(b) Iron oxides are reduced by carbon at a temperature which could be achieved by early metallurgists.
(c) (i) can be polished to a smooth surface
(ii) good conductor and low in density
(iii) non-toxic
(iv) not corroded on exposure to air

3. The value of the standard electrode potential for the discharge of Na is higher than that for Al. In cryolite, Al is part of the anion.

4. Amount of Al = 1 × 10^6/ 27 mol
Coulombs needed = 3 × 96 500 × 10^6/27 = 1.07 × 10^{10} C

5. The high ratio charge/size attracts negatively charged colloidal particles, which coagulate and precipitate from colloidal solution.

6. Hydrolysis of $[Al(H_2O)_6]^{3+}$ [see § 19.4.1] produces hydrogen ions. With NaCN they liberate poisonous hydrogen cyanide, HCN.

7. *(a)* (i) Dissolves and then the solution becomes cloudy.
$Al_2Cl_6(aq) + 12H_2O(l) \longrightarrow 2Al(H_2O)_6]^{3+}(aq) + 6Cl^-(aq)$
(ii) $[Al(H_2O)_6]^{3+}(aq) + H_2O(l) \rightleftharpoons [Al(H_2O)_5OH]^{2+}(aq) + H_3O^+(aq)$
(iii) A gelatinous ppt of $Al(OH)_3(H_2O)_3(s)$ appears.
$CO_3^{2-}(aq) + H_2O(l) \rightleftharpoons HCO_3^{2-}(aq) + OH^-(aq)$
$[Al(H_2O)_6]^{3+}(aq) + 3OH^-(aq) \longrightarrow Al(OH)_3(H_2O)_3(s) + 3H_2O(l)$

(b) (i) A gelatinous ppt of $Al(OH)_3(H_2O)_3(s)$ appears and then dissolves in excess of ammonia to form $[Al(NH_3)_6]^{3+}(aq)$.
(ii) The observations would be the same, but $Al(OH)_3(s)$ would dissolve to form $Na^+(aq)$ $[Al(OH)_4]^-(aq)$.

8. *(a)* (i) The T_m is even higher than 1200 K. The cost of electricity to keep it molten would be very high.
(ii) $Al^{3+}(l) + 3e^- \longrightarrow Al(l)$
(iii) $O^{2-}(l) \longrightarrow O(g) + 2e^-$ followed by $2O(g) \longrightarrow O_2(g)$
O_2 oxidises C to CO and CO_2.

(b) Keeping the electrolyte molten. One mol Al requires 3 faradays for discharge.

(c) (i) Saves resources of Al and saves on the energy consumed.
(ii) Collecting and separating aluminium from other metals.

9. *(a)* See § 19.3.2.

(b) (i) AlF_3 is largely ionic; $AlCl_3$ is largely covalent.
(ii) The small highly charged Al^{3+} ion can polarise the anion Cl^-, drawing the electron cloud of Cl^- towards Al^{3+} and forming a bond with a high degree of covalent character [see § 4.6.3]. The ion F^- is smaller than Cl^-, its electrons are held closer to the nucleus and are less polarisable.

(c) (i) $pV = nRT$
$1.00 \times 10^5 \text{ Pa} \times 73.6 \times 10^{-6} \text{ m}^3 = (0.500 \text{ g}/M) \times 8.314 \text{ J K}^{-1} \text{ mol}^{-1} \times 473 \text{ K}$
$M = 267$ g mol^{-1}, $M_r = 267$
(ii) Cl Cl Cl
Al Al
Cl Cl Cl

CHAPTER 20 THE HALOGENS

Checkpoint 20.3: Bonding

1. F forms ionic compounds rapidly because, being a small ion, the standard lattice enthalpies of its salts are highly exothermic, and the standard enthalpies of formation of its compounds are therefore highly exothermic. Also the F—F bond is weaker than the X—X bond in other halogens; see § 20.3. F forms covalent compounds readily because the covalent bonds between F and other elements have high standard enthalpies; see § 20.3.2.
2. *(a)* The F—F bond is weaker than other X—X bonds. The lattice enthalpies of fluorides are high; see § 20.3.1.
   (b) S, $1s^2 2s^2 2p^6 3s^2 3p^4$ can form four covalent bonds by promoting one 3p electron into a 3d orbital. The energy required is compensated for by the formation of four bonds, e.g. in SCl_4. Two more bonds can be formed by promoting a 3s electron into a 3d orbital. The energy required is compensated for by the formation of six S—F bonds but not by six S—Cl bonds, which have lower standard bond enthalpies
3. Br $(Ar)4s^2 3d^{10} 4p^5$

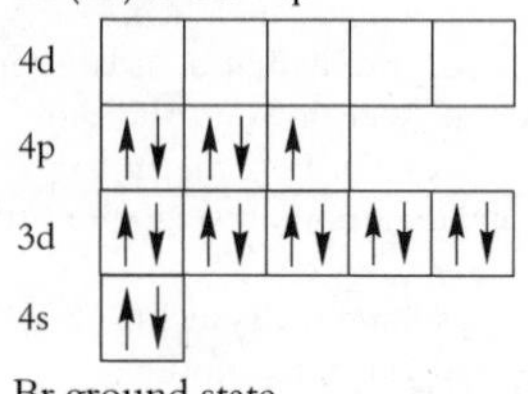

Br ground state, can form 1 covalent bond

4d, 4p, 3d, 4s

Br 1st excited state ⟶ 3 covalent bonds

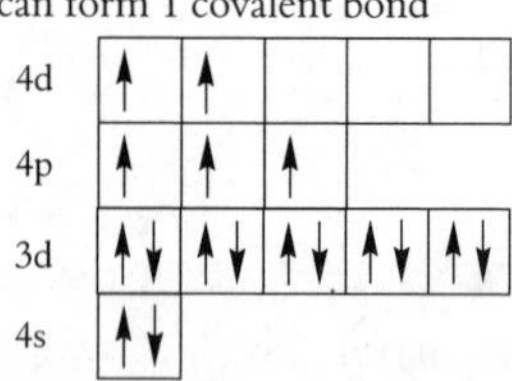

Br 2nd excited state ⟶ 5 covalent bonds

The electrons promoted in Br are in the 4th shell and further from the nucleus than the electrons promoted from the 3rd shell in Cl.

4. *(a)* The graph shows an increase from F to Cl, then a decrease Cl to Br to I.
   (b) A sharp increase from F to Cl, then a steady decrease Cl to Br to I.

Checkpoint 20.4: Reactivity

1. See standard electrode potentials, Table 20.1. Br has a higher $E^\ominus$ than **I** therefore Br oxidises I^-. Cl has a higher $E^\ominus$ than Br therefore, Cl oxidises Br^-.
2. (i) $Cl_2(aq) + SO_3^{2-}(aq) + H_2O(l) \longrightarrow 2Cl^-(aq) + SO_4^{2-}(aq) + 2H^+(aq)$
   (ii) $Cl_2(aq) + H_2S(aq) \longrightarrow 2Cl^-(aq) + S(s) + 2H^+(aq)$
   (iii) $4Cl_2(aq) + S_2O_3^{2-}(aq) + 5H_2O(l) \longrightarrow 8Cl^-(aq) + 2SO_4^{2-}(aq) + 10H^+(aq)$
   (iv) $I_2(aq) + 2S_2O_3^{2-}(aq) \longrightarrow 2I^-(aq) + S_4O_6^{2-}(aq)$
3. See Table 20.3 and § 20.4, Table 20.4A.
4. The graph shows a big fall from F to Cl, then a steady fall from Cl to Br to I.

Checkpoint 20.5: Preparations

1. Similar to Figure 20.5B. No heating is required. If chlorine is to be collected over water,it is pointless to dry it first. Collecting over water, you can see when the gas jar is full. Collecting downwards, you can dry the gas first.
2. Oxidation of X^- to X_2. No oxidising agent will oxidise F^- to F_2.
3. $KX(s) + H_2SO_4(l) \longrightarrow HX(g) + KHSO_4(s)$
   X = Cl, Br, or I
   $2X^- \longrightarrow X_2 + 2e^-$
   $MnO_2(s) + 4H^+(aq) + 2e^- \longrightarrow Mn^{2+}(aq) + 2H_2O(l)$
   $MnO_2(s) + 4H^+(aq) + 2X^-(s) \longrightarrow Mn^{2+}(aq) + X_2(g) + 2H_2O(l)$
4. Promotion of the 2p electrons does not occur in F because the nearest vacant orbitals are so distant that the energy required for promotion is too great to be compensated for by bond formation. In I, 5p electrons can be promoted to 5d orbitals and the energy required is compensated for by bond formation.
5. *(a)* $Cl_2(aq) + 2Br^-(aq) \longrightarrow Br_2(aq) + 2Cl^-(aq)$
   (b) $Br_2(aq) + SO_3^{2-}(aq) + H_2O(l) \longrightarrow 2Br^-(aq) + SO_4^{2-}(aq) + 2H^+(aq)$
6. *(a)* Similar to iodine; Table 20.2.
   (b) Astatine because HAt, like HI, is oxidised by conc. H_2SO_4.
   $NaAt(s) + H_2SO_4(l) \longrightarrow HAt(g) + NaHSO_4(s)$
   $2HAt(g) + H_2SO_4(l) \longrightarrow At_2(g) + SO_2(g) + 2H_2O(l)$

Checkpoint 20.7: Reactions

1. *(a)* $Cl_2(aq) + H_2O(l) \rightleftharpoons HCl(aq) + HClO(aq)$
   Alkali reacts with HCl(aq) and HClO(aq) and drives the position of equilibrium towards the RHS, with the formation of more HCl + HClO.
   (b) Dissolve sodium chlorate(I) in water, and acidify. Then,
   $2ClO^-(aq) + 4H^+(aq) \longrightarrow Cl_2(aq) + 2H_2O(l)$
   Alternatively, use bleaching powder, $Ca(ClO)_2.CaCl_2$.
2. +1, −1, +5
   Part of the chlorine in ClO^- (ox. no. +1) is reduced to Cl^- (ox. no. −1) and part is oxidised to ClO_3^- (ox. no. +5)
3. *(a)* F zero, O −2, F −1, F −1, O −2
   (b) F zero, O −2, O zero, F −1, O −2
4. *(a)* See § 20.6
   (b) F_2 and Cl_2 are prepared by electrolysis [see § 20.5]. Br_2 is obtained from seawater by a method which involves oxidation of Br^- by Cl_2 [see Figure 20.5A]. Iodine is obtained from sodium iodate(V) by reduction to I^- by $NaHSO_3$, followed by a disproportionation reaction between IO_3^- and I^-.

Checkpoint 20.9: Halides

1. *(a)* I *(b)* F *(c)* F *(d)* F, see Table 20.1
2. They react with water vapour in the air to form tiny droplets of HX(aq). They are strong acids and readily react:
   $HX(g) + H_2O(l) \longrightarrow H_3O^+(aq) + X^-(aq)$
3. *(a)* In electronegativity, Cl > Br > I, therefore the polarity of $H^{\delta+}$—$X^{\delta-}$ and dipole–dipole attractions between molecules increase HI < HBr < HCl
   (b) Hydrogen bonding is strong in HF; see Figure 4.8D.
4. Comparable with HI – a strong acid; a ppt of AgAt(s)
5. Hydrolysis begins by coordination of a lone pair on O of H_2O into an outer orbital. Si has empty 3d orbitals to receive lone pairs from H_2O. C ($1s^2 2s^2 2p^2$) has no empty orbitals of comparable energy to receive lone pairs.
6. Thermal stability depends on the strength of the bonds to be broken. The thermal stability order in *(b)* is the same as the order of difficulty of breaking bonds, that is the standard bond dissociation enthalpy order in *(a)*. To act as an acid,
   $HX(g) + H_2O(l) \longrightarrow H_3O^+(aq) + X^-(aq)$
   Energy must be supplied to break the bond H-X, and energy is given out when X^- is hydrated. The first of these energy terms is the larger, and the order of acid strengths is therefore the reverse of the order of H-X bond strengths.

Questions on Chapter 20

1. *(a)* strength of acids: $HF \ll HCl < HBr < HI$
   (b) stability: $HF > HCl > HBr > HI$

2. *(a)* oxidising power: $F_2 > Cl_2 > Br_2 > I_2$
   (b) (i) See Table 20.3 and § 20.9.1. (ii) See §§ 20.3.1, 20.8. (iii) See § 20.6.
3. Dissolve in distilled water, add dilute nitric acid and aqueous silver nitrate to get a pale yellow ppt of AgBr, which turns grey on exposure to light or a deep yellow ppt of AgI, which is unaffected by light.
4. *(a)* $HCl + HClO$; § 20.6 *(b)* $NaCl + NaClO$; § 20.7
   (c) $Br_2 + NaCl$; § 20.4
5. *(a)* $HCl + NaHSO_4$ *(b)* $HBr + Br_2 + NaHSO_4$
   (c) $I_2 + NaHSO_4$
6. Similar to iodine. *(a)* slowly forms HAt; Table 20.3
   (b) slowly on heating; § 20.3.1
   (c) no reaction, slightly soluble
   (d) forms $AtO_3^- + At^-$; § 20.7
7. *(a)* (i) +5 (ii) +1
   (b) $Cl_2(aq) + 2OH^-(aq) \longrightarrow ClO^-(aq) + Cl^-(aq) + H_2O(l)$
   (c) $4KClO_3(s) \longrightarrow 3KClO_3(s) + KCl(s)$
   Part of $KClO_4$ is oxidised from Cl ox. no. +5 to Cl ox. no. +7, and part is reduced to Cl ox. no. −1.
   (d) $I_2(aq) + 2NaOH(aq) \longrightarrow NaIO(aq) + NaI(aq) + H_2O(l)$
   Iodine is decolourised. Disproportionation.
   (e) $3I_2(aq) + 6NaOH(aq) \longrightarrow NaIO_3 + 5NaI(aq) + 3H_2O(l)$; disproportionation
   (f) $NaIO_3 + 5NaI(aq) + 6H^+(aq) \longrightarrow I_2(aq) + 6Na^+(aq) + 3H_2O(l)$
   The amount of I_2 liberated is the same as we started with in *(e)*.
8. *(a)* HF is a very much weaker acid than HCl.
   (b) The H—F bond is very strong; see Table 20.1. Hydrogen bonding between molecules of HF is strong.
   (c) The bonding electrons are not symmetrically distributed between the bonded atoms; they are attracted to one atom more than the other, e.g. $C^{\delta+}–Cl^{\delta-}$.
   (d) In HF, the bonding electrons are in the $n = 2$ shell of F. In HCl the bonding electrons are in the $n = 3$ shell of Cl therefore the attraction of the bonding pair by the nucleus of F in HF is greater than the attraction of the bonding pair by the nucleus of Cl in HCl.
9. *(a)* See § 18.6.5 and Figure 18.6A.
   (b) Pass chlorine from a cylinder through a solution of NaOH at r.t. Use a fume cupboard; chlorine is very poisonous. The solution will contain NaClO and NaCl. Separate by fractional crystallisation.
   (c) See § 20.11.
   (d) Table 18.6A.
10. *(a)* The ppt is silver chloride:
    $Ag + (aq) + Cl^-(aq) \longrightarrow AgCl(s)$
    A soluble complex diamminesilver ion forms:
    $AgCl(s) + 2NH_3(aq) \longrightarrow [Ag(NH_3)_2]^+(aq) + Cl^-(aq)$
    Silver bromide is precipitated from this complex because AgBr is much less soluble than AgCl. AgBr dissolves in aqueous sodium cyanide ion to form a soluble cyanosilver complex ion.
    $AgBr(s) + 2CN^-(aq) \longrightarrow [Ag(CN)_2]^-(aq) + Br^-(aq)$
    (b) There is extensive hydrogen bonding in HF.
    (c) Some proteins can form hydrogen bonds to HF, even when they cannot form hydrogen bonds to water because F is more electronegative than O:
    Protein—N(—H)—H ...... F—H ...... F—H ...... F—H
11. *(a)* (i) $I_2(aq) + 2S_2O_3^{2-}(aq) \longrightarrow 2I^-(aq) + S_4O_6^{2-}(aq)$
    (ii) starch (iii) The colour of iodine acts as indicator early in the titration.
    (iv) Amount of thio $= 20.0 \times 10^{-3} \times 0.10$ mol
    Amount of $I_2 = 1.00 \times 10^{-4}$ mol
    Mass of $I_2 = 254 \times 10^{-4}$ g, and
    $\% = 100 \times 254 \times 10^{-4} / 250 = 1.0 \times 10^{-2}$ %
    (b) $I^-(aq) + 5IO_3^-(aq) + 6H^+(aq) \longrightarrow 3I_2(aq) + 3H_2O(l)$
    (c) (i) the time taken for radioactivity to fall to half its original value; see § 1.10.6.
    (ii) $^{131}_{53}I \longrightarrow {}^{0}_{-1}e + {}^{131}_{54}Xe$
    (iii) No: isotopes have the same chemical behaviour.
    (d) (i) many examples, e.g. propanone, CH_3COCH_3, and ethanal CH_3CHO
    (ii) I (96.70/127) : C (3.050/12) : H (0.254/1) gives CHI_3.
12. *(a)* T_b increases down the group. With increasing size, the atoms have more electrons and attractions between temporary dipoles are greater; see § 4.8. 2.
    (b) See § 4.6.3; electronegativity Cl > Br > I
    The smallest of the atoms, Cl, is more able to attract the bonding electrons because the valence shell is closer to the nucleus than in Br and I.
    (c) Reducing properties $I^- > Br^- > Cl^-$
    The tendency for Cl to form Cl^- is greater than the tendency for Br to form Br^- because in Cl^- the electron added is closer to the nucleus and more energy is given out. Similarly in $Br \longrightarrow Br^-$ the electron added is closer to the nucleus and more energy is given out than in $I \longrightarrow I^-$.
    Bromide solution turns brown:
    $Cl_2(aq) + 2Br^-(aq) \longrightarrow Br_2(aq) + 2Cl^-(aq)$
    Iodide solution turns black:
    $Cl_2(aq) + 2I^-(aq) \longrightarrow I_2(aq) + 2Cl^-(aq)$
13. *(a)* See Table 20.5 in § 20.8.
    (b) The presence of sodium carbonate would cause precipitation of AgOH(s) when $AgNO_3$ was added.
    $Na_2CO_3(s) + 2HNO_3(s) \longrightarrow 2NaNO_3(aq) + CO_2(g) + H_2O(l)$
    $NaI(aq) + AgNO_3(aq) \longrightarrow NaNO_3(aq) + AgI(s)$
    0.850 g AgI
    M_r of AgI = 235, M_r of NaI = 150
    0.850 g AgI formed from (150/235) × 0.850 g NaI = 0.5425 g NaI
    % of NaI = (0.5425/1.20) × 100% = 45.2%
    (c) See § 4.6.3 for electronegativity and § 3.15.1 for reducing agent.
    The valence electrons in F are in the $n = 2$ shell, closer to the nucleus and therefore held more tightly than in the rest of the halogens. To oxidise F^- to F_2 an electron must be removed from the $n = 2$ shell, where it is close to the nucleus and tightly held.
    (d) NaCl: A misty gas is evolved, HCl(g).
    $NaCl(s) + H_2SO_4(l) \longrightarrow HCl(g) + NaHSO_4(s)$
    NaBr: A misty gas is evolved, this is HBr(g) and $SO_2(g)$. A brown vapour is also formed; this is $Br_2(g)$ formed by partial oxidation of HBr.
    $NaBr(s) + H_2SO_4(l) \longrightarrow HBr(g) + NaHSO_4(s)$
    $2HBr(g) + H_2SO_4(l) \longrightarrow Br_2(g) + SO_2(g) + 2H_2O(g)$
14. *(a)* (i) Br is more electronegative than I: Br has a greater affinity for electrons.
    (ii) F is a smaller atom than Cl. Both have 7 electrons in the outer shell. Those in F are closer to the nucleus than in Cl and are therefore more tightly held.
    (iii) Br is a larger atom than Cl with more electrons. Br_2 can therefore have bigger temporary dipoles than Cl_2 and stronger attractions between molecules.
    (b) SO_2 will be evolved as H_2SO_4 displaces HAt from its salt and then oxidises HAt.
    $NaAt(s) + H_2SO_4(l) \longrightarrow HAt(g) + NaHSO_4(s)$
    $2HAt(g) + H_2SO_4(l) \longrightarrow At_2(g) + SO_2(g) + 2H_2O(l)$
    (ii) Cl_2 will displace At_2 from NaAt:
    $Cl_2(aq) + 2NaAt(aq) \longrightarrow At_2(s) + 2NaCl(aq)$
    (iii) Like AgI, AgAt will be insoluble in $NH_3(aq)$.

CHAPTER 21 GROUP 6

Checkpoint 21.3: Reactions of oxygen and sulphur

1. *(a)* See § 21.1.
   (b) Fractional distillation of liquid air; § 21.2
   (c) Hydrogen peroxide + catalyst; collected over water
   $$2H_2O_2(aq) \longrightarrow O_2(g) + 2H_2O(l)$$
2. *(a)* (i) Many metals burn in air to form oxides. Some metals form oxides when heated in air; see Figure 21.3A.
   (ii) e.g. C, S, P; see Figure 21.3A
   (iii) Hydrocarbons, NH_3, H_2S, etc.
   e.g. $4Na(s) + O_2(g) \longrightarrow 2Na_2O(s)$
   $S(s) + O_2(g) \longrightarrow SO_2(g)$
   $CH_4(g) + 2O_2(g) \longrightarrow CO_2(g) + 2H_2O(l)$

Checkpoint 21.5: The ozone layer

1. *(a)* The product of one reaction starts off another reaction; see § 1.10.6, Figure 1.10E, § 14.15.
   (b) $O_2 + h\nu \longrightarrow O\cdot + O\cdot$
   $O\cdot + O_2 \longrightarrow O_3$
   (c) the concentration at which the rate of formation of the species, e.g. O_3, is equal to the rate of destruction of the species
   (e) Fall to a lower level. If the rate of destruction increases, more O_2 and $O\cdot$. are formed by the reaction
   $$O_3 + h\nu \longrightarrow O_2 + O\cdot$$
   and these react as in *(b)* above to form more ozone. Also if the concentration of O_3 decreases, more UV light reaches the troposphere and more O_2 dissociates, as in *(b)* above.
2. many examples in § 21.5
3. In the stratosphere it shields Earth from UV radiation; in the troposphere it damages people, vegetation, and materials; see discussion in § 21.5.

Checkpoint 21.6: Hydrides

1. (i) *(a)* $H_2O_2(aq) + 2H^+(aq) + 2e^- \longrightarrow 2H_2O(l)$
   (b) $H_2O_2(aq) \longrightarrow O_2(g) + 2H^+(aq) + 2e^-$
   (ii) *(a)* $MnO_4^-(aq) + 8H^+(aq) + 5e^- \longrightarrow Mn^{2+}(aq) + 4H_2O(l)$
   (b) $Cr_2O_7^{2-}(aq) + 14H^+(aq) + 6e^- \longrightarrow 2Cr^{3+}(aq) + 7H_2O(l)$
   (c) $Fe^{3+} + e^- \longrightarrow Fe^{2+}$
   (d) $Cl_2(aq) + 2e^- \longrightarrow 2Cl^-(aq)$
   (e) $I_2(aq) \longrightarrow 2I^-(aq)$
2. *(a)* $2I^-(aq) + H_2O_2(aq) + 2H^+(aq) \longrightarrow I_2(aq) + 2H_2O(l)$
   (b) $S^{2-}(aq) + 2H_2O_2(aq) \longrightarrow SO_4^{2-}(aq) + 4H^+(aq)$
   (c) $H_2O_2(aq) + Cl_2(aq) \longrightarrow O_2(g) + 2Cl^-(aq) + 2H^+(aq)$
   (d) $5H_2O_2(aq) + 2MnO_4^-(aq) + 6H^+(aq) \longrightarrow 2Mn^{2+}(aq) + 5O_2(g) + 8H_2O(l)$
   (e) $2Fe^{2+}(aq) + H_2O_2(aq) + 2H^+(aq) \longrightarrow 2Fe^{3+}(aq) + 2H_2O(l)$
3. *(a)* $1\ dm^3$ of $H_2O_2(aq) \longrightarrow 20\ dm^3$ of O_2
   $= 20/24$ mol $O_2 = 0.833$ mol O_2
   Since $2H_2O_2(aq) \longrightarrow O_2(g) + 2H_2O(l)$
   $1\ dm^3$ of solution contains 2×0.833 mol H_2O_2, and
   $[H_2O_2] = 1.67\ mol\ dm^{-3}$.
   (b) Titrate the $H_2O_2(aq)$ against acidified standard potassium manganate(VII). At the endpoint the purple colour of manganate(VII) turns to a very pale pink.

Checkpoint 21.8: Sulphur dioxide

1. $H_2SO_3(aq) + H_2O(l) \rightleftharpoons H_3O^+(aq) + HSO_3^-(aq)$
   $HSO_3^-(aq) + H_2O(l) \rightleftharpoons H_3O^+(aq) + SO_3^{2-}(aq)$
2. *(a)* For equations see the answer to Checkpoint 21.6, 1.
   (b) $2SO_3^{2-}(aq) + O_2(aq) \longrightarrow 2SO_4^{2-}(aq)$
   $SO_3^{2-}(aq) + H_2O(l) + Cl_2(aq) \longrightarrow SO_4^{2-}(aq) + 2H^+(aq) + 2Cl^-(aq)$
   $SO_3^{2-}(aq) + H_2O(l) + 2Fe^{3+}(aq) \longrightarrow SO_4^{2-}(aq) + 2H^+(aq) + 2Fe^{2+}(aq)$
   $3SO_3^{2-}(aq) + Cr_2O_7^{2-}(aq) + 8H^+(aq) \longrightarrow 3SO_4^{2-}(aq) + 2Cr^{3+}(aq) + 4H_2O(l)$
   $5SO_3^{2-}(aq) + 2MnO_4^-(aq) + 6H^+(aq) \longrightarrow 5SO_4^{2-}(aq) + 2Mn^{2+}(aq) + 3H_2O(l)$

Checkpoint 21.9: Sulphuric acid

1. Acts as (i) an involatile acid which displaces the lower T_b acid, HI from NaI and (ii) an oxidising agent, oxidising HI to I_2.
   $NaI(s) + H_2SO_4(l) \longrightarrow HI(g) + NaHSO_4(s)$
   $2HI(g) + H_2SO_4(l) \longrightarrow I_2(s) + 2H_2O(l)$
2. Conc. H_2SO_4 displaces HBr from KBr; then oxidises some of the HBr to Br_2. The solid is $KHSO_4$, the gases are HBr, Br_2, SO_2.
   $KBr(s) + H_2SO_4(l) \longrightarrow HBr(g) + KHSO_4(s)$
   $2HBr(g) + H_2SO_4(l) \longrightarrow Br_2(g) + SO_2(g) + 2H_2O(l)$
3. The blue colour disappears and the crystals turn into a powder. This is because conc. H_2SO_4 acts as a dehydrating agent, removing water of crystallisation.
   $CuSO_4.5H_2O(s) + H_2SO_4(l) \longrightarrow CuSO_4(s) + H_2SO_4.5H_2O(aq)$
4. SO_3, by dehydration of H_2SO_4
5. See § 21.9. 2.
6. removed from the converter to avoid release into the atmosphere

Checkpoint 21.10: Acid rain

1. See § 21.10, first paragraph.
2. The emission of S from one power station is almost twice the mass of S imported annually.
3. See the many examples in § 21.10, first five paragraphs.
4. *(a)* See § 21.10, 'Low sulphur fuels'.
   (b) See § 21.10, 'New burners'.

Questions on Chapter 21

1. See § 21.9, Figure 21.9D.
2. *(a)* conc., warm, gives $Br_2 + HBr$
   (b) dilute, warm, gives $H_2 + ZnSO_4$
   (c) conc., warm, gives $CuSO_4 + SO_2$
   (d) conc., cold, gives sugar charcoal
3. See Figure 21.9C. *(a)* dilute, with metals, e.g. Zn, Mg
   (b) conc.; with e.g. Cu, S, HI
   (c) conc.; with e.g. $CuSO_4.5H_2O$
   (d) conc., with e.g. NaCl
   (e) conc., with benzene
4. Chlorine acts by oxidising a dye to a colourless product. Sulphur dioxide acts by reducing a dye to a colourless product.
5. *(a)* FeS_2 ($M_r = 120$) $\longrightarrow 2H_2SO_4$ ($M_r = 98$)
   therefore 1 tonne $FeS_2 \longrightarrow 1.63$ tonnes H_2SO_4
   (b) It does not pollute the atmosphere.
   (c) Sulphuric acid is a more valuable commodity.
   (d) Contact process; see § 21.9.
6. *(a)* See § 21.9.
   (b) See § 21.9.2 and for (iii) see e.g. esterification, § 30.7.1.
7. *(a)* See § 21.5, equations *(a)* and *(b)*.
   (b) See § 21.5, equations *(e)*, *(f)*, *(g)*.
   (c) They involve photochemical reactions, free radicals and chain reactions.
   (d) e.g. refrigerator fluids, aerosol propellants. CFCs were introduced because of their extreme stability, e.g. non-flammability, and lack of toxicity.
   (e) Their stability to reagents in the troposphere enables CFCs to reach the ozone layer.
   (f) See § 21.5.
8. *(a)* At the upper height of the troposphere the density of air is low and winds are absent.

(*b*) non-toxic, non-flammable, non-corrosive

(*c*) Freon 12 reaches the ozone layer because it does not react with anything in the troposphere. In the stratosphere it photolyses to produce free radicals which attack ozone.

(*d*) photolysis

(*e*) free radicals

(*f*) $NO(g) + O_3(g) \longrightarrow NO_2(g) + O_2(g)$

9. (*a*) $SO_2(g) + H_2O(l) \longrightarrow H_2SO_3(aq)$

(*b*) Fe^{3+} rust-brown to green; MnO_4^- purple to pale pink

(*c*) **A** = NaOH(aq), **B** = S

$$SO_2(g) + 2NaOH(aq) \longrightarrow Na_2SO_3(aq) + H_2O(l)$$

$$Na_2SO_3(aq) + S(s) \longrightarrow Na_2S_2O_3(aq)$$

(*d*) Amount of $SO_2 = 1 \times 10^6\ dm^3/24\ dm^3\ mol^{-1}$ = amount of thiosulphate
Mass = $158\ g\ mol^{-1} \times 10^6/24\ mol^{-1} = 6.58 \times 10^6\ g$ = 6.58 tonne

(*e*) e.g. development of photographs, titration of iodine

(*f*) (i) see Figure 22.7A
$Ca_3(PO_4)_2\ (s) + 3H_2SO_4(l) \longrightarrow 2H_3PO_4(l) + 3CaSO_4(s)$
$H_3PO_4(aq) + 3NH_3(g) \longrightarrow (NH_4)_3PO_4(aq)$
(ii) $2H_2SO_4(l) + 2KI(s) \longrightarrow I_2(g) + K_2SO_4(aq) + SO_2(g) + 2H_2O(l)$
S: +6 to +4 and I: −1 to 0

10. (*a*) See § 21.9 and Le Chatelier's Principle, § 11.5. High pressure causes a decrease in volume. The volume decreases when 3 moles of gas react to form 2 moles of gas. At high pressure sulphur dioxide liquefies.

(*b*) (i) $K_p = \dfrac{p^2(SO_3)}{p^2(SO_2) \times p(O_2)}$
The reaction is exothermic, so K_p decreases with rising temperature.
(ii) Raising the temperature will drive the equilibrium from right to left.

(*c*) V_2O_5. For the effect of a catalyst on the energy of activation see § 14.4.

(*d*) Removal of product drives the equilibrium from left to right.

(*e*) Absorption in water is very exothermic and produces a dangerous mist of sulphuric acid.

(*f*) $2ZnS(s) + 3O_2(g) \longrightarrow 2ZnO(s) + 2SO_2(g)$

(*g*) The plant should be close to a port where ships can unload imported sulphur or to a source of sulphur dioxide such as a metal smelting plant or an oil refinery which removes sulphur. The site should have good access to road and rail so that the product can be transported to customers. It should be close to a power station and to a source of water for cooling purposes. A workforce must be available. As the plant discharges some sulphur dioxide it should not be close to residential areas.

(*h*) The process uses sulphur, water and electrical power.

CHAPTER 22 GROUP 5

Checkpoint 22.4: Nitrogen

1. See Figure 22.2A.
(*a*) Combination of N_2 and O_2 in vehicle engines and during lightning storms, fixation by bacteria in nodules on the roots of legumes, the Haber process.
(*b*) Denitrifying bacteria convert ammonium salts in the soil into nitrogen.
(*c*) Plants are not allowed to decay and return their nitrogen content to the soil; instead they are harvested. Animals are not allowed to decay and return their N content to the soil.
2. (*a*) +5 (*b*) +3 (*c*) +4 (*d*) +2 (*e*) −3
3. (*a*), (*b*) See § 22.3.1.

Checkpoint 22.5: Ammonia

1. See § 22.4.
2. (*a*) A pale blue ppt of $Cu(OH)_2(s)$ appears. It dissolves when more ammonia is added to form a deep blue solution of $[Cu(NH_3)_4]^{2+}(aq)$ ions.
(*b*) A ppt of CuOH(s) appears and dissolves in excess ammonia to form a solution of $[Cu(NH_3)_2]^+(aq)$ ions.
(*c*) A ppt of AgOH(s) appears and dissolves in excess ammonia to form a solution of $[Ag(NH_3)_2]^+(aq)$ ions.
Product (*a*) is used to test for aldehydes. They reduce tetraamminecopper(II) ions to copper(I) oxide which is a red solid; see § 31.7.3. Product (*c*) is used to test for aldehydes. They reduce diamminesilver ions to silver; see § 31.7.3.
3. (i) as a proton acceptor, e.g.
$NH_3(g) + H_2O(l) \longrightarrow NH_4^+ + OH^-(aq)$
(ii) using the lone pair to coordinate to another molecule, e.g.
$4H_3N{:}(g) + Cu^{2+}(aq) \longrightarrow [Cu(NH_3)_4]^{2+}(aq)$
4. NH_3 forms hydrogen bonds to H_2O.
5. It is used as a degreasing agent because, being basic, it emulsifies fats and oils. Bleaches are oxidising agents such as calcium chlorate(I). Ammonia is a reducing agent and could reduce chlorate(I) to chlorine.
6. NH_4^+ tetrahedral, NH_3 trigonal pyramidal; see Figures 5.2E, F

Checkpoint 22.7: Nitric acid

1. (i) ammonia + air (ii) nitrogen monoxide and nitrogen dioxide
(iii) platinum/rhodium
2. Explosives, dyes, fertilisers
3. aqueous iron(II) sulphate and dilute sulphuric acid

Checkpoint 22.8 Water pollution

1. nitrogen and phosphorus
2. poor in plant nutrients, rich in dissolved oxygen
3. eutrophication, see § 22.7.2
4. Soil becomes depleted of nitrogen when crops are grown on it; see § 22.2. For measures, see § 22.7.4.

Questions on Chapter 22

1. See § 22.4.
2. See § 22.1. Urea has the highest % N = 46%.
3. (*a*) For destruction of O_3 by NO see § 21.5.
(*b*) For NO in photochemical smog see § 27.11.
4. (*a*) See §§ 21.10. (*b*) See § 21.5, the end and § 26.5.
5. (*a*) $NH_4^+(s) + OH^-(aq) \longrightarrow NH_3(g) + H_2O(l)$
(*b*) Turns damp red litmus paper blue.
(*c*) 0.0500 mol NaOH, therefore 0.0500 mol NH_4^+ = 0.90 g NH_4^+
% = (0.90/10.0) × 100 = 9.0 % NH_4^+
6. (*a*) See § 22.4 for the Haber process.
(*b*) See NPK fertilisers, § 22.7.
(*c*) eutrophic lakes: § 22.7.2; ground water: § 22.7.3
7. (*a*) (i) The flame test gives a lilac flame for K compounds.
(ii) Dissolve in distilled water. Add dil. $HNO_3 + AgNO_3(aq) \longrightarrow$ white ppt of AgCl.
(*b*) Cropinc will make up for deficiency in N, P and K.
(*c*) pH
(*d*) 'Lime' will release ammonia from 'Cropinc'

$$Ca(OH)_2(s) + 2H^+(aq) \longrightarrow Ca^{2+}(aq) + 2H_2O(l)$$

8. (*a*) (i) $K_c = [NH_3(g)]^2/\{[N_2(g)]\ [H_2(g)]^3\}\ mol^{-2}\ dm^6$
(ii) $K_c = (1.46)^2/\ \{0.27(0.81)^3\} = 14.85\ mol^{-2}\ dm^6$

(b) (i) Kc will decrease with a rise in temperature because the reaction is exothermic.
(ii) The rate of the forward reaction will increase with a rise in temperature (and also the rate of the reverse reaction).
(c) (i) NH_4^+ acid, NH_3 base; H_2O base, H_3O^+ acid
(ii) $K_a = [H_3O^+(aq)]\ [NH_3(aq)]/[NH_4^+(aq)]$
$5.62 \times 10^{-10} = [H_3O^+(aq)]^2/0.100$ therefore pH 5.12
(d) A mixture of a weak base and its salt has a buffer action therefore add an equal concentration of ammonia.

9. *(a)* (i) It is close to supplies of North Sea gas.
(ii) A drop in the price of electricity would make electrolysis of water more feasible.
(iii) Synthesis gas is made from methane and steam. In some plants, air is mixed with steam to promote partial oxidation of methane. Air contains 1% argon.
(b) The reaction involves a decrease in the number of moles of gas, therefore high pressure drives the position of equilibrium towards the right, and the yield increases. A plant which will withstand high pressure is costly. The expense of running a compressor to reach high gas pressure adds to the cost of the product.
(c) (i) The reaction is exothermic, so the yield is lower at higher temperatures, but equilibrium is reached more rapidly. The use of a catalyst decreases the time required to reach equilibrium.
(ii) iron with promoters, heterogeneous
(d) (i) The mixture is cooled in a heat exchanger, ammonia liquefies and is kept under a few atm pressure.
(ii) recycled
(e) (i) $4NH_3(g) + 5O_2(g) \longrightarrow 4NO(g) + 6H_2O(g)$
(ii) $NH_3(g) + HNO_3(aq) \longrightarrow NH_4NO_3(aq)$
(f) (i) In one unit ammonia is synthesised, in another ammonia is oxidised to nitric acid, in a third unit ammonium nitrate is manufactured. It is efficient to have the three units on one site.
(ii) It is explosive and is stored under cool conditions.
(g) nylon, $-(CH_2)_6NHOC(CH_2)_4CONH-$, condensation polymerisation, e.g. clothing and ropes; see § 34.5.4

CHAPTER 23 GROUP 4

Checkpoint 23.4: Structure and reactions

1. *(a)* Each C atom is bonded to 4 others so it is difficult to separate C atoms from the structure; see Figure 6.6A.
(b) See § 6.6.

2. *(a)* Carbon atoms can be broken off from the structure because each carbon atom is bonded to only 3 others; see Figure 6.7A.
(b) The bonds between carbon atoms within a layer are strong, but the bonds between layers are weak. One layer can therefore slide over another in a lubricating action.
(c) Each carbon atom uses three of its valence electrons in the formation of covalent bonds. The fourth valence electron is delocalised and available to conduct electricity.

3. *(a)* One s electron and one p electron are promoted to give the configuration Ne(3s3p3p3p), and there are four orbitals available for bonding.
(b) A macromolecular structure with each Si atom bonded to 4 O atoms; see Figure 6.6D.
(c) The change graphite to diamond is endothermic and involves an increase in density.
(d) The energy required to promote electrons to allow 4 covalent bonds to be formed must be compensated for by the energy given out when bonds are formed. The strength of the covalent bonds between the Group 4 element and other elements decreases down the group.
(e) $SnCl_2$. (The smaller cation has more polarising power.)

Checkpoint 23.5A: Halides

1. *(a)* It is partially hydrolysed to Sn(OH)Cl(s). Add a little HCl(aq) to drive equilibrium from R to L:

$$SnCl_2(aq) + H_2O(l) \rightleftharpoons Sn(OH)Cl(s) + HCl(aq)$$

(b) A ppt of $Sn(OH)_2$ appears and dissolves in excess of $NaOH(aq) \longrightarrow Na_2SnO_2(aq)$.

2. *(a)* ECl_4: heat the element with chlorine – except C ($CS_2 + Cl_2$)
ECl_2 where **E** = Sn and Pb: Sn + HCl(g) or HCl(aq, conc.); Pb + Cl_2(g) or HCl(aq, conc.)
(b) C and Si: 4–valent only; Sn and Pb: 4–valent and 2–valent. Sn favours +4 and Sn(II) is a reducing agent; Pb favours +2.

Bond type: The compounds of oxidation state +4 are covalent. The Sn(II) and Pb(II) compounds are ionic with some covalent character, with Sn compounds having more covalent character than Pb compounds.

3. *(a)* Lead + Cl_2 + heat or lead + HCl(aq, conc.) or add soluble Pb^{2+} salt + HCl(aq)
(b) Forms soluble complex $PbCl_4^{2-}(aq)$

4. CCl_4 is hydrolysed very slowly. $SiCl_4$ is hydrolysed rapidly. Si has empty 3d orbitals into which electron pairs from H_2O molecules can coordinate as the first step in hydrolysis.

Checkpoint 23.5B: Oxides and salts

1. SiO_2 has a structure [Figure 6.6D] in which all the atoms are covalently bonded in a macromolecular structure. CO_2 consists of individual molecules. Bond energy terms make $nSiO_2 \longrightarrow (SiO_2)_n$ exothermic and $nCO_2 \longrightarrow (CO_2)_n$ endothermic; see the answer to Question 10 in Questions on Chapter 23.

2. Carbon +2 in CO, +4 in CO_2, covalent
Si: +4 only, covalent
Ge: +4 only, covalent
Sn: +2, ionic bonds with some covalent character; +4 bonds covalent with some ionic character; +4 state is more stable than +2
Pb: +2 ionic bonds, +4 covalent bonds with some ionic character; +2 state is more stable than +4, and electrovalent character of Pb(II) compounds is greater than Sn(II) compounds

3. *(a)* (i) electrovalent and basic
(ii) covalent and acidic or neutral
CO_2 covalent, dissolves in water $\longrightarrow$ weak acid;
CO covalent, very weakly acidic – reacts with molten NaOH
SiO_2 covalent, weakly acidic – reacts with molten bases
SnO_2 and SnO covalent with some electrovalent character, react with dilute acids $\longrightarrow Sn^{4+}$ and Sn^{2+} salts and react with molten base or conc. aqueous alkali $\longrightarrow$ stannate(IV) or stannate(II).
PbO_2 electrovalent with some covalent character;
PbO electrovalent with some covalent character; react with dil. acid $\longrightarrow$ Pb(IV) salts and Pb(II) salts; with molten base or conc. alkali $\longrightarrow$ plumbate(IV) or plumbate(II).

4. Incomplete combustion of hydrocarbons produces CO [see § 26.5], which is poisonous. Catalytic converters reduce CO emission; see §§14.7, 26.5, 26.6)
5. *(a)* Marble chips + HCl(aq); collect downwards or over water.
   (b) SiO_2 is widely available as sand, quartz, etc.
6. *(a)* (i) SnO_2 (ii) PbO
   (b) e.g. heat lead(II) nitrate or carbonate. SnO is oxidised to SnO_2 when heated in air.
7. *(a)* $Pb^{2+}(aq) + 2I^-(aq) \longrightarrow PbI_2(s)$
   (b) $2Fe^{3+}(aq) + Sn^{2+}(aq) \longrightarrow 2Fe^{2+}(aq) + Sn^{4+}(aq)$

Checkpoint 23.6: The greenhouse effect

1. *(a)* C (12 g) $\longrightarrow$ CO_2 (44 g)
   6×10^9 tonnes C $\longrightarrow$ 2.2×10^{10} tonnes CO_2
   (b) If 1.1×10^{10} tonnes remain in the atmosphere p.a. to add 2.5×10^{12} tonnes will take 2.5×10^{12} tonnes/1.1×10^{10} tonnes year^{-1} = 227 years
2. *(a)* The exposed land would radiate energy back towards space.
   (b) Water vapour is a greenhouse gas.
   (c) Carbon dioxide would come out of solution in the oceans.
   (d) Carbon dioxide and water vapour from volcanic action would add to the greenhouse cover.
3. Cutting down trees leaves fewer to remove carbon dioxide from the atmosphere in photosynthesis. E.g. some South American countries, some African countries, Pakistan etc. Some financial incentive, e.g. payment from richer countries or cancellation of debts, in return for a stop to deforestation.

Questions on Chapter 23

1. *(a)* electrovalent, basic *(b)* covalent, acidic or neutral
   (c) electrovalent, solids, high T_m, some partially hydrolysed by water
   (d) covalent, liquids or low T_m solids, many hydrolysed by water
   (i) Group 4 oxides, increase in basicity down the group. Oxides of C and Si are acidic; oxides of Ge, Sn and Pb are amphoteric; see Summary in § 23.2.
   (ii) Chlorides $\mathbf{E}Cl_4$ are covalent, with electrovalent character of bonds increasing down the group. All are hydrolysed readily, except $CCl_4 \longrightarrow$ silicates, stannates(IV), plumbates(IV). Chlorides $\mathbf{E}Cl_2$ formed by Sn and Pb are predominantly electrovalent and partially hydrolysed in solution; see Table 23.5A.
2. *(a)* C, Si macromolecular structure: diamond, graphite, bucky balls, Si and Ge semiconductors, Sn, Pb metallic structures
   (b) Hydrides of C are many and are stable. Hydrides of Si are spontaneously flammable and those of later members of the group are even more unstable.
   (c) CX_4 is not hydrolysed (owing to $n = 2$ shell restriction), SiX_4 and GeX_4 are readily hydrolysed, PbX_4 and SnX_4 have more electrovalent character but are hydrolysed in solution to basic salts or to stannates(IV) and plumbates(IV), SnX_2 and PbX_2 are only slightly hydrolysed in solution because they are more electrovalent than the +4 compounds.
   (d) C +4 (also +2), Si +4, Ge +4, Sn +4 (and +2), Pb +2 (and +4)
   (e) EO_2: CO_2, SiO_2 and GeO_2 weakly acidic; SnO_2 and PbO_2 amphoteric
   EO: CO very weakly acidic (molten NaOH), SnO and PbO amphoteric, mainly basic
3. The unique feature of C is its position in organic chemistry. C—C bonds are the basis of alkanes, C=C bonds of alkenes, C≡C bonds alkynes, and the benzene ring with delocalisation of electrons is the basis of aromatic chemistry. The groups >C=O and —C≡N are important in organic chemistry; see § 23.3
4. forms of an element which differ in crystal structure; see diamond Figure 6.6A, graphite Figure 6.7A, buckminsterfullerene § 35.1
   Diamond: every C atom is bonded to four others, explaining hardness and high refractive index.
   Graphite: weak bonds between layers of covalently bonded C atoms explain the lubricating quality, and delocalised electrons explain electrical conductivity.
   When completely burned, 12 g of each allotrope give 44 g of CO_2 and no other product.
5. *(a)* Burn C $\longrightarrow$ CO_2, pass CO_2 through NaOH(aq). When the indicator phenolphthalein changes colour, at pH 9, Na_2CO_3 has been formed [Figure 12.7B]. If more CO_2 is passed, $NaHCO_3$ is the product.
   (b) Pb + conc. $HNO_3 \longrightarrow Pb(NO_3)_2$;
   heat $Pb(NO_3)_2 \longrightarrow PbO(s)$
   (c) Heat Sn in air or react Sn + conc. $HNO_3 \longrightarrow SnO_2$.
   (d) Make $Pb(NO_3)_2$ as in (b).
   Add $Pb(NO_3)_2(aq) + I^-(aq) \longrightarrow$ ppt of PbI_2.
6. See § 23.3.
7. *(a)* See metallic bond, § 6.3.
   (b) Three valence electrons of each C atom are used in the formation of covalent bonds. The fourth is delocalised and available to conduct electricity.
   (c) p-type. Gp 3 elements, e.g. B, Al
   n-type Gp 5 elements, e.g. P, Sb
8. *(a)* CCl_4 no reaction
   $SiCl_4(l) + 2H_2O(l) \longrightarrow SiO_2(s) + 4HCl(g)$
   $SnCl_4(l) + 4H_2O(l) \longrightarrow [Sn(OH)_6]^{2-}(s) + 4HCl(g)$
   $SnCl_2(s) + H_2O(l) \longrightarrow Sn(OH)Cl(s) + HCl(g)$
   PCl_2 insoluble
   $PbCl_4(l) + 6H_2O(l) \longrightarrow$
   $[Pb(OH)_6]^{2-}(aq) + 4Cl^-(aq) + 6H^+(aq)$
   (b) Lead shows oxidation states +2 and +4; silicon shows only +4.
   (c) CCl_4 is not hydrolysed because there are no empty orbitals in the $n = 2$ shell into which H_2O can coordinate. $SiCl_4$ is hydrolysed because the 3d orbitals are available.
9. See Figure 6.6D.
   $SiO_2 + 2NaOH \longrightarrow Na_2SiO_3 + H_2O$
10. For polymerisation of $nSiO_2$ to $[\text{-}SiO_2\text{-}]_n$
    bonds broken are 2(Si=O) = +1276 kJ mol^{-1}
    bonds made are 4(Si—O) = −1496 kJ mol^{-1}
    Total = −220 kJ mol^{-1}, showing that energy considerations favour polymerisation.
    For polymerisation of nCO_2 to $[\text{-}CO_2\text{-}]_n$
    bonds broken are 2(C=O) = +1486 kJ mol^{-1}
    bonds made are 4(C—O) = −1440 kJ mol^{-1}
    Total = +46 kJ mol^{-1}, therefore energy considerations favour CO_2 molecules.
11. *(a)* Similar to diamond with alternating Si and C atoms
    (b) Si (Ne) $3s^2 3p^2$ uses four electrons in bond formation because the energy required for promotion is less than in the case of C.
    (c) The change graphite $\longrightarrow$ diamond is endothermic and therefore assisted by a high temperature. The change involves an increase in density and is therefore assisted by high pressure.
12. *(a)* orange through green to blue; chromium(III)(aq) is blue
    (ii) Sn(IV) is more stable than Sn(II)
    (iii) Pb(II) is more stable than Pb(IV)
    (iv) I. The stability of the +2 oxidation state increases down the group. C uses +4 and +2, Si and Ge use +4 only, Sn prefers +4, Pb prefers +2.
    II. $6s^2$
    (b) $Pb(g) \longrightarrow Pb^+(g) + e^-$
    (ii) Total of steps from $Pb(s) \longrightarrow Pb^{2+} + 2e^-$
    = −2362 kJ mol^{-1}
    Total of steps for 0.1 mol $Pb^{2+}(g) \longrightarrow Pb(s)$
    = −236 kJ mol^{-1}
    (c) I. e.g. $2CH_4(g) + 3O_2(g) \longrightarrow 2CO(g) + 4H_2O(g)$
    II. $CH_4(g) + 2O_2(g) \longrightarrow CO_2(g) + 2H_2O(g)$
    III. $2CO(g) + O_2(g) \longrightarrow 2CO_2(g)$

(ii) Group 3 (B, Al): p-type; Group 5 (P, Sb): n-type; see § 23.1

13. *(a)* (i) Si $1s^2 2s^2 2p^6 3s^2 3p^2$
Ge $1s^2 2s^2 2p^6 3s^2 3p^6 3d^{10} 4s^2 4p^2$
(ii) Further shells of electrons are added.
(iii) Between Si and Ge some of the additional electrons are in the d subshell which is closer to the nucleus than the p subshell.
(iv) In C $\longrightarrow$ C^+, the electron to be removed is in the 2p subshell, close to the nucleus.
In Si $\longrightarrow$ Si^+, the electron is in the 3p subshell. In Ge $\longrightarrow$ Ge^+, the electron is in the 4p subshell.
The distance between the 4p subshell and the nucleus is greater than the distance between the 3p subshell and the nucleus, but is less than the distance between the 3p and 2p subshells.

(b) (i) $SiCl_4(l) + H_2O(l) \longrightarrow Si(OH)_4(s) + 4HCl(aq)$
SiH_4 does not react unless traces of alkali are present.
(ii)

Cl
Cl Si Cl
Cl

tetrahedral as in CH_4, Figure 5.2F

(c) N is electronegative, the bond $N^{\delta-}$—$H^{\delta+}$ is polar and hydrogen bonds exist between molecules of NH_3. The C—H bond is not sufficiently polar for hydrogen bonds to be formed between molecules of CH_4.

(d) The bond energy of C—C in diamond is high so the energy required to break up the structure is not compensated by the energy given out in the formation of C—Cl bonds.

CHAPTER 24 THE TRANSITION METALS

Checkpoint 24.10: Properties of transition metals

1. The nuclear charge increases from L $\longrightarrow$ R, and the number of electrons increases from L $\longrightarrow$ R. Each additional electron enters the 3d subshell and helps to shield the 4s electrons from the increased nuclear charge; therefore the effective nuclear charge remains fairly constant. This is why the sizes of the atoms and the first ionisation energies are similar. The chemical reactions are dictated principally by the 4s electrons, and the addition of electrons to the 3d subshell does not completely change them.
2. *(a)* Iron has more valence electrons available for delocalisation with the formation of a stronger metallic bond than in magnesium.
(b) Mg loses two 3s electrons $\longrightarrow$ Mg^{2+}; Fe loses two 4s electrons $\longrightarrow$ Fe^{2+}, and can also lose a 3d electron $\longrightarrow$ Fe^{3+}. The energy required for Mg to lose a 2p electron is too great to be compensated for by bond formation.
3. *(a)* See § 24.8.
(b) iron, cobalt, nickel; see § 24.9
(c) an unpaired electron; see § 24.9
4. *(a)* Cu^{2+} acceptor, NH_3 ligand. The ligand is uncharged, so the complex has the same charge as Cu^{2+}.
(b) Cu^{2+} acceptor, Cl^- ligand. Coordination of $4Cl^-$ to Cu^{2+} gives a complex with a charge of 2–.

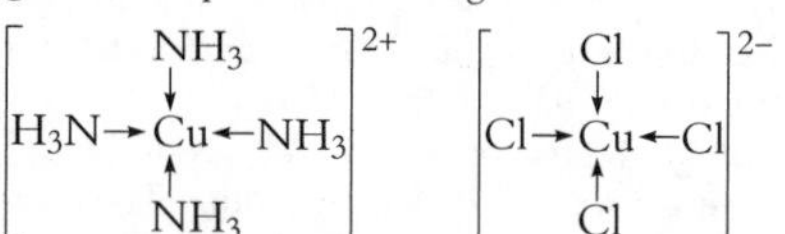

Checkpoint 24.13: Oxides and oxo-ions

1. (i) CrO (ii) MnO
2. *(a)* Mg *(b)* $\Delta H^{\ominus}_{reduction}$ of TiO_2 is extremely high.
(c) carbon
(d) Al + metal oxide $\longrightarrow$ Al oxide + metal. The reaction is very exothermic. e.g. Cr, V, Co
(e) Iron is less reactive than the metals mentioned in *(d)* and its oxides are reduced by CO. The extraction of iron in the blast furnace employs limestone and coke, not costly aluminium. It runs continuously.
3. **A** = Zn, **B** = Cu, **C** = Fe
4. *(a)* $2CrO_4^{2-}(aq) + 2H^+(aq) \longrightarrow Cr_2O_7^{2-}(aq) + H_2O(l)$
yellow to orange
(b) It is a good oxidising agent. The end point can be seen by the colour change from orange of dichromate(VI) to blue of $Cr^{3+}(aq)$.
(c) When chloride ions are present potassium manganate(VII) is not used because it oxidises chloride ions to chlorine.
5. *(a)* $a = 3, b = 4, c = 2, d = 1, e = 2$
(b) Part of MnO_4^{2-} (ox. no. = +6) is oxidised to MnO_4^- (ox. no. = +7), and part is reduced to MnO_2 (ox. no. = +4). (To balance the equation: Change in ox. no. from MnO_4^{2-} to MnO_2 is –2, Change in ox. no. from MnO_4^{2-} to MnO_4^- is +1 therefore 2 MnO_4^- must be formed for 1 MnO_2.)
(c) manganese(IV) oxide, black and manganate(VII) ion, purple
(d) $MnO_4^-(aq) + 8H^+(aq) + 5e^- \longrightarrow Mn^{2+}(aq) + 4H_2O(l)$
(e) e.g. iron(II) salts, tin(II) salts, hydrogen peroxide, ethanedioic acid

Checkpoint 24.15: Salts

1. Fe^{3+} is a small, highly charged cation able to polarise Cl^- and form a predominantly covalent bond; see § 4.6.4.
2. In aqueous solution, the ions Fe^{3+} and Cl^- are stabilised by hydration.
3. See § 24.14 and Figure 24.14A.
4. See § 24.14.1.
5. Roasting the sulphide in air to give the metal oxide followed by reduction of the oxide by carbon or carbon monoxide.

Checkpoint 24.16: Complexes

1. *(a)* A complex ion contains a central ion surrounded by other ions or molecules called ligands. The ligands are bonded to the central ion by coordinate bonds; see § 24.10.
(b) They have empty d orbitals into which ligands can coordinate.
(c) The d orbitals have slightly different energy levels. Electrons can move from a d orbital to another of lower energy; see § 24.10.2.
(d) tetrahedral, as in $[NiCl_4]^{2-}$, Figure 24.16A
2. hexaaquachromium(III), tetrahydroxyaluminate(III), tetraamminecopper(II), tetrachlorocuprate(II)
3. *(a)* +1, 2 *(b)* 0, 4 *(c)* +3, 6 *(d)* +2, 6 *(e)* +2, 4 *(f)* +1, 4 *(g)* +2, 4
4. There are mirror image forms similar to those shown for the Cr(III) complex in Figure 24.16C.
5. *(a)* octahedral, like $[Cr(NH_3)_6]^{3+}$ in Figure 24.16A
(b) octahedral, like $[Cr(NH_3)_6]^{3+}$ in Figure 24.16A.
(c) see Figure 24.16A
(d) tetrahedral, as in $[NiCl_4]^{2-}$, Figure 24.16A
6. pale blue ppt $Cu(OH)_2(s)$
deep blue solution $[Cu(NH_3)_4(H_2O)_2]^{2+}(aq)\ SO_4^{2-}(aq)$
pale blue solution $[Cu(H_2O)_6]^{2+}(aq)\ 2Cl^-(aq)$
green solution $[CuCl_4(H_2O)_2]^{2-}(aq)\ 2H^+(aq)$

7. Ligand exchange [see § 24.16.3]. Cl^- is a stronger Lewis base than NH_3, more able to coordinate a pair of electrons into a metal ion. The stability constants of complexes of two ligands with the same metal ion give a precise comparison.

Checkpoint 24.17: Iron

1. *(a)* Air, iron oxide, limestone, coke *(b)* Iron, slag
2. *(a)* The carbon content makes iron brittle.
   (b) Some iron is used as cast iron. It is easily moulded because it has a lower T_m than pure iron. Some is made into wrought iron, with a very low C content, which is malleable. Most of the iron is converted into steel; see § 24.17.3.
3. The methods of preventing or delaying rusting involve coating, alloying, sacrificial protection and cathodic protection; see § 24.17.6.
4. *(a)* iron(II) sulphide, FeS *(b)* iron(II) chloride $FeCl_2$
   (c) iron(III) chloride $FeCl_3$ *(d)* iron(II) iodide FeI_2
   (e) iron(III) oxide Fe_2O_3 *(f)* iron(II) iron(III) oxide Fe_3O_4
   (g) iron(II) sulphate $FeSO_4$.
5. Fe(II) ions + potassium hexacyanoferrate(III) ⟶ Turnbull's blue
   Fe(III) ions + potassium hexacyanoferrate(II) ⟶ Prussian blue
   Fe(III) ions + potassium thiocyanate ⟶ iron(III) thiocyanate, $FeCNS^{2+}$, blood-red colour

Checkpoint 24.19: Copper and zinc

1. Copper dissolves from the impure copper anode:
   $Cu(s) \longrightarrow Cu^{2+}(aq) + 2e^-$
   Copper is deposited on the copper cathode:
   $Cu^{2+}(aq) + 2e^- \longrightarrow Cu(s)$
   Metals higher than copper in the electrochemical series remain in solution. Metals below copper form an anode sludge.
2. See § 24.18.1.
3. *(a)* $Cu(OH)_2(s)$ copper(II) hydroxide
   (b) $[CuCl_4]^{2-}(aq)$, tetrachlorocuprate(II) ion
   (c) CuS(s), copper(II) sulphide
   (d) $Cu(OH)_2.CuCO_3(s)$, copper(II) carbonate hydroxide
   (e) $[Cu(NH_3)_4]^{2+}(aq)$, tetraamminecopper(II) ions
4. *(a)* Zinc ions Zn^{2+}, (Ar)$3d^{10}$, have a full d subshell. Zinc does not resemble the metals of Group 2; it forms complex ions, and its oxide is amphoteric.
   (b) Zinc is used for galvanising iron to protect against rust. It is a component of the alloy brass.

Questions on Chapter 24

1. *(a)* an element in which the atom or ion has an incomplete d subshell
   (b) See § 3.17.
   (c) A donor (a ligand) coordinates a lone pair (or pairs) of electrons into the empty orbital (or orbitals) of an atom or ion (an acceptor); see §24.10.
   (d) the number of ligands bonded to the central atom; see § 24.16.1
2. For electron configuration see § 24.2; physical properties § 24.3, chemical properties § 24.4, iron § 24.17.7.
3. See § 24.17.1.
4. See §§ 13.4, 24.17.6.
5. *(a)* See § 24.18.3.
   (b) (i) The complex ion $[Cu(CN)_4]^{2-}(aq)$ is formed.
   (ii) The complex ion $[Cu(NH_3)_4]^{2+}(aq)$ is formed.
6. Powerful oxidising agent, oxidises many substances, difficult to obtain completely pure. Potassium dichromate can be obtained 100% pure.
   $MnO_4^-(aq) + 8H^+(aq) + 5e^- \longrightarrow Mn^{2+}(aq) + 4H_2O(l)$
   $Fe^{2+}(aq) \longrightarrow Fe^{3+}(aq) + e^-$
   $H_2O_2(aq) \longrightarrow O_2(g) + 2H^+(aq) + 2e^-$
   (i) $MnO_4^-(aq) + 8H^+(aq) + 5Fe^{2+}(aq) \longrightarrow Mn^{2+}(aq) + 4H_2O(l) + 5Fe^{3+}(aq)$
   (ii) $2MnO_4^-(aq) + 6H^+(aq) + 5H_2O_2(aq) \longrightarrow 2Mn^{2+}(aq) + 8H_2O(l) + 5O_2(g)$
7. See § 24.17.3 for manufacture. Steel, being stronger than Al, is used for heavy machinery, frameworks for buildings etc. Al is low in density and does not corrode, and its alloys are used in the manufacture of aircraft and small boats. Steel is our chief material for the construction of machinery and means of transport.
8. *(a)* tetrahedral, similar to $[CuCl_4]^{2-}$ in Figure 24.16A
   (b) linear as in Figure 24.16A
   (c) octahedral as in Figure 24.16D
   (d) square planar, similar to $[CuCl_4]^{2-}$ in Figure 24.16A
9. *(a)* See answer to Question 1(a).
   (b)
   ```
      H              ××  −
      •×            × Cl ×
   H ו N ×         ×    •
      ו             ××
      H
   ```
   In NH_3 the N atom has a lone pair to coordinate with. Cl^- can use a pair of electrons to form a coordinate bond.
   (c) e.g. $[Cu(NH_3)_4]^{2+}$ and $CuCl_4^{2-}$
10. *(a)* See § 24.16.4 for isomers with $3Cl^-$, $2Cl^-$ and Cl^- free.
    (b) $Cr_2O_7^{2-}(aq) + 2OH^-(aq) \rightleftharpoons 2CrO_4^{2-}(aq) + H_2O(l)$
    Yellow chromate(VI) ions are formed.
    (c) $Cr_2O_7^{2-}(aq) + H_2O(l) \rightleftharpoons 2CrO_4^{2-}(aq) + 2H^+(aq)$
    Addition of $Ba^{2+}(aq)$ precipitates yellow $BaCrO_4(s)$ and drives the equilibrium from L to R.
    (d) I^- reduces Cu^{2+} to Cu^+ and then
    $Cu^+(aq) + I^-(aq) \longrightarrow CuI(s)$ which is white
    $2Cu^{2+}(aq) + 2I^-(aq) \longrightarrow 2Cu^+(aq) + I_2(aq)$
    $Cu^+(aq) + I^-(aq) \longrightarrow CuI(s)$
    (e) Cu_2O disproportionates:
    $2Cu^+(aq) \longrightarrow Cu^{2+}(aq) + Cu(s)$
    The reddish-brown solid is Cu(s); the blue solution is $CuSO_4(aq)$.
11. $Fe^{2+}(aq) \longrightarrow Fe^{3+}(aq) + e^-$
    $Cr_2O_7^{2-}(aq) + 14H^+(aq) + 6e^- \longrightarrow 2Cr^{3+}(aq) + 7H_2O(l)$
    $Cr_2O_7^{2-}(aq) + 14H^+(aq) + 6Fe^{2+}(aq) \longrightarrow 2Cr^{3+}(aq) + 6\,Fe^{3+}(aq) + 7H_2O(l)$
    Amount of $Cr_2O_7^{2-} = 15.0 \times 0.0100 \times 10^{-3}$ mol
    $= 1.50 \times 10^{-4}$ mol
    Amount of $Fe^{2+} = 9.00 \times 10^{-4}$ mol, and
    $[Fe^{2+}] = 0.036$ mol dm^{-3}
    $KMnO_4$ oxidises Cl^- to Cl_2.
12. *(a)* Conc. H_2SO_4 displaces NO_2 + NO from nitrates. NO reacts with $FeSO_4$ to form a brown complex $FeSO_4.NO$; see § 22.6
    (b) Disproportionation; $2Cu^+(aq) \longrightarrow Cu^{2+}(aq) + Cu(s)$
    (c) $[CuCl_4]^{2-}$ ions are green. Dilution gives blue $Cu(H_2O)_6]^{2+}$ ions.
13. *(a)* an element which has atoms or ions with an incomplete d subshell; § 24.2
    (b) The electrons added from left to right across the series enter the inner d subshell, while the radius is determined by the outer s subshell.
    (c) See §§ 24.3, 24.4
    (d) Cr^{2+} (Ar)$3d^4$, Mn^{3+} (Ar)$3d^4$, Mn^{7+} (Ar)
14. The mixture of hydroxides is coloured. One of the hydroxides is amphoteric; it has colourless solutions in NaOH and H_2SO_4. It is precipitated as a white ppt so it must be $Zn(OH)_2(s)$. **D** = $Na_2ZnO_2(aq)$, **H** = $Zn(OH)_2(s)$, **I** = $ZnSO_4(aq)$
    Of the colourless ppts one is soluble in $NH_3(aq)$ to form a dark blue solution; this is $Cu(OH)_2(s)$.

G = $Cu(NH_3)_4SO_4$(aq). The other coloured ppt is green therefore **E** is $Fe(OH)_2$(s) which is oxidised to F, Fe_2O_3.
C = $Fe(OH)_2$(s) + $Cu(OH)_2$(s),
B = $Fe(OH)_2$(s) + $Cu(OH)_2$(s) + $Zn(OH)_2$(s). **A** contains Fe^{2+}(aq), Cu^{2+}(aq) and Zn^{2+}(aq).

15. **A** = $Cr(OH)_3$(s), chromium(III) hydroxide
B = $2Cr(NH_3)_6{}^{3+}$(aq) $3SO_4{}^{2-}$(aq), hexaamminechromium(III) sulphate
C = $3Na^+$(aq) $Cr(OH)_6{}^{3-}$(aq), sodium chromate(III)
D = Na_2CrO_4, sodium chromate(VI), yellow
E = $Na_2Cr_2O_7$, sodium dichromate(VI), orange

16. **W** = $Cu(H_2O)_4{}^{2+}$(aq), **X** = $CuCl_4{}^{2-}$(aq), **Y** = $CuCl_2{}^-$(aq), **Z** = CuCl(s)
Disproportionation: $Cu(s) + Cu^{2+}(aq) \rightleftharpoons 2Cu^+(aq)$
$$[Cu(H_2O)_4]^{2+}(aq) + 4Cl^-(aq) \rightleftharpoons [CuCl_4]^{2-}(aq) + 4H_2O(l)$$
$$[CuCl_4]^{2-}(aq) + Cu(s) \rightleftharpoons 2[CuCl_2]^-(aq)$$
On standing Cu(I) is oxidised to Cu(II) in $CuCl_2$.

17. *(a)* $Fe^{2+}(aq) \longrightarrow Fe^{3+}(aq) + e^-$
$MnO_4{}^-(aq) + 8H^+(aq) + 5e^- \longrightarrow Mn^{2+}(aq) + 4H_2O(l)$
(b) $MnO_4{}^-(aq) + 8H^+(aq) + 5Fe^{2+}(aq) \longrightarrow Mn^{2+}(aq) + 4H_2O(l) + 5Fe^{3+}(aq)$
(c) green ⟶ yellow-brown during the titration. At the end of the titration the purple colour of $MnO_4{}^-$.
(d) See tests in Table 24.17C.
(e) Amount of $MnO_4{}^-$ = $27.4 \times 10^{-3} \times 0.0200$ mol
Amount of Fe = $5 \times 5.48 \times 10^{-4}$ mol
Mass of Fe = $56 \times 5 \times 5.48 \times 10^{-3}$ g = 0.1534 g
Percentage = 93.2 %

18. *(a)* The 2 N atoms each have a lone pair. The 4 $CO_2{}^-$ groups each have a lone pair. Thus 6 coordinate bonds can form to an acceptor ion; see §§ 12.10, 24.16.4.
(b) The —CO_2H groups are ionised in alkaline solution.
(c) M_r of $ZnSO_4.7H_2O$ = 287.4
Amount of Zn = 0.0184 mol
Amount of edta = $18.45 \times 0.1000 \times 10^{-3}$ mol
Amount of edta for 250 cm^3 = 0.184 mol
Molar ratio Zn : edta = 1 : 1

19. Amount of thio = $27.50 \times 10^{-3} \times 0.1000$ mol = 2.75×10^{-3} mol = Amount of Cu
Mass of Cu = $63.5 \times 2.75 \times 10^{-3}$ g, and percentage = 65.0%

20. *(a)* (i) $$K_1 = \frac{[Ni(NH_3)(H_2O)_5{}^{2+}(aq)]}{[Ni(H_2O)_6{}^{2+}(aq)][NH_3(aq)]}$$
(ii) unit = $mol^{-1}\ dm^3$
(iii) $K_1K_2K_3K_4K_5K_6$ = antilog – (2.67 + 2.12 + 1.61 + 1.07 + 0.63 – 0.09) = $9.77 \times 10^{-9}\ mol^{-6}\ dm^{18}$
(b) blue, pink, yellow, blue; see § 24.16.3
(c) (i) They form one coordinate bond to an acceptor.
(ii) 2
(iii) The stability constant of the cyanide complex is greater therefore CN^- is not replaced by NH_3.

21. *(a)* See § 24.16.
(b) $1s^22s^22p^63s^23p^63d^{10}4s$
(c) $Cu(H_2O)_4{}^{2+}$(aq) tetrahedral
(d) (i) $CuCl_4{}^{2-}$(aq), square planar, +2
(ii) reduction
(iii) Cu^+, the acceptor in $CuCl_2{}^-$ has a full d subshell.
(iv) $CuCl_4{}^{2-}(aq) + 4H_2O(l) \longrightarrow Cu(H_2O)_4{}^{2+}(aq) + 4Cl^-(aq)$

22. *(a)* Ratio Co 23.6/59 : N 27.9/14 : H 6.0/1 : Cl 42.5/35.5 = Co 0.4 : N 5 : H 15 : Cl 3
(b) 1.00 g *X* = 1/250.5 mol = 3.99×10^{-3} mol
1.15 g AgCl contains 1.15/143.5 mol Cl^- = 8.01×10^{-3} mol Cl^-
4.0×10^{-3} mol X contains 8.0×10^{-3} mol Cl^-
$[CoN_5H_{15}Cl]^{2+}\ 2Cl^-$
$[Co(NH_3)_5Cl]^{2+}\ 2Cl^-$, octahedral
Similar to Figure 24.16A showing $[Cr(NH_3)_6]^{3+}$
(c) Air oxidises Co^{2+} to Co^{3+}
$4Co^{2+}(aq) + O_2(g) + 4H^+(aq) \longrightarrow 4Co^{3+}(aq) + 2H_2O(l)$
NH_4Cl(aq) is acidic (salt of a weak base) and provides H^+(aq)
NH_3 coordinates to Co^{3+}.
$Co^{3+}(aq) + 6NH_3(aq) \longrightarrow [Co(NH_3)_6]^{3+}(aq)$
$[CoCl_4]^{2-}$ and $[Co(C_2O_4)_3]^{4-}$
(d) In $CoCl_4{}^{2-}$, coordination is from Cl^-; in $[Co(C_2O_4)_3]^{4-}$ coordination is from lone pairs on O atoms. More O atoms can be accommodated round Co than Cl atoms.

23. See § 24.12.2, Figures 24.12B, C.
(a) (i) $TiCl_4(g) + 2H_2(g) \longrightarrow Ti(s) + 4HCl(g)$
(ii) Mg, 1 Temperature > T_m of Mg and < temperature at which Ti combines with iron 2 atmosphere of argon
(iii) In (ii) the $MgCl_2$ formed is electrolysed and the Mg and Cl_2 are reused. In (i) there is the danger of working with hydrogen at high temperature.
(iv) The value of $\Delta H^\ominus$ for TiO_2 + C is very high, and energy considerations favour $TiCl_4$ + Mg.
(v) The high cost of running the process at high temperature and the high cost of magnesium. It is a batch process.
(b) (i) 0 (ii) It is volatile. (iii) The CO is recovered and recycled. The temperature required is low.

24 *(a)* (i) See hydrolysis of Fe^{3+}(aq); § 24.14.1. The higher the charge on the metal ion, the greater the attraction for O of H_2O and the greater the degree of hydrolysis.
(ii) See § 24.14.1.
(iii) Hydrolysis produces $Fe(OH)_3(H_2O)_6$(s). When HNO_3(aq) is added it reacts to form $Fe(NO_3)_3$(aq).
(b) (i) Reduction by Zn + acid passes from +5 through +4 to +3 to +2 oxidation state with different colours in each oxidation state.
(ii) Amount of NH_4VO_3 = 0.234 g/117 g mol^{-1} = 2.00×10^{-3} mol
Amount of $KMnO_4$ = $20.0 \times 10^{-3}\ dm^3 \times 0.200$ mol dm^{-3} = 0.40×10^{-3} mol
$$MnO_4{}^-(aq) + 8H^+(aq) + 5e^- \longrightarrow Mn^{2+}(aq) + 4H_2O(l)$$
One mol $MnO_4{}^-$ requires 5 mol electrons,
therefore 0.40×10^{-3} mol MnO_4 requires 2.00×10^{-3} mol electrons,
therefore 2.00×10^{-3} mol electrons is provided by 2.00×10^{-3} mol V in blue solution,
that is, 1 mol electrons is provided by 1 mol V in blue solution,
therefore V in blue solution changes in ox. no. by 1 unit.
Ox. no. of V in NH_4VO_3. = 5, therefore ox. no. of V in blue solution = +4.
(c) Variable oxidation state; see § 24.8. For homogeneous, see § 24.8; for heterogeneous see e.g. Haber process § 22.4, Contact process, § 21.9.

PART 4: ORGANIC CHEMISTRY

CHAPTER 25 ORGANIC CHEMISTRY

Checkpoint 25.7: Nomenclature

1. *(a)* 2-methylbutane
   (b) pent-2-ene
   (c) 4-methylpent-1-ene
   (d) 3-chloro-4-bromopentane
   (e) propanol
   (f) pentanoic acid
2. *(a)* $CH_3(CH_2)_5CH_3$
   (b) $CH_3CHClCH(CH_3)CH_2CH_2CH_3$
   (c) $CH_3CHBrCHCl(CH_2)_3CH_3$
   (d) $CH_3CH_2CH_2CHOHCH_3$
   (e) $CH_3CH{=}CHCH_2CH_2CH_3$
   (f) $CH_3CH_2CH_2CO_2H$

Checkpoint 25.8: Some reactions

1. *(a)* Homolytic fission: When the bond breaks each of the bonded atoms takes one of the bonding pair of electrons. Heterolytic fission: When the bond breaks one of the bonded atoms takes both of the bonding electrons; see § 25.8.2.
   (b) Substitution: An atom or group of atoms replaces another; see § 25.8.1.
   Addition: Two molecules react to form one; for examples see § 25.8.1.
   (c) Ion – an atom or group of atoms with a positive or negative charge
   Free radical – an atom or group of atoms with an unpaired electron, e.g. $Cl\cdot$, $CH_3\cdot$
2. *(a)* (i) carbocation – a positively charged ion containing carbon; carbanion – a negatively charged ion containing carbon
   (ii) A nucleophile has a lone pair of electrons, e.g. $:NH_3$, $:CN^-$; an electrophile has a full or partial positive charge, e.g. NO_2^+.
   (b) a carbocation because this is able to accept a lone pair of electrons from a nucleophile
3. *(a)* substitution *(b)* nucleophile *(c)* bromoethane and ethanol

Checkpoint 25.9A: Structural isomerism

1. $CH_3(CH_2)_3CH_3$, $(CH_3)_2CHCH_2CH_3$, $(CH_3)_4C$
2. $CH_3CH_2CH_2OH$, $(CH_3)_2CHOH$, $CH_3OCH_2CH_3$
3. $CH_3CH_2CH_2CHCl_2$, $C_2H_5CHClCH_2Cl$, $CH_3CHClCH_2CH_2Cl$, $CH_3CHClCHClCH_3$, $CH_2ClCH_2CH_2CH_2Cl$
4. $CH_3(CH_2)_3CHO$, $(CH_3)_2CHCH_2CHO$, $(CH_3)_3CCHO$, $(C_2H_5)_2CO$, $CH_3CH_2CH_2COCH_3$
5. $CH_3(CH_2)_3CO_2H$, $CH_3(CH_2)_2CO_2CH_3$, $CH_3CH_2CO_2C_2H_5$

Checkpoint 25.9B: Stereoisomerism

1. 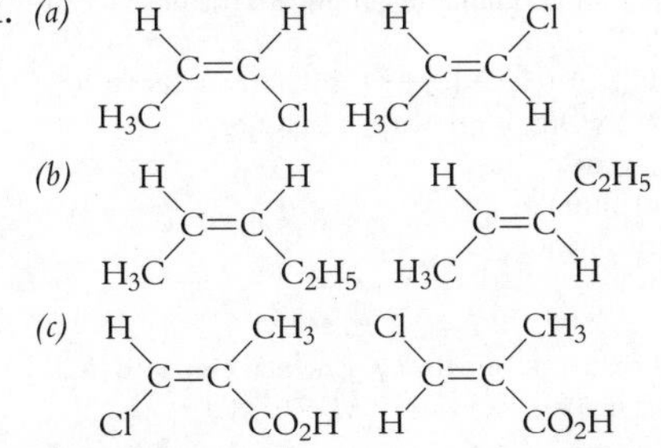

2. See the discussion of π-bonds in § 5.2.2, which leads to the planar configuration of >C=C<

Checkpoint 25.9 C: Optical activity

1. Alanine: the molecule has 4 different groups bonded to a carbon atom, therefore it is optically active. In glycine this is not the case.
2. See § 25.9.3.

   H–C(H₃C)(CO₂H)(OH) and H–C(HO₂C)(CH₃)(HO) (mirror-image tetrahedral structures)

3. *(a)* Chain isomerism: $CH_3CH_2CH_2CH_3$ and $CH_3CH(CH_3)_2$; a difference in boiling temperature
   (b) Positional isomerism: $H_2C{=}CH{-}CH_2{-}CH_3$ and $H_3C{-}CH{=}CH{-}CH_3$, which has geometric isomers, which are *cis-* and *trans-* forms:

   (H)(H₃C)C=C(H)(CH₃) and (H)(H₃C)C=C(CH₃)(H)

   (c) optical isomerism because there is a chiral C atom in $CH_3CH^*(OH)CO_2H$
   (d) geometric isomerism: *cis-trans*-isomerism
   (e) optical isomerism because there is a chiral C atom in $C_6H_5CH^*(OH)CN$
   (f) positional isomerism: $CH_3CH_2CHBr_2$, $CH_3CHBrCH_2Br$ and $CH_3CBr_2CH_3$
   (g) positional isomerism: $CH_3CH_2CH_2Cl$, $CH_3CHClCH_3$
   (h) optical isomerism because there is a chiral C atom in $C_6H_5CH_2C^*H(NH_2)CO_2H$

Questions on Chapter 25

1. *(a)* See § 25.8.3.
   (b) (i) S_E (ii) S_N
2. See § 25.8.2. (i) homolytic (ii) heterolytic
3. See § 25.9.2 and Figure 25.9A.
4. *(a)* a molecule with no plane or axis or centre of symmetry; see § 25.9.3
   (b) CO₂H–C(H₃C)(Br)(H) and CO₂H–C(Br)(CH₃)(H) (mirror-image tetrahedral structures)
   (c) They have the same chemical reactions but differ sometimes in biochemical reactions.
5. *(a)* optical C₃H₇–C(H)(CH₃)(OH) and C₃H₇–C(H₃C)(H)(HO) (mirror-image tetrahedral structures)
   (b) No, there is no C atom bonded to 4 different groups.
   (c) *cis–trans* isomerism

   (H₃C)(H)C=C(H)(CO₂H) and (H₃C)(H)C=C(CO₂H)(H)

6. *(a)* (i) There is restricted rotation about the double bond in

   (Br)(H)C=C(Br)(H) and (Br)(H)C=C(H)(Br)

   (ii) There is freedom of rotation in

   H–C(Br)(H)–C(Br)(H)–H

(iii) There are no *cis-trans* forms of

```
Br       H
  \     /
   C=C
  /     \
Br       H
```

(b) (i) hex-3-ene:

```
   H  H         H  H
   |  |         |  |
H—C—C—C=C—C—C—H
   |  |  |  |  |  |
   H  H  H  H  H  H
```

butenedioic acid: $HO_2C—C=C—CO_2H$ (each C of C=C carrying H)

```
HO2C—C=C—CO2H
     |  |
     H  H
```

(ii) hex-3-ene *cis-trans* isomers:

```
H          H          H         C2H5
  \       /             \       /
    C=C                   C=C
  /       \             /       \
C2H5       C2H5      C2H5        H
```

butenedioic acid:

```
HO2C        CO2H     HO2C         H
    \      /             \       /
     C=C                   C=C
    /      \             /       \
   H        H           H         CO2H
```

(c) (i) a group with no plane or axis or centre of symmetry; see § 25.9.3.

(ii) Two isomers which are mirror images can exist.

(iii) N (the C in the middle is bonded to 4 different groups)

(iv)

```
     CH2NHCH3                CH2NHCH3
       |                       |
       C                       C
     / | \                   / | \
   HO  |  H                 H  |  OH
    C6H3(OH)2               C6H3(OH)2
```

CHAPTER 26 THE ALKANES

Questions on Chapter 26

1. *(a)* $CH_3CH(CH_3)CH(CH_3)CH_2CH_3$
(b) $CH_3CH(CH_3)CH_2CH(CH_3)CH(CH_3)CH_2CH_3$
(c) $CH_3CHClCHBrCH_2CH_3$ and $CH_3CHClCHBrCH_2CH_3$
(d)

```
     CH2—CH2
    /       \
CH2          CH2
    \       /
     CH2—CH2
```

2. *(a)* ii *(b)* ii *(c)* i *(d)* i

3. *(a)* carbon dioxide, carbon monoxide, carbon, water
(b) chloromethane, dichloromethane, trichloromethane, tetrachloromethane + hydrogen chloride
(c) methane, ethane, hydrogen
(d) sulphur dioxide + all mentioned in *(b)*

4. *(a)* $CH_3CH_2CH_2CH_3$ and $(CH_3)_3CH$
(b) CH_2ClCH_2Cl and CH_3CHCl_2
(c) $CH_3(CH_2)_3CH_3$ and $(CH_3)_2CHCH_2CH_3$ and $(CH_3)_4C$

5. Chain initiation: $Cl_2 \longrightarrow 2Cl\cdot$
Chain propagation: $Cl\cdot + CH_3Cl \longrightarrow HCl + CH_2Cl\cdot$
$CH_2Cl\cdot + Cl_2 \longrightarrow CH_2Cl_2 + Cl\cdot$
Chain termination: $2Cl\cdot \longrightarrow Cl_2$
$2CH_2Cl\cdot \longrightarrow ClCH_2CH_2Cl$
$CH_2Cl\cdot + Cl\cdot \longrightarrow CH_2Cl_2$
See also § 26.4.7.

6. *(a)* See § 26.2.1.
(b) See § 26.4.2.
(c) See § 26.4.2.
(d) See § 26.4.4.
(e) See § 26.4.4.
(f) See § 26.4.1.
(g) See § 26.4.1.

7. *(a)* See §§ 26.2.2, 26.4.2.
(b) See Acid rain, § 21.10.

8. *(a)* heterogeneous
(b) Hydrocarbons and CO are oxidised; see § 26.6.
(c) Oxides of nitrogen are reduced; see § 26.6.
(d) lead; use unleaded petrol

9. *(a)* For photochemical substitution see § 26.4.6.
(b) See § 26.4.7.
(c) for definition see § 10.7.1.
$C(s) + 1.5\,H_2(g) + 0.5\,Cl_2(g) \longrightarrow CH_3Cl(g);\ \Delta H_f^\ominus$
(d) $CH_4(g) + Cl_2(g) \longrightarrow CH_3Cl(g) + HCl(g)$
−75   0   −82   −72 kJ mol^{-1}
$\Delta H_r^\ominus = -82 - 72 - (-75) = -79$ kJ mol^{-1}
(e) (i) Ratio H 4.1/1 : C 24.2/12 : Cl 71.7/35.5 gives the empirical formula CH_2Cl
(ii) M_r of $CH_2Cl = 49.5$ corresponding to $C_2H_4Cl_2$
(iii) Peak at 100 is due to $C_2H_4{}^{35}Cl^{37}Cl$, and peak at 102 to $C_2H_4{}^{37}Cl_2$.

10. *(a)* (i) sunlight
(ii) see § 26.4.7 for mechanism
(b) (i) van der Waals; see §4.8.2
(ii) Forces of attraction between molecules of heptane and other molecules of heptane are very similar in strength to forces of attraction between molecules of heptane and molecules of octane; see § 8.5.1.

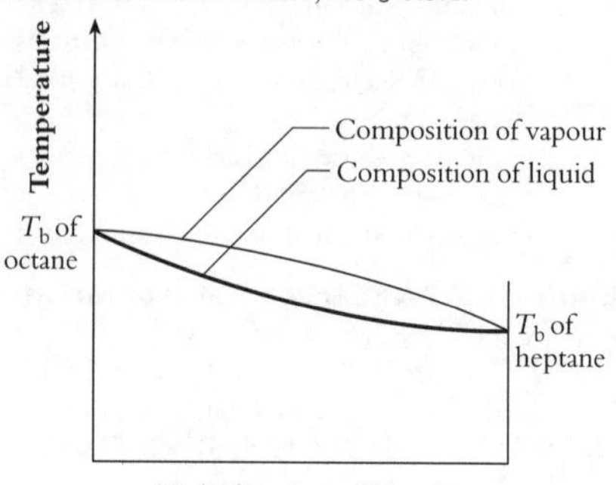

(iv) fractional distillation
(c) (i) Liquids are denser and therefore a smaller fuel tank is needed. They are less flammable and therefore safer.
(ii) Aromatic hydrocarbons are carcinogenic. Lead compounds are poisonous and cause depression and mental impairment, depending on the dose received.

11. *(a)* (i) See § 25.2.
(ii) $2C_8H_{18}(g) + 17O_2(g) \longrightarrow 16CO(g) + 18H_2O(g)$
(b) $2CO(g) + 2NO(g) \longrightarrow N_2(g) + 2CO_2(g)$
reducing agent
(c) (i) e.g. platinum
(ii) heterogeneous
(d) See § 26.4.7.
(e) cracking
(f) The final mixture contains CCl_4 which contains ^{35}Cl and ^{37}Cl. The highest value of $M_r = C^{37}Cl_4$ with $m/z = 160$.

CHAPTER 27 ALKENES AND ALKYNES

Checkpoint 27.8: Alkenes

1. *(a)* hex-2-ene
   (b) 2,5-dimethylhex-2-ene
   (c) *trans*–6-chlorohex-2-ene
   (d) 3-chlorobut-1-ene
   (e) *cis*-hex-2-ene
2. *(a)* $CH_2{=}CH{-}CH_2{-}CH_2{-}CH_3$
   (b) $CH_3{-}CH{=}CCl{-}CH{=}CH{-}CH_3$
   (c) $CH_2{=}CH{-}CH{=}CH_2$
   (d) $CH_3{-}CH{=}CH{-}C(CH_3)_3$
3. *b*
4. *(a)* $CH_3CHClCH_2Cl$
   (b) $CH_3CHOHCH_2Cl + CH_3CHClCH_2Cl + HCl$
   The mechanism for *(a)* is similar to steps 1, 2 and 3 for bromine and ethene, § 27.8.5. In the mechanism for *(b)* step 4 also is involved $\longrightarrow CH_3CHOHCH_2Cl$.
5. *(a)* H_2O; add conc. sulphuric acid, then warm with water
   (b) $CH_3CHBrCH_3$; simply mix the gases at room temperature
   (c) $(CH_3)_2C(OH)CH_2Br$; bubble the alkene through bromine water
   (d) $(CH_3)_2CHOH$; add phosphoric acid and then warm with water
   (e) 2[OH]; cold alkaline $KMnO_4$
   (f) 2[O]; hot conc. $KMnO_4$
6. The chloronium ion, $CH_3{-}CH{-}CH_2$ (bridged by Cl^+)
   is formed and is attacked:
   by $Cl^- \longrightarrow CH_3CHClCH_2Cl$, 1,2-dichloropropane
   by $H_2O \longrightarrow CH_3CHOHCH_2Cl$, 1-chloropropan-2-ol
   by $NO_3^- \longrightarrow CH_3CH(NO_3)CH_2Cl$, (chloromethyl)ethyl nitrate
   by $NOCl \longrightarrow CH_3CHClCHNO$, 2-chloro-1-nitroso-propane
7. Restricted rotation about the C=C bond gives rise to *cis-trans* geometric isomerism.

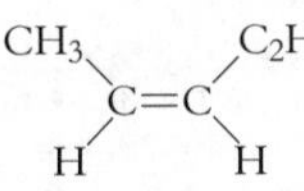

cis-1-chloropropene

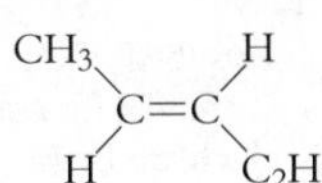

trans-1-chloropropene

$CH_3(H)C{=}C(H)C_2H_5$

cis-pent-2-ene

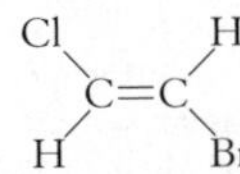

trans-pent-2-ene

$Cl(H)C{=}C(H)Br$

cis-1-bromo-2-chloroethene

$Cl(H)C{=}C(Br)H$

trans-1-bromo-2-chloroethene

Questions on Chapter 27

1. The first step is the formation of a bromonium ion,
   $CH_2{-}CH_2$ (bridged by Br^+)
   This is attacked by either Br^- or Cl^-; to give CH_2BrCH_2Br or CH_2BrCH_2Cl; it cannot give CH_2CH_2Cl.
2. The main product is $CH_3CH_2CHBrCH_3$. The other is $CH_3CH_2CH_2CH_2Br$. See § 27.8.5 for the mechanism.
3. *(a)* $CH_3CHOHCH_2Br$, 1-bromopropan-2-ol
   (b) $(CH_3)_2CHOSO_3H$, methylethyl hydrogensulphate, hydrolysed to propan-2-ol. For the mechanism see § 27.8.5.
4. $100\ cm^3$ at stp is the volume of 0.250 g therefore $22.4\ dm^3$ (the gas molar volume) is the volume of $(22\,400/100) \times 0.250$ g = 56 g. With molar mass = $56\ g\ mol^{-1}$, the formula is C_4H_8.
   but-1-ene $CH_2{=}CHC_2H_5$
   cis-but-2-ene: $CH_3(H)C{=}C(H)CH_3$ (both CH_3 on the same side)
   trans-but-2-ene: $CH_3(H)C{=}C(CH_3)H$ (CH_3 groups on opposite sides)
5. *(a)* sunny, calm
   (b) valleys
   (c) They favour a temperature inversion; see Figure 27.11A.
6. *(a)* For the π-bond see § 5.3.2, which explains why the atoms d, e, f and g in
   $d(e)C{=}C(f)g$
   are coplanar. It also explains why the electron cloud in a π-bond, being above and below the line joining the two carbon atoms, is readily attacked by electrophiles.
   (b) Addition. Electrophiles, e.g. $Br^{\delta+}{-}Br^{\delta-}$, $H^{\delta+}{-}Br^{\delta-}$, $H^{\delta+}{-}O^{\delta-}SO_3H$
7. *(a)* (i) **C** (ii) **C** (iii) **B** (iv) **E** (v) **C**
   (b) **B** and **D**; **C** and **E**
8. *(a)* Cracking of petroleum fractions
   (b) Propene reacts readily to form addition compounds.
   (c) either high pressure or atmospheric pressure and a catalyst
   $\left(CH_2{-}CH(CH_3) \right)_n$
   (d) They do not absorb moisture.
   (e) See Table 27.8.
9. *(a)* from butan-1-ol by dehydration [see Figure 27.3A and § 30.7.2] and from 1-bromobutane by refluxing with sodium hydroxide in ethanol [see Figure 27.3A and § 29.8.2]
   (b) (i) I. steam + phosphoric acid catalyst $\longrightarrow$ ethanol
   II. hydrogen + heated nickel catalyst $\longrightarrow$ ethane
   (ii) Ethanol is an important industrial solvent.
   (c) (i) electrophilic addition, A_E
   (ii) carbocation
   (iii) addition of HBr
   (iv) I. Steam is involved in the fast step so changing the pressure will not alter the rate.
   II. Since $K_p = p(C_2H_5OH(g))/(p(C_2H_4(g)) \times p(H_2O(g)))$ an increase in $p(H_2O(g))$ increases $p(C_2H_5OH(g))$ that is, increases the equilibrium yield.
   (v) Propan-2-ol is the main product. In $CH_3{\rightarrow}C^{\delta+}H{=}C^{\delta-}H_2$, the alkyl group is electron-repelling so the CH_2 group has a δ–charge which is attacked by H^+ to form $CH_3{-}CH{-}CH_3^+$, followed by an attack by $H_2O \longrightarrow CH_3CHOHCH_3 + H^+$.
   (d) Bonds broken are (C=C) + (H—O) and bonds made are (C—C) + (C—O) + (C—H)
   The difference is $-45\ kJ\ mol^{-1}$.
10. *(a)* $CH_2{=}CH_2 + H_2SO_4 \longrightarrow CH_3CH_2SO_4H$
    electrophilic addition, A_E
    (b) water; nucleophilic substitution, S_N
    (c) $2CH_2{=}CH_2 + O_2 \longrightarrow 2CH_2{-}CH_2$ (bridged by O)
    The bond angles of the C atoms are strained; they are less than the tetrahedral bond angle normal for C.

(*d*) $CH_3CHBrCH_2CH_3$
The alkyl group is electron-repelling in $H_2C^{\delta-}{=}C^{\delta+}H \leftarrow CH_2 \leftarrow CH_3$, so the CH_2 group has a $\delta-$ charge and is attacked by the H of $H^{\delta+}{-}Br^{\delta-}$.

11. (*a*) (i) C_nH_{2n+2}
(ii) $12n + 2n + 2 = 170 \Rightarrow n = 12 \Rightarrow C_{12}H_{26}$
(iii) fuel for jet engines; see Table 26.2; e.g. gasoline, lower T_b range

(*b*) **D** and **E** are unsaturated, **F** is saturated; it must be cyclohexane. To show geometrical isomerism **D** must have two different groups attached to each of the doubly bonded C atoms.

D= $H_3C(H)C{=}C(C_2H_5)CH_3$ **E**= $(H_3C)(CH_3)C{=}C(CH_3)CH_3$

F= cyclohexane ring of six CH_2 groups

CHAPTER 28 AROMATIC COMPOUNDS

Checkpoint 28.8: Benzene

1. (*a*) Addition takes place $\longrightarrow C_6H_6Cl_6$.
(*b*) Substitution takes place $\longrightarrow C_6H_5Cl + HCl$.

2. Electrophiles. (*a*) NO_2^+
(*b*) R^+ where R is an alkyl group
(*c*) RCO^+ where RCO is an acyl group

3. Conc. nitric and conc. sulphuric acids. The nitryl cation NO_2^+ is the nitrating agent.

$$HNO_3 + 2H_2SO_4 \rightleftharpoons NO_2^+ + H_3O^+ + 2HSO_4^-$$

For the mechanism see § 28.8.2.

4. Benzene undergoes substitution reactions; see Figure 28.8C for examples.
There are π-bonds between the carbon atoms in ethene and in benzene. In benzene, the π-electrons are delocalised [see § 28.6], spread between six carbon–carbon bonds which are intermediate between C—C and C=C in character and therefore less reactive towards electrophiles than the C=C bond in an alkene.

5. (*a*) See Figure 28.8B. (*b*) See § 28.8.7.

6. E.g., a solution of bromine in an organic solvent is rapidly decolourised by cyclohexene but not by benzene. E.g., a solution of cold alkaline $KMnO_4$ is rapidly decolourised by cyclohexene, not by benzene. E.g., HBr adds rapidly to cylcohexene but not to benzene. See also Table 28.1.

Checkpoint 28. 11: Methylbenzene

1. (*a*) (i) $C_6H_5CH_3$
(ii) 1,4-$CH_3C_6H_4CH_3$ and also some 1, 2-
(*b*) (i) $C_6H_5COCH_3$
(ii) 1,4-$CH_3C_6H_4COCH_3$ and also some 1, 2-
(*c*) (i) $C_6H_5NO_2$
(ii) 1,4-$CH_3C_6H_4NO_2$
(*d*) (i) no reaction
(ii) $C_6H_5CO_2H$
(*e*) (i) $C_6H_6Cl_6$
(ii) $C_6H_5CH_2Cl$
(*f*) (i) C_6H_5Cl
(ii) 1,4-$CH_3C_6H_4Cl$ and also some 1, 2-

2. [Structures: benzene ring with Cl and adjacent CH_3; benzene ring with Cl and para CH_3; benzene ring with CH_2Cl]

Methylbenzene + Cl_2 + $FeCl_3$ (catalyst) $\longrightarrow$
1-chloro-2-methylbenzene + 1-chloro-4-methylbenzene
Separate by fractional distillation under reduced pressure. For (chloromethyl)benzene, pass chlorine into boiling methylbenzene. Stop when the boiling temperature has risen to that of (chloromethyl)benzene to avoid further substitution.

3. (*a*) Fractional distillation of petroleum or coal tar
(*b*) Benzene + bromomethane + $AlBr_3$(catalyst). Reflux.

Questions on Chapter 28

1. See § 28.8.1

2. (*a*) $Cl_2 + AlCl_3$(catalyst) (or Al or Fe or $FeCl_3$), room temperature; see § 28.8.6
(*b*) $C_2H_5Cl + AlCl_3$(catalyst), 60 °C; see § 28.8.4
(*c*) $CH_3COCl + AlCl_3$(catalyst), 60 °C; see § 28.8.5
(*d*) H_2SO_4; warm with fuming sulphuric acid or reflux with conc. sulphuric acid; see § 28.8.3

3. Substitution in the ring is similar to benzene but easier. Substitution in the side chain is not shared by benzene; see Figure 28.11A for examples.

4. (*a*) (i) Propene adds bromine $\longrightarrow CH_3CH_2BrCH_2Br$, 1,2-dibromopropane
Benzene is substituted $\longrightarrow$ bromobenzene, $C_6H_5Br + HBr$
(ii) Sulphuric acid adds to propene $\longrightarrow CH_3CH_2(CH_3)OSO_3H$, methylethyl hydrogensulphate. Benzene is substituted by fuming sulphuric acid or hot conc. sulphuric acid $\longrightarrow$ benzenesulphonic acid, $C_6H_5SO_3H$.
(*b*) (i) Cyclohexene is oxidised $\longrightarrow HO_2C(CH_2)_4CO_2H$, hexane-1,6-dicarboxylic acid. Benzene does not react.
(ii) Cyclohexene does not react.
Benzene $\longrightarrow C_6H_5COCH_3$; see § 28.8.5

5. Electrophilic substitution, S_E, e.g. halogenation, alkylation, acylation; see § 28.8 for equations. They need Friedel–Crafts catalysts, which are Lewis acids, e.g. $AlCl_3$, $FeBr_3$. For the mechanism see § 28.8.7.

6. (*a*) electrophilic substitution, S_E
(*b*) nitryl cation
(*c*) For mechanism see § 28.8.2.

7. (*a*) phenylethene; styrene
(*b*) B = phenylethane, $C_6H_5C_2H_5$; **C** = ethylcyclohexane, $C_6H_{11}C_2H_5$, **D** = poly(phenylethene) or polystyrene,

$$\left({-}CH_2{-}\underset{C_6H_5}{CH}{-} \right)_n$$

8. (*a*) $C_6H_6(l) + Br_2(l) \longrightarrow C_6H_5Br(l) + HBr(g)$
(*b*) Benzene is carcinogenic, bromine is toxic and caustic, with a very pungent smell. HBr is given off in the reaction.
(*c*) (i) The organic layer (benzene and bromobenzene) is immiscible with the aqueous layer. Unreacted bromine passes from the organic layer into the aqueous layer. Several successive portions of NaOH(aq) are required to remove all the bromine.
(ii) Bromine leaves the organic layer which is red owing to the bromine dissolved in it.

$$Br_2(l) + 2NaOH(aq) \longrightarrow NaBrO(aq) + NaBr(aq) + H_2O(l)$$

(d) To remove traces of water which have entered the organic layer because of its treatment with NaOH(aq) and shaking with water

(e) Mass of benzene = $30\ cm^3 \times 0.87\ g\ cm^{-3} = 26.1\ g$
M_r(benzene) = 78, M_r(bromobenzene) = 157
Mass of bromobenzene calculated = $26.1 \times 157/78$ = 52.53 g
% yield = $100 \times 25.9/52.53 = 49.3\%$

9. (a) **A** = 4-nitromethylbenzene, **B** + C = conc. nitric and sulphuric acids

(b) (i) $H_3C-C_6H_4-SO_3H$

(ii) SO_2
(iii) detergents

(c) (i) $Br_2 + FeBr_3 \rightleftharpoons Br^+FeBr_4^-$
(ii) electrophilic substitution

(d) (i) Step 1: H_2, catalyst, heat (200°C)
Step 2: Reflux with NaOH(aq)
(ii) bromine water, changing from brown to colourless

10. (a) (i) $3 \times (-119.6) = -358.8\ kJ\ mol^{-1}$
Benzene is more stable by 150.4 kJ mol^{-1} than expected from the formula: [benzene ring structure]
The stabilisation is due to delocalisation of the π-electrons; see § 5.4.1.

(b) Nitryl cation, NO_2^+

$$HNO_3 + 2H_2SO_4 \rightleftharpoons NO_2^+ + H_3O^+ + 2HSO_4^-$$

For the mechanism see § 28.8.2.

(c) explosives

11. (a) **A** = cyclohexane, **B** = hydrogen, **C** = bromomethane, **D** = iron(III) bromide, **E** = bromobenzene, **F** = conc. sulphuric acid

(b) (i) **E**: CH_3^+; nitrobenzene: NO_2^+
(ii) to avoid further substitution
(iii) reduction to amines from which many other compounds can be made; see Chapter 32.

(c) (i) Pass benzene vapour and hydrogen over heated nickel catalyst.
(ii) $C_6H_6(l) + 3Cl_2(g) \longrightarrow C_6H_6Cl_6(s)$

12. (a) (i) $C_2H_5Cl + AlCl_3 \rightleftharpoons C_2H_5^+ + AlCl_4^-$
(ii) $C_2H_4 + HCl + AlCl_3 \rightleftharpoons C_2H_5^+ + AlCl_4^-$
(iii) electrophilic substitution; for mechanism see § 28.8.4

(b) Ethene is a product of cracking in the petroleum industry, whereas chloroethane must be made.

(c) phenylethene (styrene) $C_6H_5CH{=}CH_2$, poly(phenylethene) or polystyrene; see § 27.8.10 and Table 27.8

13. (a) The mixture obeys Raoult's Law: vapour pressure of mixture of A and B = (saturated vapour pressure of A × mole fraction of A + (saturated vapour pressure of B × mole fraction of B)

(b) (i) Cyclohexane 25/82 mol = 0.305 mol
Benzene 40/78 mol = 0.513 mol
Mole fractions are cyclohexane = 0.305/0.818 = 0.373 and benzene 0.627
Vapour pressure = $(0.373 \times 11\,830) + (0.627 \times 9975)$ Pa = 10.7 kPa

(c) Cyclohexane: $0.305 \times (-3752) = -1144.4$ kJ
Benzene: $0.513 \times (-3267) = -1676.0$ kJ; Total = -2820.4 kJ

(d) (i) Nickel (ii) Cyclohexane

(e) See HBr + ethene; § 27.8.6.

(f) (i) **A** = PBr_3, **B** = KOH(ethanolic solution); see §§ 29.4, 29.6
(ii) **X** = cyclohexanol, **Y** = bromocyclohexane

(g) petroleum oil

CHAPTER 29 HALOGENOALKANES AND HALOGENOARENES

Checkpoint 29.6: CFCs

1. (a) It is not flammable or toxic and is stable.
(b) It is not toxic and is not odorous like liquid ammonia and liquid sulphur dioxide which were used formerly.
(c) Since it is not able to react with substances in the lower atmosphere, it therefore reaches the stratosphere unchanged.
(d) homolytic fission
2. See § 29.6 for HCFCs and HFCs as alternatives to CFCs.

Checkpoint 29.7: Reactions

1. (a) 2-iodobutane (b) 1-bromo-1,1-dimethylethane
2. C_5H_{12} has a higher T_b than C_3H_8 because stronger van der Waals forces operate between the longer molecules of C_5H_{12}. C_3H_7Cl has a higher T_b than C_3H_8 because replacement of one H atom by a Cl atom makes the molecule polar and dipole–dipole interactions between molecules are stronger than van der Waals forces; see § 29.3.1.
3. See § 29.5 for uses. Stability of fluoroalkanes.
4. **B**
5. (a) $CH_3-C(CH_3)(H)-CH_2-Br$
(b) $CH_3-C(CH_3)(H)-CH_2-OH$ 2-methylpropan-1-ol
(c) $CH_3-C(CH_3){=}CH_2$ 2-methylpropene
(d) $CH_3-C(CH_3)(Br)-CH_3$ 2-bromo-2-methylpropane
6. (i) Add aqueous alkali and warm, acidify, add aqueous silver nitrate. **A** gives a white precipitate, **B** gives no precipitate.
(ii) Add aqueous alkali and warm, acidify, add aqueous silver nitrate. **A** gives a white precipitate, **B** gives a pale yellow precipitate.
(iii) Add water. **E** has no reaction, **F** gives hydrogen chloride (which gives white smoke with ammonia)
7. Via a halogenoalkane intermediate:
$C_3H_8(g) + Cl_2(g) \longrightarrow C_3H_7Cl(l) + HCl(g)$
$C_3H_7Cl(l) + OH^-(aq) \longrightarrow C_3H_7OH(l) + Cl^-(aq)$
8. alcohols, alkenes, nitriles, amines; see Figure 29.6A

Checkpoint 29.8: Reactivity

1. (a) Reflux with aqueous sodium hydroxide.
(b) Reflux with alcoholic sodium hydroxide; distil.
(c) Warm with ammonia in a sealed tube.
(d) Warm with potassium cyanide in propanone; distil.
2. In alkanes the C—C bonds are non-polar and C—H bonds have very little polarity [see §4.6.3]. In halogenoalkanes, the $C^{\delta+}$—Halogen$^{\delta-}$ bond is polar and $C^{\delta+}$ is therefore attacked by nucleophiles. However, the $C^{\delta+}$—Halogen$^{\delta-}$ bond is less polar than bonds in other organic compounds, e.g. alcohols and acids, and the reactions of halogenoalkanes are slow.
3. (a) A reagent with a lone pair of electrons which can form a coordinate bond to an atom with an incomplete outer electron shell, e.g. $:OH^-$, $CN:^-$, $:NH_3$. $H_2\ddot{O}$:

(*b*) The C—halogen bond is polarised, $-C^{\delta+}-X^{\delta-}$ and $C^{\delta+}$ is attacked by a nucleophile.
(*c*) Substitution of —X by another group or elimination of HX to form an alkene. Propan-1-ol and propene.

4. See § 29.8.3. The intermediate in (*a*) is

$$\left[\begin{array}{c} R \\ | \\ HO\cdots C\cdots Br \\ / \quad \backslash \\ H \qquad H \end{array}\right]^-$$

It reacts rapidly because five atoms are bonded or partly bonded to a carbon atom.
The intermediate in (*b*) is R_3C^+. It reacts rapidly because a carbon atom carries a positive charge.

Checkpoint 29.9: Reaction mechanisms

1. See § 29.8.1. (*b*) See § 29.8.3.
2. C because the reaction between two oppositely charged ions would be fast and $[OH^-]$ would not then occur in the rate equation.
3. (*a*) (i) See § 25.8.1.
   (ii) See § 25.8.3.
   (iii) Rate $\propto$ [concentration]^n, n = order; see § 14.13.2
   (iv) Molecularity = number of species taking part in the formation of the transition state; see § 14.17.2
4. See §§ 29.8.3, 29.9.1 for the transition state. The polarity of the $C^{\delta+}-Br^{\delta-}$ bond makes it possible for OH^- to make a partial bond to $C^{\delta+}$. This cannot happen in alkanes because the C—H bond is not polar. S_N1 and S_N2 differ in the order of reaction: the number of species required to form the transition state. For the 3° halogenoalkane [see § 29.9.2] hydrolysis is S_N1. A carbocation is formed more easily than in a 1° halogenoalkane because the positive charge is spread out over adjoining carbon atoms.

Checkpoint 29.11: Grignard reagents

1. See § 29.10.
2. $C_2H_5CH_2CH_2OH$ butan-1-ol, $C_2H_5CH_2OH$ propan-1-ol,

$C_2H_5CH(OH)CH_3$ 2-methylpropan-1-ol

$C_2H_5-C(CH_3)_2-OH$ 2,2-dimethylpropan-1-ol

3. $C_2H_5CH_2MgBr$:
   (i) CO_2
   (ii) dilute acid $\longrightarrow C_2H_5CH_2CO_2H$
   $C_2H_5CH_2MgBr$:
   (i) HCHO
   (ii) dilute acid $\longrightarrow C_2H_5CH_2CH_2OH$;
   $C_2H_5CH_2CH_2OH$:
   oxidation by $K_2Cr_2O_7$, $H^+ \longrightarrow C_2H_5CH_2CO_2H$
4. (*a*) C_2H_5MgBr:
   (i) CO_2
   (ii) dil. acid $\longrightarrow C_2H_5CO_2H$
   (*b*) C_2H_5MgBr:
   (i) CH_2-CH_2 (epoxide, bridged by O)
   (ii) dil. acid $\longrightarrow C_2H_5CH_2CH_2OH \longrightarrow C_2H_5CH_2CO_2H$

Questions on Chapter 29

1. (*a*) Br_2 + ethane + sunlight
   (*b*) benzene + Br_2 + $AlBr_3$
   (*c*) Br_2, light
   (*d*) Br_2, UV light, boil
   (*e*) Br_2, $FeBr_3$ catalyst, warm
   (i) $AgNO_3$(aq) no reaction with (*a*), (*b*), (*c*), (*e*); with (*d*) a white precipitate slowly appears
   (ii) aqueous alkali + (a), reflux $\longrightarrow$ ethanol;
   aqueous alkali + (*b*), (*c*) (*e*) no reaction;
   aqueous alkali + (*d*) reflux $\longrightarrow$ phenylmethanol
2. See Figure 29.4B.
   $KBr(s) + H_2SO_4(l) \longrightarrow HBr(g) + KHSO_4(s)$
   $C_2H_5OH(l) + HBr(g) \longrightarrow C_2H_5Br(l) + H_2O(l)$
   impurities: ethoxyethane, ethene; fractional distillation
3. (*a*) similar to Figure 29.4B, using butan-2-ol
   (*b*) 1-bromobutane $CH_3CH_2CH_2CH_2Br$ (1°)
   2-bromobutane $CH_3CH_2CHBrCH_3$ (2°)
   2-bromo-2-methylpropane $(CH_3)_3CBr$ (3°)
   rate: 3° > 2° > 1°
   (*c*) (i) Reflux with conc. NaOH(aq); butan-2-ol
   $C_2H_5CHBrCH_3(l) + OH^-(aq) \longrightarrow C_2H_5CHOHCH_3(l) + Br^-(aq)$
   (ii) Reflux with KOH(ethanol); but-2-ene
   $C_2H_5CHBrCH_3(l) + OH^-(aq) \longrightarrow C_2H_5CH{=}CH_2(l) + Br^-(aq) + H_2O(l)$
   (iii) Add KCN in ethanol, warm, distil;
   2-methylbutanenitrile
   (iv) Warm with ammonia in a sealed container;
   2-aminobutane
   $C_2H_5CHBrCH_3(l) + NH_3(g) \longrightarrow C_2H_5CHNH_2CH_3(l) + H_2O(l)$
4. (*a*) alcohols, alkenes, nitriles, amines
   (*b*) See Figure 29.7A.
   (*c*) RX $\longrightarrow$ Grignard reagent RMgX $\longrightarrow$ primary alcohols RCH_2OH and RCH_2CH_2OH (adding 1C or 2C to the chain), secondary alcohols RR′CHOH, tertiary alcohols RR′R″COH and carboxylic acid RCO_2H.
5. (*a*) (i) Bromine + $FeBr_3$; see § 28.8.6
   (ii)

$$H_2C{=}CH_2 + Br_2 \longrightarrow Br-CH_2-CH_2-Br$$ electrophilic addition

   (iii) The π electrons in the ethene C=C bond and the delocalised electrons in the benzene ring both attract bromine which is electrophilic.
   (*b*) (i) $F-CClF-CClF-F$ (i.e. $CClF_2-CClF_2$)
   (ii) CF_3CH_2F contains 2 H atoms and is therefore more reactive than a CFC.
   (iii) I. $CCl_2{=}CHCl + 3HF \longrightarrow CF_3\text{-}CH_2Cl + 2HCl$
   II. $CF_3CH_2Cl + HF \longrightarrow CF_3CH_2F + HCl$
6. (*a*) (i) The halogenoalkanes are insoluble in water.
   (ii) butan-2-ol
   (iii) $C_4H_9Br(l) + H_2O(l) \longrightarrow C_4H_9OH(aq) + HBr(aq)$
   (iv) yellow
   (v) silver chloride: $Ag^+(aq) + Cl^-(aq) \longrightarrow AgCl(s)$
   (vi) The C—Halogen bond strengths are different;
   C—Cl > C—Br > C—I
   (*b*) (i) The apparatus is a round-bottomed flask, similar to Figure 29.4B but fitted with a reflux condenser. The mixture is heated, and the temperature is controlled so that bromobutane refluxes and but-1-ene, with the lower boiling temperature, distils over. It is collected over water.
   (ii) Bromine water changes from brown to colourless (without the evolution of HBr which happens when bromine substitutes a phenol or an aromatic amine).
7. (*a*) (i) $C_6H_6(l) + Br_2(l) \longrightarrow C_6H_5Br(l) + HBr(g)$
   (ii) $FeBr_3$ or Fe

(b) (i) Br_2, sunlight; electrophilic substitution, photochemical
(ii) $CH_2{=}CH_2(g) + HBr(g) \longrightarrow CH_3CH_2Br(g)$
(iii) nucleophilic substitution

(c) (i) phosphoric(V) acid
(ii) It oxidises HBr to Br_2.
(iii) HBr reacts with ethanol as it is formed.
(iv) Water rises up the test tube because HBr is a very soluble gas.

8. *(a)* (i)

```
     H   H   H   H                 H  CH3  H
     |   |   |   |                 |   |   |
  H—C—C—C—C—Br            H—C—C—C—Br
     |   |   |   |                 |   |   |
     H   H   H   H                 H   H   H
```

(ii) 2-bromo-2-methylpropane

(b) (i) nucleophilic substitution
(ii)

```
     H   H   H    H
     |   |   |    |
  H—C—C—C——C—H
     |   |   |    |
     H   H  NH2   H
```

(i) $(CH_3)_3Br$, tertiary

(c) (i) KOH(ethanolic); reflux
(ii) $CH_3CH{=}CHCH_3$ and $CH_3CH_2CH{=}CH_2$

(d) (i) electrophilic addition
(ii) See § 27.8.5.

9. *(a)* (i) See § 29.9.1.
(ii) S_N2 reaction
(iii) evidence from the rate equation; see § 29.9.1

(b) A white precipitate of silver chloride will form. No reaction with chlorobenzene. The lack of reactivity of chlorobenzene is explained in § 29.10.

(c) $C_3H_7Br \longrightarrow C_3H_7CN$; reflux with KCN(ethanolic)
$C_3H_7CN \longrightarrow C_3H_7CO_2H$; Reflux with a dilute acid; see § 33.6.2

(d) (i) I e.g. DDT; see § 20.1
II e.g. trichlorofluoromethane; see CFCs § 29.9
III e.g. tetrachloroethene, see § 29.5
(ii) The references give the drawbacks of these compounds

10. *(a)* (i) I. Bonds broken: (C—H) = +435 kJ mol^{-1}
Bonds made: (H—Cl) = −432 kJ mol^{-1}
Total = +3 kJ mol^{-1}
II. Bonds broken: (C—H) = +435 kJ mol^{-1}
Bonds made: (C—Cl) = −243 kJ mol^{-1}
Total = +192 kJ mol^{-1}
therefore I is more likely.
(ii) In I C_2H_6 would be formed; in II H_2 would be formed.

(b) S_N2
Nucleophilic substitution in a bimolecular reaction. Attack by CN^- on $C^{\delta+}$ in $H_3C^{\delta+}—I^{\delta-}$. The reaction is second order.

(c) $CH_3I \xrightarrow{(1)} CH_3OH \xrightarrow{(2)} HCO_2H$
(1) Reflux in ethanolic KOH (2) Oxidise with acidified potassium dichromate

11. *(a)*

```
     H   H   H   H
     |   |   |   |
  H—C—C—C—C—Br            1-bromobutane
     |   |   |   |
     H   H   H   H

     H   H   Br  H
     |   |   |   |
  H—C—C—C—C—H             2-bromobutane
     |   |   |   |
     H   H   H   H

     H   H   H
     |   |   |
  H—C—C—C—Br              1-bromo-2-methylpropane
     |   |   |
     H   |   H
      H—C—H
         |
         H

     H   Br  H
     |   |   |
  H—C—C—C—H               2-bromo-2-methylpropane
     |   |   |
     H   |   H
      H—C—H
         |
         H
```

Note that this question asks you to show all the covalent bonds.

(b) (i) An atom or group with a lone pair of electrons which it can donate to another atom. (ii) OH^-
(iii) Rate = k [C_4H_9Br] (iv) For the mechanism of S_N1 reaction, see § 29.9.2. The 3° halogenoalkane is most likely to react by a 1st order reaction. There are 3 carbon atoms bonded to the positively charged carbon atom in the carbonium ion, and the charge can be more spread out.

(c) (i) 2-bromobutane exists in mirror-image forms:

```
   C2H5           C2H5
    |              |
    C              C
  / | \          / | \
 H  |  Br      Br  |  H
   CH3            H3C
```

(ii) The intermediate carbocation is planar:

```
 [   C2H5   ]+
 [    |     ]
 [    C     ]
 [   / \    ]
 [  H   CH3 ]
```

OH^- can add to form a racemic mixture of

```
   C2H5     and     C2H5
    |                |
    C                C
  / | \            / | \
 H  |  OH        HO  |  H
   CH3              H3C
```

CHAPTER 30 ALCOHOLS AND PHENOLS

Checkpoint 30.4: Properties

1. *(a)* a hydroxyl group, $\gt$C—O—H

(b)

```
     H   H                       H
     |   |                       |
  H—C—C—(O—H)            H3C—C—CH3
     |   |                       |
     H   H                     (O—H)
```

2. (i) O is more electronegative than H and the —OH group is polarised $—O^{\delta-}—H^{\delta+}$. $H^{\delta+}$ in one molecule is attracted to $O^{\delta-}$ in another molecule; see Figure 30.3A.
(ii) Ethanol molecules can form hydrogen bonds with water molecules; see Figure 30.3B.
(iii) The hydrogen bonds between molecules of ethanol are stronger than the van der Waals forces between molecules of ethane.

3. Fermentation of sugars and catalytic hydration of ethene.
(i) fermentation: batch process
catalytic hydration: continuous

(ii) fermentation: uses renewable sugars and starches
catalytic hydration: uses ethene from petroleum, a non-renewable resource

(iii) fermentation: no heat required
catalytic hydration: heat required

(iv) fermentation is slow, catalytic hydration is faster

Checkpoint 30.5: Uses

1. *(a)* Oxygenates are compounds containing oxygen; petroleum fractions are hydrocarbons.
   (b) Oxygenates burn more cleanly to form carbon dioxide and water with less carbon monoxide and carbon.
   (c) Methanol and MTBE are made from natural gas (non-renewable). Ethanol is made from ethene (from petroleum, non-renewable) or from sugar and starch (renewable).
2. *(a)* The boiling temperature must be similar to that of petrol. The fuel must be soluble in petrol. The combustion products must be harmless. It should not require a big adjustment of the carburettor.
   (b) It saves on imports of petroleum, and it reduces pollution; see § 30.5.3. Countries with agricultural land to spare and enough sunshine to ripen sugar cane.

Checkpoint 30.7: Reactions

1. *(a)* e.g. reaction with sodium and esterification; see § 30.7.1
   (b) e.g. halogenation, dehydration, oxidation; see § 30.7.2
2. *(a)* conc. H_2SO_4, heat
   (b) I_2 + red P, distil
   (c) NaBr + conc. H_2SO_4, distil
   (d) HCl(g) + $ZnCl_2$ (catalyst); reflux and then distil
   (e) ethanoic acid + conc. H_2SO_4
   (f) (i) I_2 + red P, reflux, distil $\longrightarrow C_2H_5I$
   (ii) KCN(ethanol), warm, distil $\longrightarrow C_2H_5CN$
3. *(a)* $CH_3CH_2CH_2ONa$, sodium propoxide
   (b) $CH_3CH_2CH_2Cl$, 1-chloropropane
   (c) $CH_3CH{=}CH_2$, propene
   (d) $CH_3CO_2CH_2CH_2CH_3$, propyl ethanoate
4. *(a)* $CH_3CH_2CH_2OH \xrightarrow{\text{conc. } H_2SO_4} CH_3CH{=}CH_2 \xrightarrow{HBr} CH_3CHBrCH_3 \xrightarrow{KOH(aq)} CH_3CHOHCH_3$
   (b) $CH_3CH_2CH_2OH \xrightarrow{\text{conc. } H_2SO_4} CH_3CH{=}CH_2 \xrightarrow{Cl_2} CH_3CHClCH_2Cl$
   (c) $CH_3CH_2CH_2OH \xrightarrow{\text{conc. } H_2SO_4} CH_3CH{=}CH_2 \xrightarrow{KMnO_4\text{(cold, dilute)}} CH_3CHOHCH_2OH$
5. Names: see §§ 30.2.1, 30.2.2. For distinguishing test with conc. HCl acid + $ZnCl_2$ see Table 30.7.
6. **A** = C_2H_5Br
   B = $CH_3CH(OH)CH_3$
   (a) KBr + conc. H_2SO_4
   (b) KCN (ethanol solution)
   (c) KOH(aq), reflux
   (d) $K_2Cr_2O_7$, acid
7. *(a)* C_4H_9Br
   (b) $CH_3{-}CH(CH_3){-}CH_2OH$ $\quad$ $CH_3{-}CH(CH_3){-}CH_2Br$
   (c) $CH_3{-}C(CH_3){=}CH_2$ $\quad$ 2-methylpropene
   (d) $CH_3{-}C(CH_3)_2{-}Br$ $\quad$ 2-bromo-2-methylpropane

Checkpoint 30.11: Phenols

1. 1 = conc. HNO_3 + conc. H_2SO_4, 2 = Cl_2 + $AlCl_3$, 3 = fuming H_2SO_4, 4 = NaOH(aq), high temperature and pressure, 5 = melted with NaOH(s), **X** = Sn + HCl(aq), **Y** = diazotise with $NaNO_2$ + HCl(aq) and warm
2. *(a)* conc. H_2SO_4, r.t.
   (b) $CH_3COCl + AlCl_3$, reflux
   (c) NaOH(aq), Br_2(aq), acidify
   (d) conc. HNO_3
   (e) esterify by CH_3COCl or $(CH_3CO)_2O$
3. delocalisation of charge on $C_6H_5O^-$; see § 30.11.1

Questions on Chapter 30

1. (i) Ethanol molecules form hydrogen bonds to water molecules; ethane molecules cannot do this. (ii) Hydrogen bonding between ethanol molecules means that more heat is required to vaporise the liquid. In ethane there are weak van der Waals forces between molecules.
2. *(a)* cracking of petroleum fractions; see § 26.4.2
   (b) $CH_2{=}CH_2 + HBr \longrightarrow CH_3CH_2Br \xrightarrow{KOH(aq)} CH_3CH_2OH$
   (c) Produces less pollution and saves resources of petroleum – provided that ethanol is obtained through fermentation.
   (d) $C_2H_5OH + 3O_2 \longrightarrow 2CO_2 + 3H_2O$
   (e) Potassium dichromate(VI) changed from orange through green to blue as $Cr_2O_7^{2-}$ ions (orange) were reduced to Cr^{3+} ions (blue).
3. NaOH reacts with the phenol to form $CH_3C_6H_4ONa$ but not with the alcohol.
   $FeCl_3$ gives a violet colour with the phenol.
   PCl_5 reacts with the alcohol to form $C_6H_5CH_2Cl$ + HCl(g), but reacts very slowly with the phenol.
4. *(a)* See § 27.8.7 for the catalytic hydration of ethene and § 30.4.3 for fermentation.
   (b) (i) sodium ethoxide, C_2H_5ONa (absence of water, r.t.)
   (ii) ethyl ethanoate $CH_3CO_2C_2H_5$ (reflux with conc. sulphuric acid as catalyst)
   (iii) bromoethane C_2H_5Br (distil)
5. *(a)* benzene + fuming $H_2SO_4 \longrightarrow C_6H_5SO_3H$, benzenesulphonic acid; fuse with NaOH $\longrightarrow C_6H_5ONa$; with water and acid $\longrightarrow C_6H_5OH$; see § 30.10.1
   (b) (i) 2,4,6-tribromophenol forms
   (ii) phenyl benzoate forms
   (c) 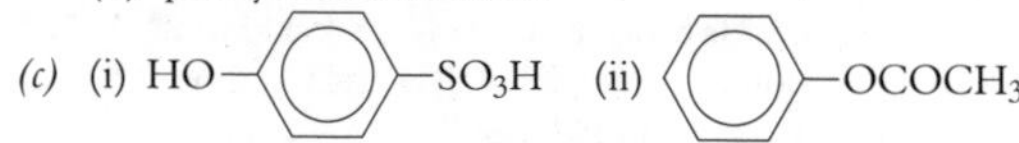

6. *(a)* $CH_2{=}CHCHO$ oxidised $\longrightarrow CH_2{=}CHCO_2H$.
   On further oxidation $\longrightarrow HCHO + OHCCO_2H \longrightarrow HCO_2H + (CO_2H)_2$
   (b) $CH_2BrCHBrCH_2OH$, 2,3-dibromopropan-1-ol; addition, electrophile
   (c) $CH_3CH_2CH_2OH$, propan-1-ol
   (d) $CH_3CO_2CH_2CH{=}CH_2$; propenyl ethanoate: esterification
7. *(a)* $CH_3CH{=}CH_2 + H_2O$ (conc. H_2SO_4, heat)
   (b) $C_6H_5ONa + NaHSO_3$ (melt with NaOH)
   (c) $CH_3CH_2ONa + H_2$ (anhydrous, r.t.)
   (d) $CH_3CH_2C(CH_3)_2OSO_3H$ (conc. H_2SO_4, r.t.)
   (e) $(CH_3)_3CCl + H_2O$ (add at r.t.)
8. *(a)* catalytic hydration; see § 27.8.7
   (b) hydrolysis; see § 29.8.1 and Figure 29.8A
   (i) reflux together with conc. H_2SO_4 as catalyst
   (ii) conc. H_2SO_4 >170 °C $\longrightarrow$ ethene
9. *(a)* NaOH(aq)
   (b) conc. HNO_3, r.t.
   (c) Br_2(aq), r.t.

10. Dissolve the mixture in ethoxyethane. Pour the solution into a separating funnel. Add NaOH(aq), shake, allow the layers to separate. Run off the bottom layer, which contains the sodium salt of **A**. Add HCl(aq) to precipitate **A**. Take the top layer, dry it, distil in a fume cupboard to remove ethoxyethane (highly flammable) and leave behind **B**.

11. See Table 30.11.

12. *(a)* Ethanol is a weaker acid than water because the $C_2H_5O^-$ ion is less stable than the OH^- ion [§ 30.6]. Phenol is a stronger acid than water because in the $C_6H_5O^-$ ion the negative charge is spread over the ring to some extent, and this stabilises the ion; see § 30.11.1.

(b) See Table 30.11. Ethanol reacts slowly with Na to form sodium ethoxide, C_2H_5ONa. Phenol reacts more rapidly to form sodium phenoxide, C_6H_5ONa. Ethanol reacts with ethanoyl choride, with conc. sulphuric acid as catalyst, at room temperature to form ethyl ethanoate. Phenol must be converted into C_6H_5ONa which then reacts rapidly with ethanoyl chloride at room temperature to form phenyl ethanoate. Ethanol reacts with ethanoic acid, with conc. sulphuric acid as catalyst to form ethyl ethanoate. Phenol does not react with ethanoic acid: the acid chloride or anhydride is used for esterification of the ion $C_6H_5O^-$. Bromine does not react with ethanol. Bromine water and phenol or sodium phenoxide react rapidly to form a ppt of 2,4,6-tribromophenol.

$2C_2H_5OH(l) + 2Na(s) \longrightarrow 2C_2H_5ONa(s) + H_2(g)$

$2C_6H_5OH(s) + 2Na(s) \longrightarrow 2C_6H_5ONa(s) + H_2(g)$

$C_2H_5OH(l) + CH_3COCl(l) \longrightarrow CH_3CO_2C_2H_5(l) + HCl(g)$

$C_6H_5ONa(s) + CH_3COCl(l) \longrightarrow CH_3CO_2C_6H_5(l) + NaCl(s)$

$C_2H_5OH(l) + CH_3CO_2H(l) \longrightarrow CH_3CO_2C_2H_5(l) + H_2O(l)$

$C_6H_5OH(aq) + 3Br_2(aq) \longrightarrow Br_3C_6H_2OH(s) + 3HBr(aq)$

(c) (i)

```
CH2OH(l) + 2Na(s) ──► CH2ONa(s) + H2(g)
|                     |
CH2OH                 CH2ONa
```

(ii) $C_6H_5CH_2OH(l) + CH_3CO_2H(l) \longrightarrow CH_3CO_2CH_2C_6H_5(l) + H_2O(l)$

(iii)

```
CH2OH(l) + 3CH3COCl(l) ──► CH2OCOCH3(l) + 3HCl(g)
|                          |
CHOH                       CHOCOCH3
|                          |
CH2OH                      CH2OCOCH3
```

13. *(a)* $(CH_3)_2CHCH_2OH$

(b) (i) elimination
(ii) $CH_3CH{=}CHCH_3$ or $CH_2{=}CHCH_2CH_3$

(c) (i) butanal $CH_3CH_2CH_2CHO$
(ii) butanoic acid $CH_3CH_2CH_2CO_2H$
(iii) butanone $CH_3COCH_2CH_3$
(iv) oxidation

(d) (i) $CH_3CO_2C(CH_3)_2$
(ii) ethanoic acid
(iii) conc. sulphuric acid

(e) (i) 1° alcohol, cloudiness appears slowly
2° alcohol, cloudiness appears in 5 minutes
3° alcohol cloudiness appears in 1 minute; see Table 30.7
(ii) $CH_3CHClCH_2CH_3$

14. *(a)* (i) ethene by catalytic hydration and sugars by fermentation
$CH_2{=}CH_2 + H_2O \longrightarrow CH_3CH_2OH$; phosphoric acid catalyst
$C_6H_{12}O_6 \longrightarrow 2C_2H_5OH + 2CO_2$; enzyme in yeast as catalyst
Ethene is a product of the cracking of petroleum oil fractions. As oil runs out, the renewable resource, sugar, is liable to become more important.
(ii) $CH_3CO_2H + 4[H] \longrightarrow C_2H_5OH + H_2O$; $LiAlH_4$(ethoxyethane)

(b) $C_2H_4 \longrightarrow C_2H_6$, ethane by hydrogenation with a nickel catalyst
$\longrightarrow (CH_2)_n$, poly(ethene) by polymerisation

15. *(a)* Substitution. The reagent is a nucleophile.

```
           CH3             ┌      CH3     ┐-
           |               │      |       │
HO- + H—C—Br  ──►          │ HO····C····Br │
           |               │     / \      │
           CH(CH3)2        └    H   CH(CH3)2┘
                                  |
                                  ▼
                                 CH3
                                 |
                          HO—C—CH(CH3)2 + Br-
                                 |
                                 H
```

(b) Elimination. The reagent is a base.
$CH_2{=}CH{-}CH(CH_3)_2$ is also formed

```
           CH3                       ┌ CH3      ┐-
           |                         │ |        │
HO- + H—C—Br  ──►  H2O +             │ C—Br     │
           |                         │ |        │
           CH(CH3)2                  └ CH(CH3)2 ┘
                                        |
                                        ▼
                                       CH3
                                       |
                                       CH + Br-
                                       ||
                                       C(CH3)2
```

CHAPTER 31 ALDEHYDES AND KETONES

Checkpoint 31.4: Carbonyl compounds

1. *(a)* $CH_3CH_2CH_2CHO$

(b) $CH_3CH_2CH_2COCH_3$

(c) $CH_3CH_2COCH_2CH_3$

(d)

```
  CH2—CH2
 /       \
CH2       C=O
 \       /
  CH2—CH2
```

(e) $CH_3CH_2CH_2CH(CH_3)CH_2CHO$

(f) $CH_3COCH_2COCH_3$

(g) $CH_3CH(CH_3)COCHClCH_2CH_3$

(h)

```
H3C       H
   \     /
    C=C
   /     \
  H       CHO
```

(i) HO–(benzene ring)–CHO (para)

(j) (benzene ring)–CHO with Cl on the ring (meta)

2. (a) butanal (b) butan-2-one (c) pentan-3-one (d) 2-methylpropanal (e) 3-methylbutan-2-one (f) but-2-enal (g) 4-chlorophenylethanone (h) 4-nitrobenzaldehyde
3. Polarisation of the carbonyl group makes it easy for nucleophiles to attack; see § 31.4.
4. Bromine is an electrophile; see § 27.8.5. The carbonyl group is attacked by nucleophiles on the $\delta+$ carbon atom in $>C^{\delta+}{=}O^{\delta-}$; see §§ 31.4.1, 31.4.2.
5. In $C_3H_7{-}O^{\delta-}{-}H^{\delta+}$ the O—H bond is polarised and the H atom is attracted to the O atom of a neighbouring molecule. In

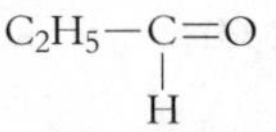

```
C2H5—C=O
     |
     H
```

the C—H bond is only very slightly polarised and there is no similar attraction between $-H^{\delta+}$ and $-O^{\delta-}$.

Checkpoint 31.6: Preparations

1. Oxidation to the carboxylic acid can occur. Distil off the aldehyde as it is formed; see Figure 31.6A.
2. (a) $(CH_3)_2C{=}CHCH_3$
   (b) $(CH_3)_2C{=}CHCH_2CH_2CH{=}CHC_2H_5$
   (c) $CH_2{=}C(CH_3)CH_2C(CH_3){=}CH_2$
   (d) $CH_2{=}CHCH_2CH{=}CH_2$

Checkpoint 31.7: Reactions

1. (a) $(CH_3)_2C{=}NNH_2$
   (b) $(CH_3)_2C{=}NNHC_6H_5$
   (c) 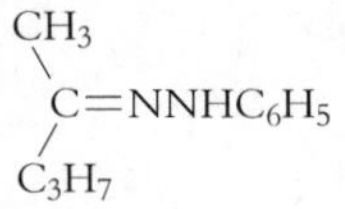
```
CH3
   \
    C=NNHC6H5
   /
C3H7
```
   (d) 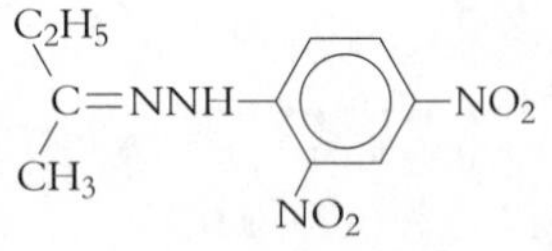
```
C2H5
   \
    C=NNH—⟨ring⟩—NO2
   /
CH3          NO2
```
   (e) 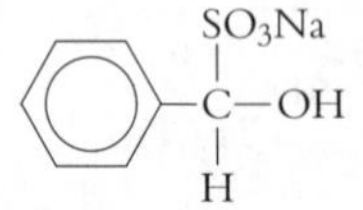
```
          SO3Na
          |
⟨ring⟩—C—OH
          |
          H
```
2. (a) 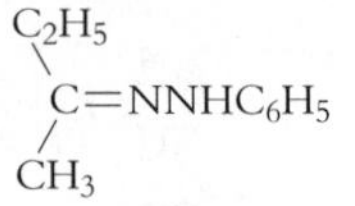
```
C2H5
   \
    C=NNHC6H5
   /
CH3
```
   (b) $C_6H_5CH_2OH$
   (c) $C_2H_5CO_2H$
   (d) $C_6H_5CH_2CH_2CHO$
   (e) $C_6H_5CH{=}CHCH_2OH$
   (f) $C_2H_5CHOHCH_3$
3. In common are e.g. addition reactions with HCN, $NaHSO_3$ [§ 31.7.4], addition–elimination reactions with $C_6H_5NHNH_2$ etc. [§ 31.7.5] and halogenation [§ 31.7.6]
   Aldehydes but not ketones with Tollens' reagent give silver and with Fehling's solution give copper(I) oxide [§ 31.7.3] because aldehydes are more easily oxidised than ketones.
4. (a)
```
C2H5  OH
   \ /
    C
   / \
CH3   CN
```
   (b)
```
C2H5
   \
    C=NNHC6H5
   /
CH3
```
   (c)
```
C2H5
   \
    C=O
   /
CBr3
```
   (d) $CHI_3 + C_2H_5CO_2^-$
   (e) 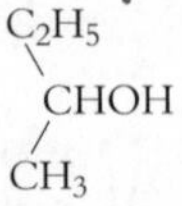
```
C2H5
   \
    CHOH
   /
CH3
```
5. (a) aqueous sodium chlorate(I) or chlorine + NaOH(aq)
   (b) CH_3CHO reduce with $NaBH_4 \longrightarrow C_2H_5OH$; with conc. $H_2SO_4 \longrightarrow CH_2{=}CH_2$
   (c) CH_3CHO reduce with $NaBH_4 \longrightarrow C_2H_5OH$
   CH_3CHO oxidise with $K_2Cr_2O_7$, acid $\longrightarrow CH_3CO_2H$
   $C_2H_5OH + CH_3CO_2H$ with conc. H_2SO_4
   $\longrightarrow CH_3CO_2C_2H_5 + H_2O$
6. (a) C, E, F, H (b) A, C, E
7. $CH_3CH_2COCH_3$ reacts faster because the 2° alcohol must first be oxidised to CH_3COCH_2CHO before it reacts with iodine.
   $CH_3CH_2COCH_3 \longrightarrow CH_3CH_2CO_2Na + CHI_3$
   $CH_3CHOHCH_2CH_2OH \longrightarrow CHI_3 + NaO_2CCH_2CHO$

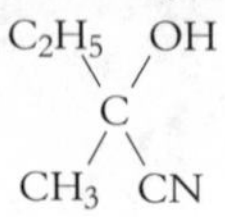

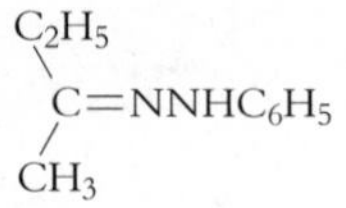

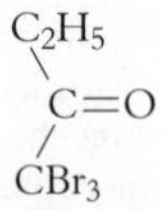

Checkpoint 31.8: Reactivity

1. $X = -Cl, -Br, -I, -OSO_3H, -C_nH_{2n+1}$
   $Y = -CN, -SO_3Na, -NHNH_2, -NHNHC_6H_5$
   For a comparison of the reactivity of C=C and C=O see § 31.8.2.
2. Addition of CN^- increases the speed of reaction because CN^- is the attacking nucleophile [see § 31.8.1]. The ionisation of HCN to give CN^- ions is suppressed by H^+ ions.
3. (a) 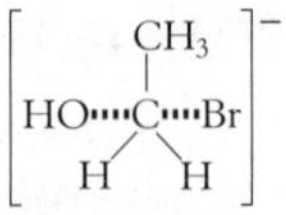
```
[     CH3     ]-
[      |      ]
[ HO····C····Br ]
[     / \     ]
[    H   H    ]
```
   5 pairs, with the negative charge spread over the species, including C atoms
   (b) 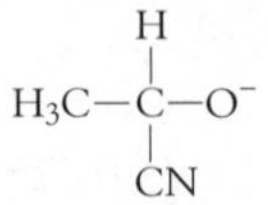
```
       H
       |
H3C—C—O⁻
       |
       CN
```
   4 pairs, with O^- carrying the negative charge
   (c) (b) is more stable because oxygen is electronegative and able to carry a negative charge.
4. In $H^{\delta+}{-}Br^{\delta-}$: the $H^{\delta+}$ attacks the π electrons of the C=C bond. In $>C^{\delta+}{=}O^{\delta-}$ the $\delta+$ C atom is attacked by nucleophiles.

Questions on Chapter 31

1. (a) pentan-2-one, $CH_3CH_2CH_2COCH_3$
   (b) $Cr(VI) \longrightarrow Cr(III)$
   (c) $KMnO_4$, acid
   (d) Forms a yellow ppt with DNP and does not reduce Tollens' reagent or Fehling's solution.
2. (a) Oxidised to a mixture of products
   (b) Reduced to propan-2-ol
   (c) $\longrightarrow CHI_3 + CH_3CO_2^-$
   (d) $(CH_3)_2C(OH)CN$. The $[CN^-]$ is low because HCN is a weak acid. Adding KCN provides CN^- ions.
3. $CH_3CH{=}CH_2 \xrightarrow{(i)} CH_3CHOHCH_3 \xrightarrow{(ii)} CH_3COCH_3$
   (i) conc. H_2SO_4, warm (ii) $K_2Cr_2O_7$, acid, warm
   CH_3CH_2CHO, propanal
   The aldehyde reduces Tollens' reagent and Benedict's/Fehling's solution.

4. **P** is an alkene, **Q** is an aldehyde with 2 CHO groups. This suggests **P** = cyclohexene and **Q** = hexane-1, 6-dial

P **Q**

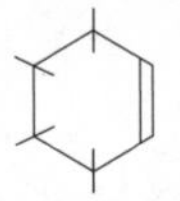

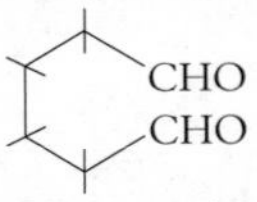

CHO
CHO

5. Oxidation of **A** removes 2H: it is possibly an alcohol. **A** is oxidised to a carbonyl compound, **B**, which has a CH_3CO— group. Dehydration of **A** gives **C**, an alkene C_5H_{10}. Ozonolysis shows that **C** is $CH_3CH_2CH_2CH{=}CH_2$. The formation of butanal shows that **A** does not have a branched chain; it is $CH_3CH_2CH_2CHOHCH_3$.

6. **P** = $C_5H_8O_2$. The hydroxynitrile has 2 N so **P** contains two >*C*=O groups. **P** contains —$COCH_3$ because it gives the iodoform test and —CHO because it reduces Tollens' reagent. It has an unbranched chain because it is reduced to pentane. **P** is $CH_3COCH_2CH_2CHO$.

7. *(a)* C_2H_5CHO reduces Benedict's/Fehling's solution to a reddish brown ppt of Cu_2O. CH_3COCH_3 does not reduce Fehling's solution but gives a coloured ppt with DNP. C_2H_5OH is a 1° alcohol, and $(CH_3)_2CHOH$ is a 2° alcohol; to distinguish see Lucas test in Table 30.7.

(b) C_6H_5CHO reduces Fehling's solution. $C_6H_5CH_2OH$ reacts with ethanoic acid (conc. H_2SO_4 catalyst) to form a sweet-smelling ester. $C_6H_5COCH_3$ gives a coloured ppt with DNP but does not reduce Fehling's solution. $C_6H_5CH{=}CH_2$ decolourises bromine water.

8. *(a)* Chlorinate $\longrightarrow CH_3COCH_2Cl$. Hydrolyse with NaOH(aq), warm.

(b) Reduce with $LiAlH_4$(ethoxyethane) $\longrightarrow CH_3CHOHCH_3$. Dehydrate with conc. $H_2SO_4 \longrightarrow CH_3CH{=}CH_2$.

(c) Reduce with $NaBH_4(aq) \longrightarrow C_6H_5CH_2OH$. With KBr + conc. $H_2SO_4 \longrightarrow C_6H_5CH_2Br$

9. *(a)* (i) Ethanal reduces ammoniacal $AgNO_3 \longrightarrow Ag$, but propanone does not react.

(ii) Ethanal is oxidised to ethanoic acid, but propanone is oxidised only with prolonged treatment.

(iii) Both form addition products, $CH_3CHOHCN$ and $(CH_3)_2COHCN$.

(iv) Both form addition–elimination products, 2,4-dinitrophenylhydrazones, $CH_3CH{=}NNHC_6H_3(NO_2)_2$ and $(CH_3)_2C{=}NNHC_6H_3(NO_2)_2$.

(b) Addition of a base increases ionisation of HCN; see § 31.8.1.

10. *(a)* (i) $K_2Cr_2O_7$, acid

(ii) NaIO(aq) or I_2 + NaOH(aq)

(iii) HCN followed by dilute acid, warm

(b) $CH_3CHO + 3I_2 \longrightarrow CI_3CHO + 3HI$

$CI_3CHO + OH^- \longrightarrow CHI_3 + HCO_2^-$

$CH_3CHO + HCN \longrightarrow CH_3CHOHCN$

$CH_3CHOHCN + 2H_2O \longrightarrow CH_3CHOHCO_2H + NH_3(g)$

(c)

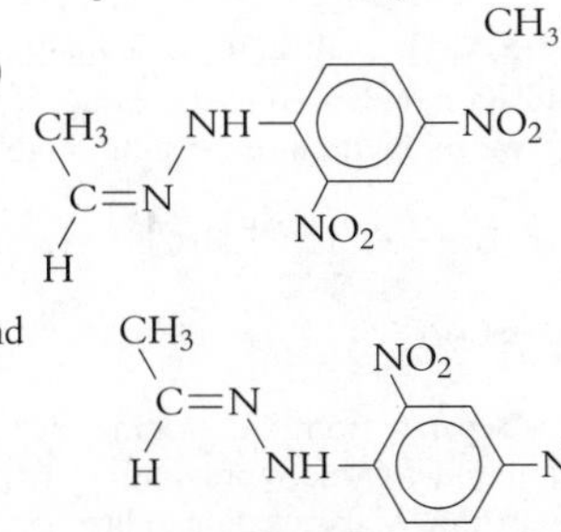

CH_3 NH— —NO_2
C=N
H NO_2

and

CH_3 NO_2
C=N
H NH— —NO_2

11. *(a)* **A**: $C_6H_5CO_2H$, **B**: $C_6H_5CH_2OH$, **C**: $C_6H_5CHOHSO_3Na$, **D**: C_6H_5CClO

(b) **A**: $K_2Cr_2O_7$, acid, warm, **B**: $NaBH_4$(aq), warm, **C**: $NaHSO_3$(aq), r.t., **D**: Cl_2, boil

(c) Addition to >C=O is by a nucleophile; addition to >C=C< is by an electrophile; see § 31.8.2.

(d) Benzaldehyde reduces Benedict's/Fehling's solution to red Cu_2O and reduces Tollens' reagent to a silver mirror. Phenylethanone does neither.

12. *(a)* **A** is a carbonyl compound. The reaction is addition-elimination to form the 2,4-dinitrophenylhydrazone of **A**, which can be recrystallised and **A** can be identified from the T_m of the derivative.

(b) **A** must be an aldehyde RCHO, not a ketone, oxidised to **B**, a carboxylic acid, RCO_2H.

(c) **A** is reduced to an alcohol, **C**, RCH_2OH.

(d) **A** reduces Ag^+(aq) to Ag.(s)A silver mirror is seen and **A** is oxidised to **B**.

(e) RCO_2CH_2R

(f) (i) RCO_2H: strong hydrogen bonds between molecules

(ii) RCO_2CH_2R: there is no $\delta+$ H atom to form hydrogen bonds.

13. *(a)* Propene: addition of the electrophile HBr; see § 27.8.6. Propanal: addition of a nucleophile, e.g. CN^-; see § 31.8.1 and 31.8.2.

(b) Warm dilute $K_2Cr_2O_7$ + acid oxidises propanal but not propanone. The oxidising agent changes from orange through green to blue.

14. *(a)* (i) see Figure 31.6A.

(ii) To avoid further oxidation to ethanoic acid

(b) See § 31.4.1.

15. The evidence shows **X** is a carbonyl compound (adds DNP). **X** contains a CH_3CO— group (gives iodoform). It is not an aldehyde (not easily oxidised). It has no C=C bond (does not add Br_2), so hydrogen must reduce the >CO group to >CHOH.

X = $CH_3COCH_2CH_3$, **Y**and **Z** = $CH_3C^*HOHCH_2CH_3$. Since C* is chiral, a mixture of stereoisomers is formed.

16. *(a)* (i) **E** = $CH_3CH{=}CHOH$ or $CH_2{=}CHCH_2OH$, **F** = CH_3COCH_3, **G** = CH_3CH_2CHO

(ii) 1. With CH_3CO_2H + conc. H_2SO_4, **E** gives a sweet-smelling ester; **F** and **G** do not react.

2. With DNP, **F** and **G** give coloured ppts; **E** does not react.

3. With Tollens' reagent, **G** gives a silver mirror; **E** and **F** do not react.

$CH_2{=}CHCH_2OH + CH_3CO_2H \longrightarrow CH_3CO_2CH_2CH{=}CH_2 + H_2O$

$(CH_3)_2CO + H_2NNHC_6H_3(NO_2)_2 \longrightarrow (CH_3)_2C{=}NNHC_6H_3(NO_2)_2 + H_2O$

$CH_3CH_2CHO + H_2NNHC_6H_3(NO_2)_2 \longrightarrow CH_3CH_2CH{=}NNHC_6H_3(NO_2)_2 + H_2O$

$CH_3CH_2CHO + H_2O + Ag^+(aq) \longrightarrow CH_3CH_2CO_2H + 2H^+(aq) + Ag(s)$

(b) (i) $CH_3CHOHCHOHCH_3$

(ii) $2CHI_3 + HO_2CCO_2H$

17. *(a)* alkene and carbonyl

(b) (i) The bromine solution is decolourised.

(ii) $C_6H_5CH{=}CHCHO + Br_2 \longrightarrow C_6H_5CHBrCHBrCHO$

(iii) For mechanism see § 27.8.5.

(iv) electrophilic attack

(c) DNP gives a coloured ppt.

(d) C_6H_5 and CHO on one carbon, H and H on the other, joined as C=C

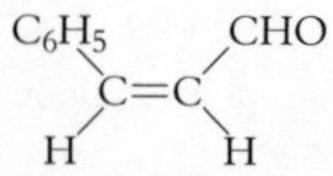

cis–trans isomerism arises from restricted rotation about the C=C bond.

(e) $C_6H_5CH_2CH_2CH_2OH$ obtained by H_2, Ni

18. (a) (i) CHO reacts to give a coloured ppt.
(ii) —CHO reacts to give a silver mirror.
(b) —CHO is oxidised to $—CO_2H$; Ag^+ is reduced to Ag.
(c) (i) HO–C_6H_3(OCH$_3$)–CH_2OH (benzene ring with HO, CH_2OH and CH_3O)
(ii) I. $1\frac{1}{2}$ mol because 1 mol reacts with —OH, and $\frac{1}{2}$ mol reacts with aromatic —CHO in the Canizzarro reaction:

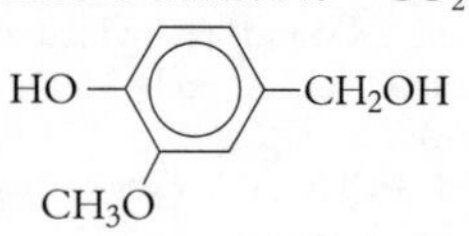

$$2ArCHO + NaOH \longrightarrow ArCH_2OH + ArCO_2Na$$

II. 1 mol reacts with —OH; $—CH_2OH$ does not react with NaOH.

(d) (i) tri-iodomethane
(ii) sodium iodate (I)(aq) or iodine + NaOH(aq)
(iii) No, it must contain a group $—COCH_3$.

19. (a) See § 27.8.5.
(b) $CH_3CHOHCH_2CH_3$
(c) (i) electrophilic addition ⟶ (ring structure with H, Br and =O)
(ii) nucleophilic addition ⟶ (ring structure with OH and CN)
(iii) 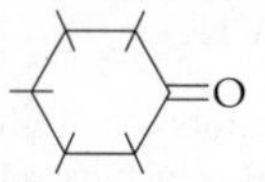 (ring structure with =O)

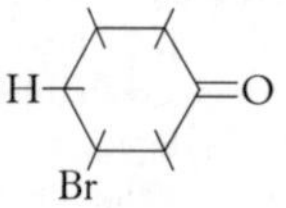

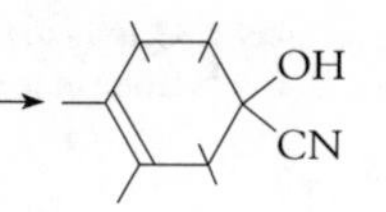

20. (a) C 71.4%, H 9.5%, O 19.1%
(b) (i) Bromine water is decolourised.
(i) DNP gives a coloured ppt.
(c) **X** contains a —CHO group: C_4H_7CHO. The isomers which do not show *cis–trans* isomerism are $CH_2=CHCH_2CH_2CHO$ and $(CH_3)_2C=CHCHO$.
(d) (i) $(CH_3)_2C=CHCHO + HBr \longrightarrow$
A: $(CH_3)_2CBrCH_2CHO$
+ **B**: $(CH_3)_2CHC^*HBrCHO$
(ii) For the mechanism and the reason why product **A** is preferred see § 27.8.6.

21. (a) carbonyl group, C=C double bond, hydroxyl group, benzene ring
(b) (i) Aqueous bromine is decolourised because Br_2 adds across C=C double bond.
(ii) A yellow ppt of iodoform CHI_3 forms as I_2 + NaOH(aq) react with the $—COCH_3$ group $\longrightarrow —COCI_3 \longrightarrow —CO_2H + CHI_3$
(c) (i) One. DNP will react with **A**. It will not react with **B** which is part of an ester group.
(ii) No, it is not an aldehyde.

CHAPTER 32 AMINES

Checkpoint 32.5: Formulae

1. (a) $C_2H_5—N(CH_3)—C_3H_7$
(b) $C_2H_5—CH(CH_3)—NH_2$
(c) $CH_3—CH(Cl)—CH_2—NH_2$
(d) $[CH_3—N(C_2H_5)_2—CH_3]^+ Cl^-$
(e) $C_6H_5—N(CH_3)_2$
(f) $O_2N—C_6H_4—N(CH_3)_2$

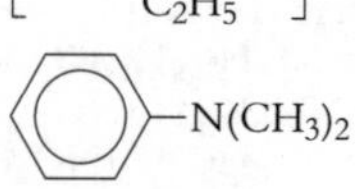

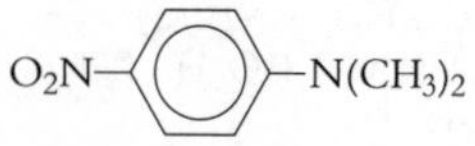

2. (a) dimethylamine, 2°
(b) diethylmethylamine, 3°
(c) diphenylamine, 2°
(d) *N*-ethyl-4-iodophenylamine, 2°
(e) ethyltrimethylammonium bromide, 4°
(f) *N*-methyl-4-methylphenylamine, 2°

3. $CH_3(CH_2)_5NH_2$ The linear molecule can form more extensive van der Waals forces. Also $—NH_2$ has 2 H atoms to form hydrogen bonds to other molecules.

Checkpoint 32.6: Preparations of amines

1. (a) NH_3(ethanolic) + CH_3CH_2Cl(ethanolic); heat in a 'bomb'
(b) (i) CH_3CH_2Cl + KCN(ethanolic), warm $\longrightarrow CH_3CH_2CN$
(ii) $CH_3CH_2CN + LiAlH_4$(ethoxyethane) $\longrightarrow CH_3CH_2CH_2NH_2$
(c) $C_6H_5CHO \xrightarrow{(i)} C_6H_5CH_2OH \xrightarrow{(ii)} C_6H_5CH_2Br \xrightarrow{(iii)} C_6H_5CH_2NH_2$
(i) $LiAlH_4$(ethoxyethane) or $NaBH_4$(aq)
(ii) $KBr + H_2SO_4$
(iii) NH_3 (ethanol); heat in a 'bomb'
(d) $C_6H_5—CH_3 \xrightarrow{(i)}$ 2-NO_2-C_6H_4—$CH_3 \xrightarrow{(ii)}$ 2-NH_2-C_6H_4—CH_3
(i) conc. HNO_3, r.t. Separate from the 4-isomer by fractional distillation under reduced pressure
(ii) Sn + HCl(aq), warm. Neutralise the solution to obtain the product.
(e) $CH_3CH=CH_2 + HBr \longrightarrow CH_3CHBrCH_3$.
(f) $C_6H_5—CH_3 \longrightarrow O_2N—C_6H_4—CH_3$
Use conc. HNO_3 at r.t. Separate from the 2-isomer by fractional distillation under reduced pressure.

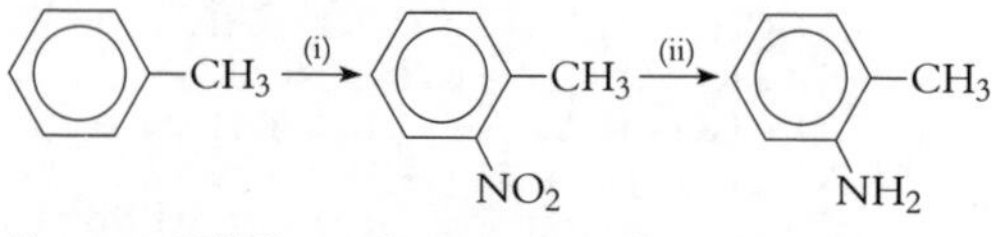

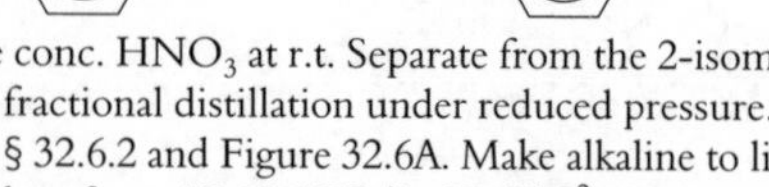

2. See § 32.6.2 and Figure 32.6A. Make alkaline to liberate the product from $(C_6H_5NH_3^+)_2\,[SnCl_6]^{2-}$. Extract with ethoxyethane, purify by distillation under reduced pressure.

3. *(a)* $\longrightarrow [(CH_3)_3NC_2H_5]^+I^-$ Heat in ethanolic solution in a 'bomb'.
   (b) $C_6H_5NO_2 + 3Zn + 7HCl \longrightarrow C_6H_5NH_3^+Cl^- + 3ZnCl_2 + 2H_2O$ (for conditions see Figure 32.6A)
   (c) $\longrightarrow C_3H_7NH_2 + H_2O$; Al_2O_3, heat
   (d) $LiAlH_4$(ethoxyethane)
   (e) $C_2H_5Br + NH_3 \longrightarrow C_2H_5NH_2 \longrightarrow (C_2H_5)_2NH \longrightarrow (C_2H_5)_3N \longrightarrow (C_2H_5)_4N^+Br^-$; heat with C_2H_5Br in a 'bomb'.
4. Add NaOH(aq) to **E** in a separating funnel, shake, separate the two layers. To the aqueous layer add enough acid to neutralise; **P** is thrown out of solution. To the ethoxyethane layer in a separating funnel, add dilute hydrochloric acid, shake, separate the two layers. Neutralise the aqueous layer with NaOH(aq); **A** is thrown out of solution.

Checkpoint 32.7: Reactions of amines

1. In $[CH_3-NH_3]^+$ (structure: H above and below N, bracketed, charge +) distribution of charge between the C atom and the N atom stabilises the cation.

   In $C_6H_5-\ddot{N}H_2$ (benzene ring–N: with two H) the lone pair on the N atom is partially delocalised by interaction with the p-electron cloud of the benzene ring and less available for coordination to a proton to form a cation.
2. *(a)* phenylammonium chloride $C_6H_5-NH_3^+Cl^-$
   (b) 2,4,6-tribromophenylamine (benzene ring with NH_2, and Br at 2, 4, 6 positions)
   (c) *N*-phenylethanamide $C_6H_5-NHCOCH_3$
   (d) *N*-(4-bromophenyl)ethanamide
   $Br-C_6H_4-NHCOCH_3$
   (e) (i) phenol $C_6H_5-OH + N_2$
   (ii) benzene diazonium chloride $C_6H_5-N^+{\equiv}NCl^-$
3. *(a)* Add ethanoic anhydride. The product solidifies.
   (b) Add $NaNO_2$(aq) + HCl(aq) below 10 °C.
   (c) Prepare *(a)* then add conc. HNO_3 + conc. H_2SO_4. Separate *N*-(4-nitrophenyl)ethanamide from the mixture of 2- and 4-isomers by recrystallisation. Warm with HCl(aq) to remove the ethanoyl group and yield the product
4. (i) Add to form butylamine hydrobromide.
   $C_4H_9NH_2(l) + HBr(aq) \longrightarrow C_4H_9NH_3^+\,Br^-(s)$
   (ii) Add, and shake until the product, N-butylethanamide, solidifies.
   $C_4H_9NH_2(l) + CH_3COCl(l) \longrightarrow C_4H_9NHCOCH_3(s) + HCl(g)$
   (iii) Add at r.t. to form butan-1-ol and nitrogen.
   $C_4H_9NH_2(l) + HNO_2(aq) \longrightarrow C_4H_9OH(l) + N_2(g) + H_2O(l)$

Checkpoint 32.8: Diazonium compounds

1. *(a)* Add the diazonium compound to boiling dilute sulphuric acid. Phenol distils over.
   (b) Dissolve phenol in NaOH(aq). Add a solution of benzene diazonium chloride. $C_6H_5N^+{\equiv}N$ is the electrophile. The —OH group increases the availability of electrons in the benzene ring; see § 30.11.2.
   (c) Warm with (i) conc. HCl + CuCl (ii) KI(aq) (iii) neutralise (iv) add KCN(aq) + CuCN
2. *(a)* $C_6H_5NO_2$; reduce with Sn + HCl $\longrightarrow C_6H_5NH_2$
   (b) $C_6H_5NH_2$ diazotise and warm $\longrightarrow C_6H_5OH$
   (c) $C_6H_5NH_2 \longrightarrow C_6H_5N_2^+\,Cl^-$; warm with conc. HCl + CuCl $\longrightarrow C_6H_5Cl$
   (d) $C_6H_6 \longrightarrow C_6H_5NO_2 \longrightarrow O_2N-C_6H_4-NO_2$ (1,3-dinitrobenzene)
   (e)

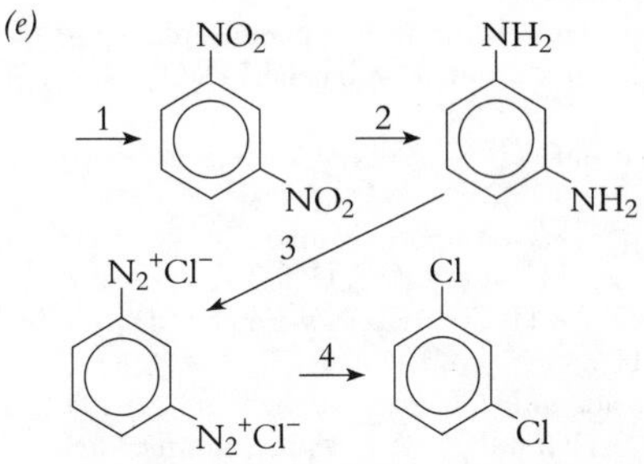

   1. nitration: conc. HNO_3 + conc. H_2SO_4; 2. reduction: Sn + HCl; 3. diazotisation: $NaNO_3$ + HCl(aq); 4. replacement by —Cl: conc. HCl + CuCl
   (f) $C_6H_6 \longrightarrow C_6H_5NO_2 \longrightarrow C_6H_5NH_2$; with $C_6H_5COCl \longrightarrow C_6H_5NHCOC_6H_5 + HCl$

Questions on Chapter 32

1. *(a)* conc. HNO_3 + conc. H_2SO_4; see § 24.8.1
   (b) Make nitrobenzene as in *(a)* reduce with Sn + HCl; see § 32.6.2.
   (c) Convert phenylamine into benzenediazonium chloride [§ 32.7.3] then add conc. HBr(aq) + CuBr (catalyst).
   (d) benzene diazonium chloride + KI
   (e) $C_6H_5-N{=}N-C_6H_4-OH$
   Make benzenediazonium chloride as in *(c)*, warm some of the product to give phenol; couple benzenediazonium chloride with phenol to give 4-(phenylazo)phenol.
2. Convert the sulphonic acid into the diazonium compound, $HO_3SC_6H_4N_2^+Cl^-$. Convert the amine into $C_6H_5N(CH_3)_2$, using CH_3I. The diazonium compound and the amine combine readily to form methyl orange.
3. *(a)* $CH_3CH_2CH_3$ with $Cl_2(S_E) \longrightarrow CH_3CH_2CH_2Cl$; with $NH_3(S_N) \longrightarrow CH_3CH_2CH_2NH_2$
   (b) $CH_3CH_2CH_3$ with $Cl_2(S_E) \longrightarrow CH_3CH_2CH_2Cl$; with KOH(ethanol) $(E_N) \longrightarrow CH_3CH{=}CH_2$; with HCl(g)$(A_E) \longrightarrow CH_3CHClCH_3$; with $NH_3(S_N) \longrightarrow CH_3CH(NH_2)CH_3$
4. *(a)* (i) $C_6H_6 + HNO_3 \longrightarrow C_6H_5NO_2 + H_2O$
   (heat with conc. HNO_3 + conc. H_2SO_4)
   $C_6H_5NO_2 + SnCl_2 + 6H^+ + 2Cl^- \longrightarrow C_6H_5NH_2 + SnCl_4 + 2H_2O$
   $2C_6H_5NH_2 + SnCl_4 + 2HCl \longrightarrow [C_6H_5NH_3^+]_2[SnCl_6]^{2-}$
   (ii) $[C_6H_5NH_3^+]_2[SnCl_6]^{2-} + 6OH^-(aq) \longrightarrow 2C_6H_5NH_2 + Sn(OH)_4 + 6Cl^- + 2H_2O$

(b) (i) $C_6H_5NH_2(l) + HCl(aq) \longrightarrow C_6H_5NH_3^+Cl^-(s)$
(ii) $C_6H_5NH_2 + CH_3COCl \longrightarrow C_6H_5NHCOCH_3 + HCl$

(c) (i) $C_6H_5NHCOCH_3$ phenylethanamide
(ii) $C_6H_5N_2^+Cl^-$ benzenediazonium chloride
(iii) C_6H_5OH phenol
(iv) 2,4,6-tribromophenylamine

NH₂ (structure: benzene ring with NH_2, Br at 2, 4, 6 positions)

5. **A**: Nitrate (conc. HNO_3 + conc. H_2SO_4); then reduce (Sn + HCl)
B: With $CH_3Br + AlBr_3 \longrightarrow C_6H_5CH_3$; boil, pass $Cl_2 \longrightarrow C_6H_5CH_2Cl$
With NH_3 in ethanolic solution, heat in a 'bomb' $\longrightarrow C_6H_5CH_2NH_2$.
C: benzene ⟶ nitrobenzene ⟶ phenylamine ⟶ N-phenylethanamide; nitrate with conc. HNO_3 + conc. $H_2SO_4 \longrightarrow O_2N-C_6H_4-NHCOCH_3 \longrightarrow$ hydrolyse with HCl(aq) ⟶ 4-nitrophenylamine
D: benzene (conc. HNO_3 + conc. H_2SO_4) ⟶ nitrobenzene (Sn + HCl) ⟶ phenylamine (CH_3I) ⟶ $C_6H_5NHCH_3$
A is a 1° aromatic amine; **B** is a 2° aliphatic amine.
Add $NaNO_2 + HCl < 10\,°C$: **A** ⟶ diazonium compound; **B** ⟶ N_2
With phenol in NaOH(aq) **A** ⟶ coloured compound

6. *(a)* For basicity see the answer to Checkpoint 32.7, Question 1.
(b) $C_2H_5NH_2 + Br_2$: no reaction
$C_6H_5NH_2 + Br_2$ react rapidly ⟶ 2,4,6-tribromophenylamine
(c) The $—NH_2$ group is acylated. Both amines react readily at room temperature.
$C_2H_5NH_2 + CH_3COCl \longrightarrow C_2H_5NHCOCH_3 + HCl$
$C_6H_5NH_2 + CH_3COCl \longrightarrow C_6H_5NHCOCH_3 + HCl$

7. *(a)* (i) Add $NaNO_2 + HCl < 10\,°C$
(ii) Add KI(aq)
(iii) Reduce with $NaBH_4(aq)$
(b) $C_6H_5—N{=}N—C_6H_4—OH$
(c) (i) Forms salt $C_6H_5NHNH_3^+Cl^-$
(ii) Forms a phenylhydrazone, $CH_3CH{=}NNHC_6H_5$
(d) It forms solid derivatives which can be recrystallised and the T_m used to identify the carbonyl compound. The 2, 4-dinitrophenylhydrazones have lower solubility and higher T_m than the phenylhydrazones.

8. *(a)* **A** = C_2H_7N. For a 1° amine, **A** = $C_2H_5NH_2$. Then **B** = C_2H_5I
D: $C_4H_9NO + NaOH(aq) \longrightarrow C_2H_5NH_2 +$ **C**
Subtracting (C_2H_5NH) from the formula of **D** leaves $C_2H_3O = CH_3CO$, therefore **D** = $C_2H_5NHCOCH_3$ and **C** = CH_3CO_2Na. Since $C_2H_5I + NaOH(aq) \longrightarrow$ **E**, **E** = C_2H_5OH
(b) (i) hydrolysis (ii) $OH^-(aq)$ (iii) nucleophile

9. *(a)* (i) $CH_3CH_2CH_2Br + FeBr_3$, warm; see § 28.8.4
(ii) **X** = $C_6H_5CH_2CHBrCH_3$
Heat with NH_3 in a sealed container.
(b) $C_6H_5CHNH_2CH_2CH_3$ if HBr adds differently
1,4-$CH_3CHNH_2CH_2C_6H_4CH_2CHNH_2CH_3$ if polyalkylation occurs at Step 1.
(c) volatile liquid, similar to phenylamine, basic, soluble in NaOH(aq)
(d) The isomer is an aromatic amine. Diazotize ($NaNO_2$ + HCl(aq) < 5 °C) a sample. Add a little of the original. The two will react to form a dye:

$C_3H_7-C_6H_4-N{=}N-C_6H_3(NH_2)(C_3H_7)$

(e) Benzedrine shows an IR peak due to aliphatic $—NH_2$. Compare with the spectrum of an authentic specimen. The NMR spectrum of benzedrine shows H atoms in different positions: 5 in the ring, 2 in CH_2, 1 in CH, 2 in NH_2, 3 in CH_3.

10. *(a)* (i) —OH
(ii) 1. acidic, carboxylic acid 2. contains $—NH_2$ group 3. No C=C double bond
(iii) $H_2N-C_6H_4-CO_2H$
(iv) The $—NH_2$ could be in the 2- or 3- position.
(b) (i) oxidation
(ii) **B:** $H-\underset{H}{\overset{H}{C}}-\underset{H}{\overset{H}{C}}-O-H$ **D:** $H-\underset{H}{\overset{H}{C}}-C(=O)-O-H$
(c) (i) H_2O
(ii) esterification
(iii) $H_2N-C_6H_4-CO_2C_2H_5$
(d) (i) ethanoyl chloride
(ii) $CH_3COCl(l) + H_2O(l) \longrightarrow CH_3CO_2H(aq) + HCl(aq)$
(e) $CO_2C_2H_5-C_6H_4-NHCOCH_3$ (para)

11. *(a)* The electron pair on the N of NH_2 is partially delocalised by interaction with the π electron cloud of the benzene ring; see § 32.5.
(b) $C_6H_5CN + 4[H] \longrightarrow C_6H_5CH_2NH_2$, reduction (by $LiAlH_4$ in ethoxyethane)
(c) Nucleophilic substitution. A mixture of amines, e.g. $(C_6H_5CH_2)_2NH$, is obtained.
(d) quaternary ammonium compound
$C_6H_5CH_2—N^+(CH_3)_2—(CH_2)_{11}CH_3 \quad Cl^-$

12. *(a)* In $CH_3CH_2CH_2NH_2$ the N has a lone pair of electrons which can accept a proton to form $C_3H_7NH_3^+$.
(b) The positive charge is distributed over the carbon atoms as well as the N atom, stabilising the cation.
(c) nucleophilic substitution. For mechanism, similar to $OH^- + RX$, see § 29.8.3.

$H_3\ddot{N} + HC(H)(C_2H_5)Br \longrightarrow [H_3N\cdots C(H)(H)(C_2H_5)\cdots Br] \longrightarrow [H_3N-CH_2C_2H_5]^+ + Br^- \longrightarrow H_2N-CH_2C_2H_5 + H^+$

(d) reduction: $CH_3CH_2CN + 4[H] \longrightarrow CH_3CH_2CH_2NH_2$
Method *(c)* gives a mixture of 1°, 2° and 3° amines, e.g. $(CH_3CH_2CH_2)_2NH$.

13. *(a)* 1 Acylation. Ethanoyl chloride, $CH_3COCl + AlCl_3$
3 Reduction, Sn + conc. HCl(aq)
(b) $CH_3COCl + AlCl_3 \rightleftharpoons CH_3CO^+ + AlCl_4^-$; for mechanism see § 28.8.7
14. *(a)* Sn + HCl; cool to keep the mixture at r.t. [see § 32.6.2], add alkali to liberate phenylamine, steam distil, extract with ethoxyethane, distil under reduced pressure.
(b) (i) the basic $—NH_2$ group The energy given out when the strong bond N—H forms in $C_6H_5NH_3^+$ is greater than the energy given out when the weaker O—H bond forms between $—NH_2$ and H_2O.
(ii) $NO_2^-(aq) + H^+(aq) \rightleftharpoons HNO_2(aq)$
HNO_2 and NO_2^- are a conjugate acid-base pair.
(iii) To moderate the rate of reaction and control the temperature, avoiding a rise in temperature and resulting decomposition of the product.
(c) The reaction vessel must be thermostatted. The gas evolved is collected in a gas syringe. Measurements of gas volume are taken at intervals of time after the start of the reaction. A plot of volume of nitrogen against time is made. The tangent to this curve at a certain time gives the rate of reaction at this time; see § 14.11.

CHAPTER 33 ORGANIC ACIDS AND THEIR DERIVATIVES

Checkpoint 33.6: Acids

1. *(a)* heptanoic acid *(b)* 3-methylpropanoic acid
(c) trifluoroethanoic acid *(d)* propan-1,3-dioic acid
(e) 4-methylbenzoic acid *(f)* benzene-1,2-dicarboxylic acid
(g) phenylethanoic acid
2. $d < b < c < a$
In *(d)* there are weak van der Waals forces between molecules.
In *(b)* there are stronger dipole-interactions between $>C=O$ groups. In *(c)* hydrogen bonds exist between molecules. In acids *(a)* hydrogen bonding is stronger than in alcohols because the CO group withdraws electrons from the OH bond:

$$R—\overset{\delta+}{C}=\overset{\delta-}{O}$$
$$\nwarrow O—H$$

3. *(a)* $a < b < c < d$
4. *(a)* $RCH_2Cl + KCN \longrightarrow RCH_2CN + KCl$
Warm with KCN (in ethanol); distil off the product.
(b) $H_2C{=}CHCN(l) + NaOH(aq) + H_2O(l) \longrightarrow H_2C{=}CHCO_2Na(aq) + NH_3(g)$
Reflux with NaOH(aq) – or with HCl(aq)
Prop-2-enoic acid. Polymers, e.g. poly(propenenitrile), are used to make acrylic fibres, which are used in the clothing industry as e.g. Acrilan®.
5. *(a)* With $NaHSO_3$ followed by $KCN \longrightarrow CH_3CH(OH)CN$
Reflux with $H^+(aq) \longrightarrow CH_3CH(OH)CO_2H$
(b) 2-hydroxypropanoic acid
(c) (i) Oxidation gives a ketone. Ketones react with DNP but not with Tollens' reagent.
(ii) Liberates CO_2 from $Na_2CO_3(aq)$.
(d) Rotates plane of polarisation of polarised light because the molecule contains a chiral carbon atom.

Checkpoint 33.8: Reactions of acids

1. Dissolve butter in ethoxyethane, extract with NaOH(aq). Separate the aqueous layer, acidify $\longrightarrow$ butanoic acid(l). Dissolve in ethoxyethane, separate the ether layer, dry, distil in fume cupboard to remove ether and leave butanoic acid.
(a) Make the sodium salt, recrystallise, acidify to obtain butanoic acid.
(b) Find the boiling temperature.
2. *(a)* Chlorinate $\longrightarrow CH_3CHClCO_2H$
(b) Convert half the acid into its sodium salt. Then weak acid + salt of weak acid = buffer.
3. Oxidise ($K_2Cr_2O_7$, acid) $\longrightarrow CH_3CHO$. Add $NaHSO_3$ followed by $KCN \longrightarrow CH_3CH(OH)CN$. Reflux with acid $\longrightarrow CH_3CH(OH)CO_2H$
4. *(a)* $H_2NC_6H_4CHBrCHBrCO_2H$
(b) $CH_3CONHC_6H_4CH{=}CHCO_2H$
(c) $H_2NC_6H_4CH_2CH_2CO_2H$
(d) $H_2NC_6H_4CH{=}CHCH_2OH$
(e) $H_2NC_6H_4CHO + OHCCO_2H$

5.
$$—\overset{\delta+}{C}=\overset{\delta-}{O}$$
$$\nwarrow O—H$$

The flow of electron density from OH towards $C^{\delta+}$ reduces the reactivity of the CO group towards nucleophiles.

6. $C_2H_5OH(aq) \rightleftharpoons C_2H_5O^-(aq) + H^+(aq)$
The dissociation constant is very small.
$C_6H_5OH(aq) \rightleftharpoons C_6H_5O^-(aq) + H^+(aq)$
The dissociation constant is greater than in ethanol because the negative charge can be delocalised over the benzene ring.
$CH_3CO_2H(aq) \rightleftharpoons CH_3CO_2^-(aq) + H^+(aq)$
The dissociation constant is greater than in phenol because the anion $\left[H_3C—C\begin{smallmatrix}O\\O\end{smallmatrix}\right]^-$ is stabilised by delocalisation of the charge between the 2 O atoms.

Checkpoint 33.12: Acid chlorides and anhydrides

1. *(a)* $C_2H_5CO_2H(l) + PCl_5(s) \longrightarrow C_2H_5COCl(l) + POCl_3(l) + HCl(g)$
(b) $CH_3CH_2CO_2Na + CH_3CH_2COCl \longrightarrow (CH_3CH_2CO)_2O + NaCl$
(c) $(C_6H_5CO)_2O(s) + 2NH_3(g) \longrightarrow 2C_6H_5CONH_2(s) + H_2O(l)$
(d) $(CH_3)_2CHCOCl(l) + C_2H_5OH(l) \longrightarrow (CH_3)_2CHCOC_2H_5(l) + H_2O(l)$
2. *(a)* Ethanoic acid + PCl_5 or $SOCl_2$; warm, distil.
(b) Distil sodium ethanoate + ethanoyl chloride
(i) **A** + water $\longrightarrow$ ethanoic acid + HCl(g);
B + water $\longrightarrow$ ethanoic acid
(ii) **A** $\longrightarrow$ ethyl ethanoate + HCl(g);
B $\longrightarrow$ ethyl ethanoate + ethanoic acid
(iii) **A** $\longrightarrow$ phenyl ethanoate + HCl(g);
B $\longrightarrow$ phenyl ethanoate + ethanoic acid
(iv) **A** $\longrightarrow$ N-ethanoylphenylamine + HCl(g);
B $\longrightarrow$ *N*-ethanoylphenylamine + ethanoic acid
3. *(a)* C_2H_5Cl is hydrolysed with difficulty: reflux with NaOH(aq).
CH_3COCl is hydrolysed when added to water. The polar CO group makes attack by the nucleophile H_2O easier:

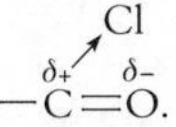

(b) CH_3COCl reacts with ethanol in the presence of a base $\longrightarrow$ ethyl ethanoate; C_2H_5Cl does not react.
(c) C_2H_5Cl reacts with NH_3 when heated under pressure $\longrightarrow$ aminoethane, $C_2H_5NH_2$; CH_3COCl reacts with NH_3 with ease $\longrightarrow$ ethanamide, CH_3CONH_2.
(d) C_2H_5Cl reacts with KCN(ethanol) warm, distil $\longrightarrow$ propanenitrile C_2H_5CN; CH_3COCl does not react.
4. $CH_3COCl(l) + H_2O(l) \longrightarrow CH_3CO_2H(aq) + HCl(aq)$
Amount of $OH^- = 5.00 \times 10^{-3}$ mol; amount of $CH_3COCl = 2.5 \times 10^{-3}$ mol; $m = 0.196$ g

5. *(a)* Make the solid benzoyl derivatives, $C_6H_5NHCOC_6H_5$ and $C_6H_5CH_2NHCOC_6H_5$. Recrystallise, dry, find the melting temperatures.
   (b) Make the two amides of phenylamine. $C_6H_5NHCOC_6H_5$ has a higher melting temperature than $C_6H_5NHCOCH_3$. Or study IR and NMR spectra.

Checkpoint 33.14: Esters

1. | | |
   |---|---|
   | $HCO_2CH_2CH_2CH_2CH_3$ | butyl methanoate |
   | $HCO_2CH_2CH(CH_3)_2$ | 2-methylpropyl methanoate |
   | $HCO_2CH(CH_3)CH_2CH_3$ | 1-methylpropyl methanoate |
   | $HCO_2C(CH_3)_3$ | 1,2-dimethylethyl methanoate |
   | $CH_3CO_2CH_2CH_2CH_3$ | propyl ethanoate |
   | $CH_3CO_2CH(CH_3)_2$ | 2-methylethyl ethanoate |
   | $C_2H_5CO_2CH_2CH_3$ | ethyl propanoate |
   | $CH_3CH_2CH_2CO_2CH_3$ | methyl butanoate |
   | $(CH_3)_2CHCO_2CH_3$ | methyl 2-methylpropanoate |
2. $C_3H_7CO_2H$ and $C_2H_5{}^{18}OH$
3. *(a)* propanol + propanoic acid
   (b) methanol + benzoic acid
   (c) ethanol + methanoic acid
   (d) methanol + pentanoic acid
   (e) methylethanol + ethanoic acid
   (f) methylethanol + benzoic acid
4. *(a)* $C_6H_5NH_2 + NaNO_2 + HCl(aq)$, <10 °C $\longrightarrow C_6H_5N_2{}^+Cl^-$; Warm $\longrightarrow C_6H_5OH$
   (b) $C_6H_5NH_2 + NaNO_2 + HCl(aq)$, <10 °C $\longrightarrow C_6H_5N_2{}^+Cl^-$
   With $KCN + CuCN \longrightarrow C_6H_5CN$.
   Reflux with acid $\longrightarrow C_6H_5CO_2H$.
   With $SOCl_2 \longrightarrow C_6H_5COCl$
   (i) Treat phenol, C_6H_5OH, with NaOH(aq) $\longrightarrow C_6H_5ONa$
   Heat benzoyl chloride + sodium phenoxide:
   $C_6H_5COCl + C_6H_5ONa \longrightarrow C_6H_5CO_2C_6H_5 + NaCl$
   (ii) $2C_6H_5NH_2 \longrightarrow C_6H_5CO_2C_6H_5$;
   10.0 g $\longrightarrow$ 10.6 g product
5. Ester RCO_2R'. Amount of ester = Amount of NaOH $= 2.0 \times 10^{-2}$ mol = 1.76 g
   $M = 88$ g mol^{-1}. Subtracting 44 for CO_2 leaves 44, which corresponds to C_3H_8. The formula is $C_4H_8O_2$.

$HCO_2CH_2CH_2CH_3$	propyl methanoate
$HCO_2CH(CH_3)_2$	methylethyl methanoate
$CH_3CO_2CH_2CH_3$	ethyl ethanoate
$CH_3CH_2CO_2CH_3$	methyl propanoate
6. *(a)* NaOH(aq), heat $\longrightarrow CH_3CH{=}CHCH_2CO_2Na + C_2H_5OH$
   (b) H_2, Ni $\longrightarrow CH_3CH_2CH_2CH_2CO_2C_2H_5$
   (c) $Br_2 \longrightarrow CH_3CHBrCHBrCH_2CO_2C_2H_5$
   (d) $CH_3CHO + OHCCH_2CO_2C_2H_5$
   (e) $LiAlH_4 \longrightarrow CH_3CH{=}CHCH_2CH_2OH + C_2H_5OH$
7. $RCH_2CO_2H \xrightarrow{LiAlH_4(\text{ethoxyethane})} RCH_2CH_2OH \xrightarrow{\text{red P} + I_2}$
   $RCH_2CH_2I \xrightarrow{KCN(\text{ethanol})} RCH_2CH_2CN$
   $\xrightarrow{\text{Acid, Reflux}} RCH_2CH_2CO_2H$

Checkpoint 33.16: Amides and nitriles

1. *(a)* Heat with NaOH(aq) $\longrightarrow RCO_2Na + NH_3(g)$. Then add HCl(aq) to liberate RCO_2H.
   (b) $LiAlH_4$(ethoxyethane)
   (c) Br_2 + conc. NaOH(aq)
   (d) conc. NH_3(aq)
   (e) conc. NH_3(aq)
   (f) H_2, Pt, heat
2. *(a)* (i) ethanamide, CH_3CONH_2
   (ii) aminoethane, $C_2H_5NH_2$
   (b) Differences: Amides are readily hydrolysed by dilute acid or alkali to form e.g. $RCO_2H + NH_4Cl$ or $RCO_2Na + NH_3(g)$. Amines are not hydrolysed. Amines react with halogenoalkanes to form 2° amines, e.g. $RNH_2 + R'Br \longrightarrow RR'NH + HBr$. Amides do not react with halogenoalkanes.
   Similarities: Amines and amides are basic. Amines are much stronger bases than amides. Both react with $HNO_2(aq)$: $RCONH_2 \longrightarrow RCO_2H$, $RNH_2 \longrightarrow ROH$
   (c) $CH_3CONH_2 + Br_2$ + conc. $NaOH(aq) \longrightarrow CH_3NH_2$
   (d) $C_2H_5NH_2 + CH_3COCl \longrightarrow C_2H_5NHCOCH_3$
3. *(a)* $CH_3CH_2CH_2OH \xrightarrow{PBr_3} CH_3CH_2CH_2Br \xrightarrow{KCN(\text{ethanol})}$
   $CH_3CH_2CH_2CN \xrightarrow{H^+(aq)} CH_3CH_2CH_2CO_2H$
   (b) $CH_3CH_2OH \xrightarrow{K_2Cr_2O_7,\ \text{acid}} CH_3CO_2H$
   $CH_3CO_2H + C_2H_5OH \xrightarrow{\text{conc. } H_2SO_4} CH_3CO_2C_2H_5$
   (c) $C_6H_6 \xrightarrow{\text{conc. } HNO_3 + H_2SO_4} C_6H_5NO_2 \xrightarrow{Sn + HCl(aq)}$
   $C_6H_5NH_2 \xrightarrow{HNO_2(aq),\ \text{cold}} C_6H_5N_2{}^+Cl^- \xrightarrow{KCN(aq),\ CuCN} C_6H_5CN$
   $C_6H_6 \longrightarrow C_6H_5CN$ (as above); controlled hydrolysis $\longrightarrow C_6H_5CONH_2$
   $C_6H_6 \xrightarrow{CH_3COCl + AlCl_3} C_6H_5COCH_3 \xrightarrow{KMnO_4,\ \text{acid}} C_6H_5CO_2H$
4. **A** = C_2H_5COCl, **B** = $C_2H_5CONH_2$, **C** = C_2H_5OH, **D** = $CH_3CO_2C_2H_5$, **E** = $C_2H_5CO_2CH_3$
   $x = Br_2$ + conc. NaOH(aq), $y = NaNO_2 + HCl(aq)$, $z = CH_3OH$ + conc. H_2SO_4.
   $C_2H_5CO_2H(l) + PCl_5(s) \longrightarrow C_2H_5COCl(l) + POCl_3(l) + HCl(g)$
   $C_2H_5COCl(l) + NH_3(s) \longrightarrow C_2H_5CONH_2(l) + HCl(g)$
   $C_2H_5CONH_2(s) + Br_2(aq) + 4OH^-(aq) \longrightarrow C_2H_5NH_2(l) + 2Br^- + CO_3{}^{2-}(aq) + 2H_2O(l)$
   $C_2H_5NH_2(g) + HNO_2(s) \longrightarrow C_2H_5OH(l) + N_2(g) + H_2O(l)$
   $C_2H_5OH(l) + CH_3CO_2H(l) \longrightarrow CH_3CO_2C_2H_5(l) + H_2O(l)$
   $CH_3OH(l) + C_2H_5CO_2H(l) \longrightarrow C_2H_5CO_2CH_3(l) + H_2O(l)$
5. **A** = C_6H_5CHO, **B** = $C_6H_5CH_2OH$, **C** = C_6H_5COCl, **D** = $C_6H_5CO_2CH_2C_6H_5$, **E** = $C_6H_5CONH_2$, **F** = $C_6H_5NH_2$, **G** = $C_6H_5NHCOC_6H_5$
   $C_6H_5CHO(l) + 2[H] \longrightarrow C_6H_5CH_2OH(l)$
   $C_6H_5CO_2H(s) + SOCl_2(l) \longrightarrow C_6H_5COCl(l) + HCl(g) + SO_2(g)$
   $C_6H_5CH_2OH(l) + C_6H_5COCl(l) \longrightarrow C_6H_5CO_2CH_2C_6H_5(s) + HCl(g)$
   $C_6H_5COCl(l) + 2NH_3(aq) \longrightarrow C_6H_5CONH_2(s) + NH_4Cl(aq)$
   $C_6H_5CONH_2(s) + Br_2(aq) + 4OH^-(aq) \longrightarrow C_6H_5NH_2(l) + 2Br^-(aq) + CO_3{}^{2-}(aq) + 2H_2O(l)$
   $C_6H_5NH_2(l) + C_6H_5COCl(l) \longrightarrow C_6H_5NHCOC_6H_5COCl(s) + HCl(g)$

Checkpoint 33.17: Amino acids and proteins

1. $CH_3CH_2CO_2H$, boil, pass $Cl_2 \longrightarrow CH_3CHClCO_2H$.
   Add conc. $NH_3(aq) \longrightarrow H_2NCH(CH_3)CO_2H$, 2-aminopropanoic acid
   Reactions of $-NH_2$, e.g. with anhydride $(RCO)_2O \longrightarrow -NHCOR$
   Reactions of $-CO_2H$, e.g. with $SOCl_2 \longrightarrow -COCl$
2. *(a)* CH_3CO_2H, boil, pass $Cl_2 \longrightarrow ClCH_2CO_2H$. With conc. $NH_3(aq) \longrightarrow H_2NCH_2CO_2H$
   The species $H_2NCH_2CO_2H$, $H_3N^+CH_2CO_2H$, $H_2NCH_2CO_2{}^-$ and $H_3N^+CH_2CO_2{}^-$ are all present in aqueous solution. The species in highest concentration is $H_2NCH_2CO_2H$.
   $H_2NCH_2CO_2H(s) + SOCl_2(l) \longrightarrow H_2NCH_2COCl(l) + SO_2(g) + HCl(g)$
   $H_2NCH_2CO_2H(s) + (CH_3CO)_2O(l) \longrightarrow CH_3CONHCH_2CO_2H(s) + CH_3CO_2H(l)$

3. peptides, polypeptides and proteins. For names of proteins see § 33.17.2. The peptide linkage/peptide bond

```
—N—C—
 |  ||
 H  O
```

hydrolysed $\longrightarrow$ $-NH_2 + HO_2C-$ by dilute acids and alkalis

4. On reaction of glycine with $SOCl_2$, a mixture of pungent smelling, acidic gases is formed
$H_2NCH_2CO_2H(s) + SOCl_2(l) \longrightarrow H_2NCH_2COCl(l) + SO_2(g) + HCl(g)$
Alkaline hydrolysis of ethanamide gives the alkaline gas ammonia.
$CH_3CONH_2(s) + NaOH(aq) \longrightarrow CH_3CO_2Na(aq) + NH_3(g)$

5. Amount of $N_2 = 6.67 \times 10^{-4}$ mol = Amount of amino acid
$0.110\ g/M = 6.67 \times 10^{-4}$; $M = 166\ g\ mol^{-1}$

Questions on Chapter 33

1. **A** = CH_3CH_2Br, **B** = CH_3CH_2OH, **C** = $CH_3CH(OH)CN$, **D** = CH_3CH_2CN, **E** = $CH_3CHClCO_2H$, product = 2-hydroxypropanoic acid
(a) $CH_3CCl(OH)CO_2H$ *(b)* $CH_3CHClCOCl$
(c) $CO_2(g) + CH_3CH(OH)CO_2Na(aq)$
(d) rotate the plane of polarisation because it has a chiral carbon atom

2. *(a)* Oxidise part with $K_2Cr_2O_7$ + acid $\longrightarrow CH_3CH_2CO_2H$
Esterify with the remainder of
$CH_3CH_2CH_2OH \longrightarrow CH_3CH_2CO_2CH_2CH_2CH_3$
(b) $(CH_3)_2CHOH \xrightarrow{K_2Cr_2O_7,\ acid} (CH_3)_2C{=}O \xrightarrow{(i)\ NaHSO_3\ (ii)\ KCN} (CH_3)_2C(OH)CN \xrightarrow{HCl(aq),\ warm} (CH_3)_2C(OH)CO_2H$
(c) Oxidise part with $K_2Cr_2O_7$, acid $\longrightarrow CH_3CO_2H$
Reduce part with $LiAlH_4$(ethoxyethane) $\longrightarrow CH_3CH_2OH$
Esterify (conc. H_2SO_4) $\longrightarrow CH_3CO_2CH_2CH_3$

3. *(a)* With $SOCl_2$ or $PCl_5 \longrightarrow RCOCl$
(b) Make the Na salt RCO_2Na. Make RCOCl as in *(a)*.
Heat $RCO_2Na + RCOCl \longrightarrow (RCO)_2O + NaCl$
(c) Make RCOCl as in *(a)*. Heat with conc. $NH_3(aq) \longrightarrow RCONH_2 + HCl$
(d) Heat with an alcohol R'OH and conc. $H_2SO_4 \longrightarrow RCO_2R' + H_2O$
$RCO_2H + SOCl_2 \longrightarrow RCOCl + SO_2 + HCl$
$RCO_2Na + RCOCl \longrightarrow (RCO)_2O + NaCl$
$RCOCl + NH_3 \longrightarrow RCONH_2 + HCl$
$RCO_2H + R'OH \longrightarrow RCO_2R' + H_2O$
$RCOCl + H_2O \longrightarrow RCO_2H + HCl$: carboxylic acid + hydrogen chloride
$(RCO)_2O + H_2O \longrightarrow 2RCO_2H$: carboxylic acid
$RCONH_2 + H_2O \longrightarrow RCO_2NH_4$: ammonium salt of carboxylic acid
$RCO_2R' + H_2O \longrightarrow RCO_2H + R'OH$: carboxylic acid + alcohol

4. **D** must be a diazonium compound, $RC_6H_4N_2^+Cl^-$.
Subtracting $C_6H_4N_2^+Cl^-$ from $C_7H_5O_2N_2Cl$ leaves CO_2H, a carboxyl group, so **D** is $HO_2CC_6H_4N_2^+Cl^-$.
C must be an aromatic amine, $HO_2CC_6H_4NH_2$.
B gives **C** on Hofmann degradation, so **B** is $HO_2CC_6H_4CONH_2$.
F, obtained by hydrolysis of **B**, is $HO_2CC_6H_4CO_2H$.
E, formed from the diazonium compound + KCN, is $HO_2CC_6H_4CN$.
A, made by heating a dicarboxylic acid, must be an anhydride, and the carboxyl groups in **F** must be adjacent.

A is [benzene ring fused with –C(=O)–O–C(=O)– ring: C=O, O, C=O]   **B** is [benzene ring with CONH₂ and CO₂H on adjacent carbons]

C is [benzene ring with NH_2 and CO_2H on adjacent carbons]   **D** is [benzene ring with $N_2^+Cl^-$ and CO_2H on adjacent carbons]

E is [benzene ring with CN and CO_2H on adjacent carbons]   **F** is [benzene ring with CO_2H and CO_2H on adjacent carbons]

5. In $>\overset{\delta+}{C}{=}\overset{\delta-}{O}$ the lone pair of a nucleophile, e.g. CN^-, attacks the $\delta+$ C atom.
In $>\overset{\delta+}{C}{=}\overset{\delta-}{O}$ with O—H on C
the $\delta+$ charge is reduced by a flow of electron density from —OH towards $C^{\delta+}$.

6. $C_6H_{12}O_2$ corresponds to RCO_2R', and $R + R' = C_5H_{12}$.
Representing the esters as **A** = $R^1CO_2R^2$ and **B** = $R^3CO_2R^4$,
A: $R^1CO_2R^2 + NaOH \longrightarrow CH_3CO_2Na + R^2OH$:
$R^1 = CH_3-$ and $R^2 = C_4H_9-$
B: $R^3CO_2R^4 + NaOH \longrightarrow R^3CO_2Na + CH_3OH$:
$R^3 = C_4H_9-$, and $R^4 = CH_3-$
There must be a chiral C atom therefore the formulae are

A = $H_3C-C(=O)-O-CH(CH_3)-C_2H_5$

B = $C_2H_5-CH(CH_3)-C(=O)-O-CH_3$

7. C_3H_8O is formed when an ester is hydrolysed: it must be an alcohol, C_3H_7OH. An alcohol which gives an iodoform test must contain the group CH_3CHOH-: it is $(CH_3)_2CHOH$. The ester is $C_4H_9CO_2CH(CH_3)_2$. The group $-OCH(CH_3)_2$ is not chiral therefore the group C_4H_9- must be chiral. The ester is

$C_2H_5-CH(CH_3)-C(=O)-O-CH(CH_3)-CH_3$

8. *(a)* Water, $:\!O(H)-H$
is a nucleophile. The lone pairs on the O atom attack a centre of positive charge.
In $CH_3-\overset{\delta+}{C}(Cl){=}\overset{\delta-}{O}$
the nucleophile attacks the $\delta+$ C atom.
In $Cl^{\delta-}-C^{\delta+}H_2-CH_3$ the C of CH_2 is $\delta+$ but carries a smaller positive charge than the $C^{\delta+}{=}O$ in CH_3COCl.
The halogenoalkane is attacked by powerful nucleophiles, e.g. OH^-, but not by H_2O molecules.
(b) There is a chiral carbon atom in 2-hydroxypropanoic acid,

$CH_3-C^*H(OH)-CO_2H$

There are two optical isomers, and a laboratory preparation gives a mixture of the two which is optically inactive – a racemic mixture.

9. *(a)* $K_2Cr_2O_7$ + acid, warm
(b) e.g. propanal $\longrightarrow$ propanoic acid
$CH_3CH_2CHO + [O] \longrightarrow CH_3CH_2CO_2H$

(c) 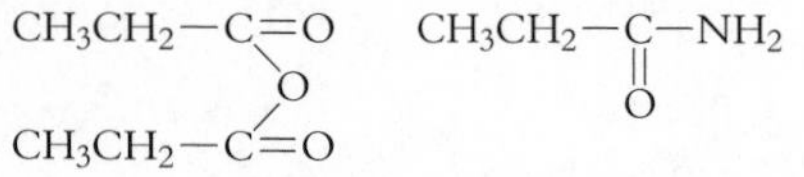 $CH_3CH_2-C{=}O$ / O / $CH_3CH_2-C{=}O$ $CH_3CH_2-C(=O)-NH_2$

(d) (i) Add water.
(ii) Heat with NaOH(aq) ⟶ $CH_3CH_2CO_2Na$
Add dilute HCl(aq) ⟶ $CH_3CH_2CO_2H$

10. **A**: $C_5H_{10}O_2 + LiAlH_4 \longrightarrow$ **B** + **C**
The alcohols **B** and **C** give the tri-iodomethane test; therefore one or both contain the group CH_3CHOH— or one of them is C_2H_5OH. With 5 C between them, they could be C_2H_5OH and $(CH_3)_2CHOH$. The ester which is reduced to these alcohols is $CH_3CO_2CH(CH_3)_2$.
A is $CH_3-C(=O)-O-CH(CH_3)_2$
B and **C** are $CH_3-CH(CH_3)-OH$ and C_2H_5OH, **D** is CHI_3

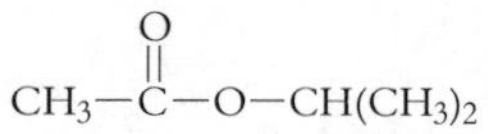

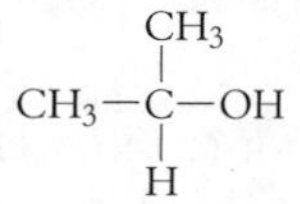

11. **A** gives only two monochloro-derivatives therefore it probably has only 3 carbon atoms per molecule. **B** and **C** are halogenoalkanes which are hydrolysed to alcohols. **B** must be hydrolysed to a 1° alcohol which is oxidised to an acid, while **C** must be hydrolysed to a 2° alcohol which is oxidised to a ketone.
A = $CH_3CH_2CH_3$, **B** = $CH_3CH_2CH_2Cl$,
C = $CH_3CHClCH_3$, **D** = $CH_3CH_2CO_2H$, **E** = $(CH_3)_2CO$

12. (a) Gives a purple colour with $FeCl_3$
(b) 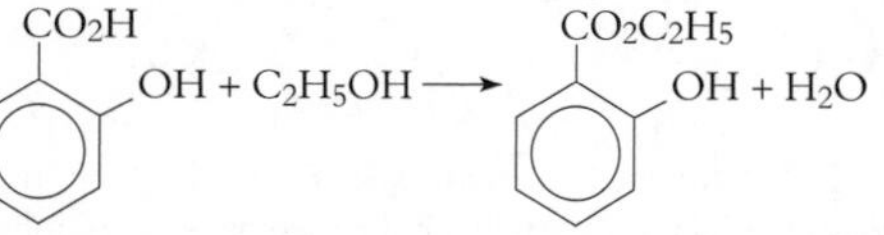 $C_6H_4(CO_2H)OH + C_2H_5OH \longrightarrow C_6H_4(CO_2C_2H_5)OH + H_2O$
(c) (i) H^-
(ii) Polarisation of the $C^{\delta+}{=}O^{\delta-}$ bond makes the C atom δ+.
(d) (i) 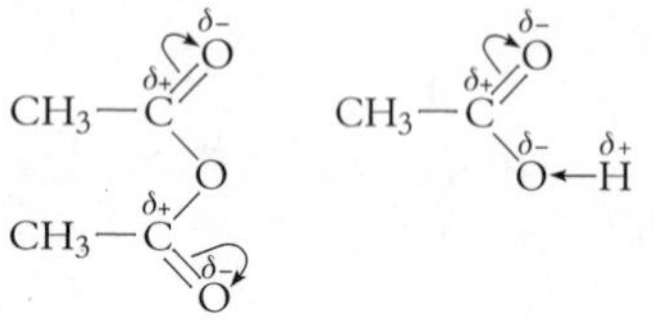 $CH_3-C^{\delta+}(=O^{\delta-})-O-C^{\delta+}(=O^{\delta-})-CH_3$ $CH_3-C^{\delta+}(=O^{\delta-})-O^{\delta-}\leftarrow H^{\delta+}$
(ii) In ethanoic acid, the δ+ charge on the C atom is reduced by the $O^{\delta-}$ of the —OH group.
(e) 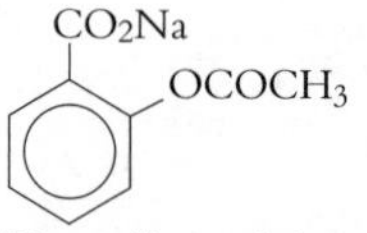 $C_6H_4(CO_2Na)OCOCH_3$
The sodium salt is more soluble and therefore more rapidly absorbed. It does not cause acid indigestion in the stomach.

13. (a) I HCN II Warm with dilute HCl(aq).
J = $C_6H_5CHOHCN$
(b) (i) $C_6H_5CHBrCO_2H$
(ii) $C_6H_5CHClCOCl$
(iii) 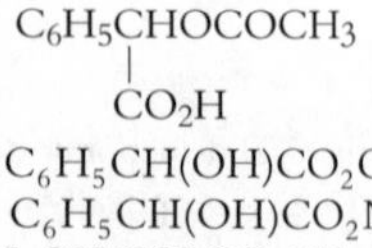 $C_6H_5CH(OCOCH_3)CO_2H$
(iv) $C_6H_5CH(OH)CO_2C_2H_5$
(v) $C_6H_5CH(OH)CO_2Na$
(c) $C_6H_5CH(OH)CO_2H$ has $M_r = 152$
Amount of NaOH = 6.00×10^{-4} mol so 0.100 g of sample contains 6.00×10^{-4} mol acid = 0.0912 g therefore sample is 91.2% pure

14. (a) (i) 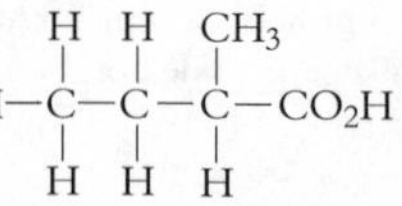 $H-CH_2-CH_2-CH(CH_3)-CO_2H$ (H H CH₃ / H—C—C—C—CO₂H / H H H)
(ii) $C_2H_5OH(l) + C_2H_5CHCH_3CO_2H(l) \longrightarrow C_2H_5CHCH_3CO_2C_2H_5(l) + H_2O(l)$
(b) (i) Heat in a flask fitted with a condenser [as in Figure 32.6A]
(ii) to remove sulphuric acid and unreacted 2-methylbutanoic acid
(iii) CO_2
(iv) ethanol, 9.2 g/46 g mol^{-1} = 0.20 mol
acid: 20.4 g/102 g mol^{-1} = 0.20 mol
(v) M of ester $C_7H_{14}O_2$ = 130 g mol^{-1}
Mass expected = 130 g mol^{-1} × 0.20 mol = 26.0 g
% yield = 100 × 15.6/26.0 = 60%
(c) CH_3CO_2H and $(CH_3)_2CHCH_2CH_2OH$

15. (a) (i) a substance that can donate a proton to another substance; see § 12.6.1
(ii) **C** is the weakest acid because the ion $C_2H_5O^-$ readily accepts a proton. **B** is a stronger acid than **C** because the negative charge on $C_6H_5O^-$ is spread over the ring to some extent, stabilising the ion. **A** is the strongest acid of the three. In the ion 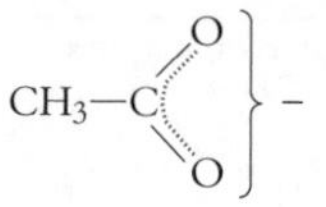
$\{CH_3-C(O)(O)\}^-$
the negative charge is spread over the $—CO_2^-$ group, stabilising the anion.
(iii) $pK_a = —\lg K_a$
(iv) **A** 4.76, **B** 10.00, **C** 16.00
(v)

	A	B	C
NaOH(aq)	reaction	reaction	no reaction
$NaHCO_3$(aq)	reaction	no reaction	no reaction

(b) phenyl ethanoate, ethanoyl chloride
$C_6H_5OH(l) + CH_3COCl(l) \longrightarrow C_6H_5OCOCH_3(s) + HCl(g)$
(c) The colour of Br_2 fades and a ppt appears.
2,4,6-tribromophenyl ethanoate: $C_6H_2Br_3OCOCH_3$ (OCOCH₃ with Br, Br, Br on ring)

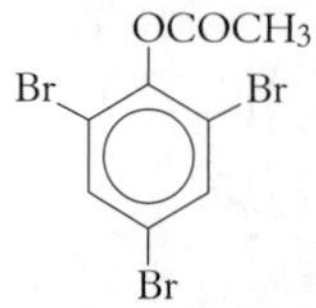

16. Hydrolysis splits **A** into **B** and **C** but does not remove —Cl therefore **A** is not an acid chloride. **B** could be $ClCH_2CO_2H$, and **C** could be CH_3OH. This would make
A = $ClCH_2CO_2CH_3$
Hydrolysis of **A** with NaOH(aq) gives **D**: $HOCH_2CO_2Na$ + **C**: CH_3OH, and **E** = $HOCH_2CO_2H$.
With Na_2CO_3(aq), **E** gives CO_2 + **D**
E + **C**: $HOCH_2CO_2H + CH_3OH \longrightarrow HOCH_2CO_2CH_3 + H_2O$
Conditions: add conc. H_2SO_4 and warm.

17. (a) (i) no plane or axis or centre of symmetry, see § 5.2.4
(ii) Two mirror image forms exist; see Figures 5.2J, K.
(iii) 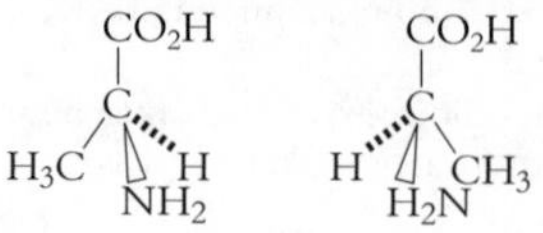 CO_2H / C / H_3C H NH_2 CO_2H / C / H CH_3 H_2N

(b) $\left\{ H_3N\text{—}CH(CH_3)\text{—}CO_2 \right\}^-$ (structure: H—N(H)(H)—C(H)(CH₃)—C(O)(O), carboxylate delocalised)

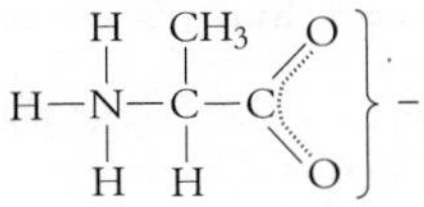

pH 2.0 $H_3N^+\text{—}CH(CH_3)\text{—}CO_2H$

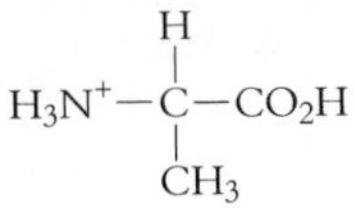

pH 10.0 $H_2N\text{—}CH(CH_3)\text{—}CO_2^-$

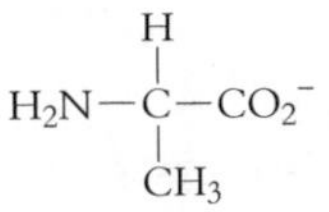

(c) (i) —C(=O)—N(H)—

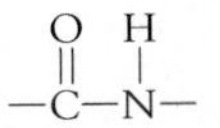

(ii) H—N(H)—CH(CH(CH₃)₂)—C(=O)—O—H (H—N—C(H)—C(=O)OH, with H—C—CH₃ / CH₃ on the α-carbon)

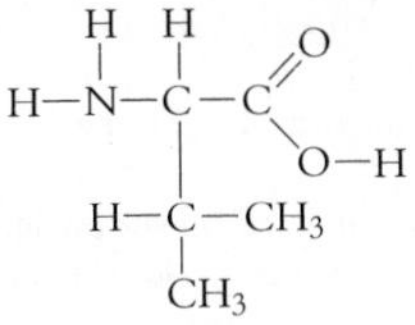

(iii) $H_2N\text{—}CH(CH(CH_3)_2)\text{—}CO\text{—}NH\text{—}CH(CH_3)\text{—}C(=O)\text{—}O\text{—}H$

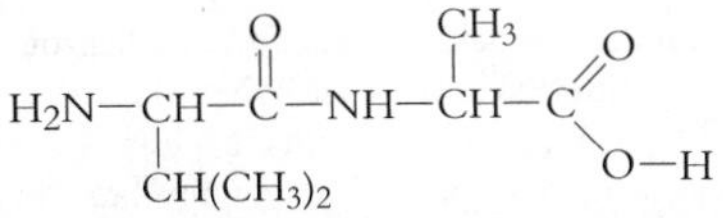

18. *(a)* **A** = $C_5H_{12}O$, oxidised by $Cr_2O_7^{2-}$, acid therefore could be an aldehyde or a ketone, but $C_5H_{12}O$ is not the formula of an aldehyde; it could be an alcohol, $C_5H_{11}OH$. **B** is chiral therefore could be

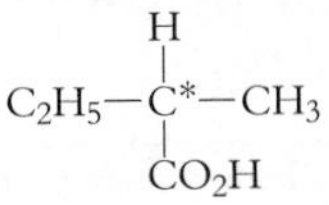

$C_2H_5\text{—}C^*H(CH_3)\text{—}CO_2H$

(b) Oxidation of **A** to **C**, which can be further oxidised, suggests **A**: 1° alcohol ⟶ **C**: aldehyde – confirmed by Tollens' reagent. **C** is $C_2H_5\text{—}CH(CH_3)\text{—}CHO$,

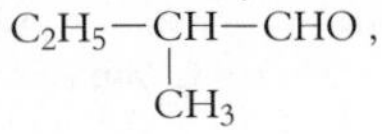

A is $C_2H_5\text{—}CH(CH_3)\text{—}CH_2OH$

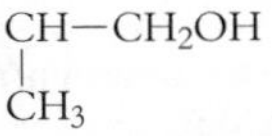

(c) The aldehyde has a lower T_b than the acid or the alcohol because fewer hydrogen bonds can form between molecules.

(d) $LiAlH_4$(ethoxyethane); reduction

(e) The molecule has no centre, plane or axis of symmetry.

(f) 2,4-dinitrophenylhydrazine. The ketone also reacts.

(g) Oxidation–reduction: **C** reduces Tollens' reagent.

19. *(a)* **A** = $CH_3CHBrCH_3$, 2-bromopropane
B = $CH_3CH_2CH_2Br$, 1-bromopropane
C = $CH_3CHOHCH_3$, propan-2-ol
D = $CH_3CH_2CH_2OH$, propan-1-ol
E = $(CH_3)_2CO$, propanone
F = $CH_3CH_2CO_2H$, propanoic acid
Reasoning: The acid formed by addition of HBr followed by hydrolysis and oxidation is propanoic acid, **F**. Since **E** reacts with DNP and not with Tollens' reagent, **E** is a ketone. **C** must be a 2° alcohol, $CH_3CHOHCH_3$, making **E** = CH_3COCH_3 and **A** = $CH_3CHBrCH_3$. **F** is formed by oxidation of **D** which contains —OH, therefore **D** = $CH_3CH_2CH_2OH$ and **B** = $CH_3CH_2CH_2Br$.

(b) (i) An acid is a substance which can donate a proton to another substance. A base is a substance which can accept a proton from another substance; see § 12.6.1.

(ii) $K_a = [H^+(aq)]\,[A^-(aq)]/[HA(aq)]$

(iii) I HCl, II HCl, III HCl (K_a values are not given for strong acids such as HCl(aq).)

CHAPTER 34 POLYMERS

Checkpoint 34.4: Addition polymers

1. *(a)* (i) Hdpe is manufactured at atmospheric pressure; ldpe at high pressure (15 atm).

(ii) Hdpe has linear molecules with little branching which pack closely together. In ldpe the molecules are branched and pack less closely.

(b) Ldpe is used when flexibility is required, e.g. waterproof covers and insulation for electrical cables. Hdpe is used when a stiff, hard plastic is required, e.g. for pipes and tanks and also for equipment which must be sterilised by heat.

2. *(a)* PVC is harder and stiffer than PE.

(b) Cl atoms increase the forces of attraction between molecules.

(c) uses; see § 34.4.2

3. *(a)* heating with sulphur to form cross-links between rubber molecules

(b) prevents creep; see § 34.4.3

(c) $\text{—}(CH_2\text{—}CH\text{=}CH\text{—}CH_2)\text{—}_n$

Checkpoint 34.5: Condensation polymers

1. *(a)* See § 34.5.1.

(b) unsaturation; see § 34.5.2

(c) Cross-linked polymers are harder, tougher, higher melting, thermosetting.

2 *(a)* See §§ 34.5.4, 34.6.

(b) nylons

3. *(a)* Thermosoftening – can be softened by heat, set and resoftened many times.
Thermosets are not softened by heat; § 34.3.

(b) cross-linking in thermosets; § 34.3.

(c) Can be bought as solid granules, fed into a machine to be melted and moulded in a continuous process. Pigments can be added, and offcuts can be recycled.

(d) e.g. kitchen work surface which must be heat-resistant, electrical plugs and sockets; see §§ 34.5–8, 34.6

4. *(a)* Phenol has three reactive positions, the 2-, 4- and 6-positions in the ring.

(b) See § 34.5.5.

5. *(a)* e.g. epoxyethane, § 34.5.6 *(b)* uses, § 34.5.6

Questions on Chapter 34

1. Addition: nCHR=CHR′ ⟶ (CHR—CHR′)$_n$, e.g. ethene, chloroethene, see § 27.8.10.
Condensation: Molecules with two reactive groups react with elimination of water molecules (or other small molecules); see § 34.5. E.g. $H_2NCHRCO_2H$; and $H_2N(CH_2)_4NH_2 + HO_2C(CH_2)_4CO_2H$

2. Cross-linking: Long molecules are joined by bridging groups at intervals; see §§ 34.5.2, 34.5.5, 34.5.6.
Thermosetting: can be shaped during manufacture but once set cannot be resoftened by heat. Suitable for use when a hard, rigid, waterproof material is required, e.g. pipes and tanks, and for equipment which needs to be heat-sterilised.

3. Consists of long hydrocarbon chains. Can be used for food containers etc. Non-biodegradable: waste plastic is difficult to dispose of; see § 34.7.

4. *(a)* amide, —CONH—
(b) Both contain —CONH— as the group linking residues of monomer.
(c) hydrogen bonding, similar to nylon as shown in § 34.3

5. **A** $C_6H_5COCH_3$ reduce with $LiAlH_4$ (ethoxyethane) ⟶ $C_6H_5CHOHCH_3$. Heat with conc. H_2SO_4 ⟶ $C_6H_5CH{=}CH_2$. Polymerise by adding an initiator.
B $H_3CC_6H_4COCH_3 + KMnO_4$, acid ⟶ $HO_2CC_6H_4CO_2H$

Polymerise with epoxyethane, $CH_2{-}CH_2$ (bridged by O)

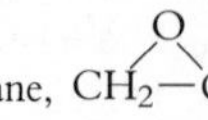

(a) **A** *(b)* **A** *(c)* **A**. The ester group in **B** is hydrolysed by acids and alkalis.

6. *(a)* $HOCH_2CH_2CH_2CO_2H$
(b) $HOCH_2CH_2CH_2CO_2CH_2CH_2CH_2CO_2H$
(c) $—CH_2CH_2CH_2CO_2—$

7. *(a)* **A**: $HO_2C(CH_2)_4CO_2H$, **B**: $ClOC(CH_2)_4COCl$, **C**: $H_2N(CH_2)_6NH_2$
(b) $—CONH(CH_2)_6NHOC(CH_2)_4—$
(c) Drawn out into threads [§§ 34.3, 35.5.4], aligns the molecules and increases intermolecular forces of attraction, thus increasing strength, but reducing water absorbancy.

8. *(a)* (i) The monomers have two functional groups. In the case of nylon, 1, 6-diaminohexane has two $—NH_2$ groups and decanoyl chloride has two —COCl groups.
(ii) Many molecules join to form a large molecule with the elimination of many small molecules, e.g. H_2O, HCl.
(iii) A polymer in which the group which links the repeating units is the group —C(=O)—N(H)—

(b) When a monofunctional monomer adds to a polymer chain, the polymer chain acquires a non-functional end group and ceases to polymerise at this end of the molecule.

(c) dimethylcyclohexane + $KMnO_4$, acid ⟶ cyclohexane(CO_2H)(CO_2H) $\xrightarrow{NH_3}$

cyclohexane(CO_2NH_4)(CO_2NH_4) $\xrightarrow{\text{Heat with parent acid}}$ cyclohexane($CONH_2$)($CONH_2$) $\xrightarrow{LiAlH_4 \text{ (ethoxyethane)}}$

cyclohexane(CH_2NH_2)(CH_2NH_2)

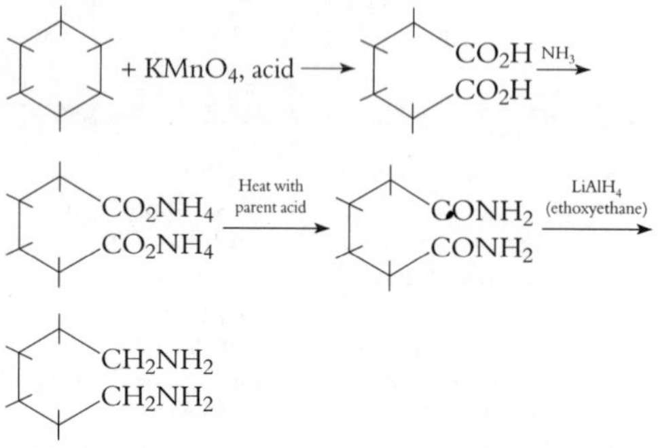

$n HO_2C(CH_2)_4CO_2H + n H_2N(CH_2)_6NH_2 \longrightarrow$
$-\!\!\!\!+ (CH_2)_4CONH(CH_2)_6NHCO -\!\!\!\!+_n + nH_2O$

(d) (i) Three molecules of urea condense to form one molecule of melamine:

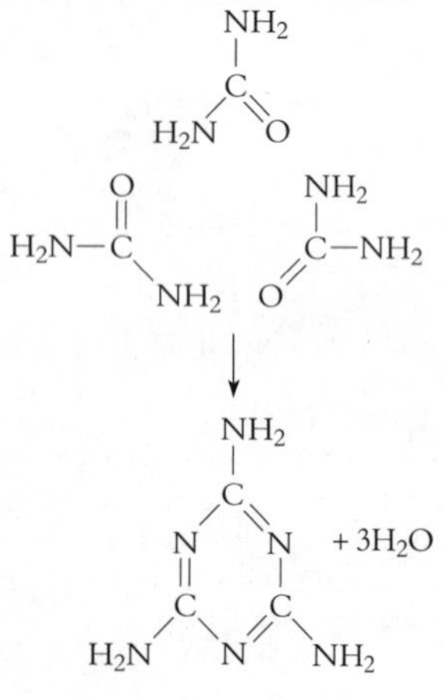

$H_2N{-}C(=O){-}NH_2$ (three molecules) ⟶ melamine (triazine ring with three NH_2 groups) $+ 3H_2O$

(ii) Resistant to chemical attack, hard with a smooth finish.

(e) (i) Hydrogen chloride can be formed – toxic. There is a possibility of the formation of chlorine also.
(ii) Flame retardants in PVC. There is a danger of forming $HCl + Cl_2$ when PVC burns.

9. *(a)* (i) H—C(H)(H)—C(H)(H)—O—H C_6H_5—C(=O)—O—H

(ii) C_6H_5—C(H)(H)—O—C(=O)—C(H)(H)—H

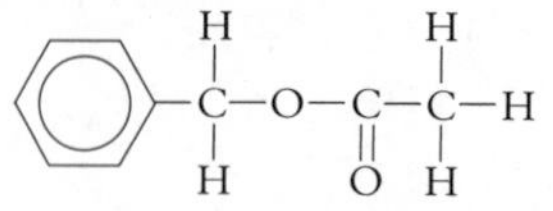

(b) (i) $-\!\!\!\!+ CH_2{-}O{-}C(=O){-}C_6H_4{-}C(=O){-}O -\!\!\!\!+$
(ii) Used in the clothing industry; can be drawn into fibres.
(iii) Have to be dumped in land-fill sites where they do not decay because they are non-biodegradable.

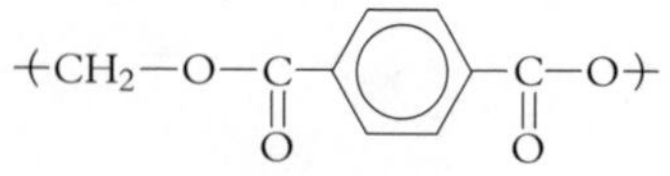

(c) (i) $H_2NCHRCO_2H$
(ii) There is an acidic group and a basic group; therefore the molecule ionises as $H_3N^+CH_2CO_2^-$. Attraction between these ions results in a high T_m. Since it is an ionic compound, it does not bond to and therefore dissolve in hydrocarbons.
(iii) Optically inactive because

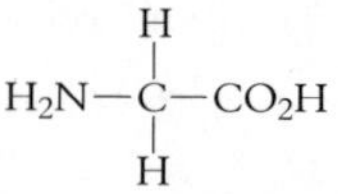

$H_2N{-}C(H)(H){-}CO_2H$

has a plane of symmetry.
(iv) Peptides are products of the hydrolysis of proteins and are further hydrolysed by digestive enzymes in the gut.

(c) (i) —C(=O)—N(H)—
(ii) $CH_3CH_2CO_2H \longrightarrow CH_3CH_2CONH_2$
Make the ammonium salt by reaction with ammonium carbonate. Heat ammonium propanoate with excess of propanoic acid at 100 °C ⟶ propanamide.

10. *(a)* See § 34.2.
(b) (i) $H_2N{-}C(H)(CH_3){-}C(=O){-}N(H){-}C(H)(CH_3){-}C(=O){-}O{-}H$
(ii) peptide link, —CO—NH—
(iii) peptides and proteins
(c) (i) $nCH_2{=}CH_2 \longrightarrow -\!\!\!\!+ CH_2{-}CH_2 -\!\!\!\!+_n$
(ii) ldpe branched chain, hdpe unbranched chain
The chains in hdpe have little branching and are able to pack more closely together.
(ii) Flexibility: ldpe is more flexible
(iv) $R\cdot + CH_2{=}CH_2 \longrightarrow RH + \cdot CH{=}CH_2$
(v) Ziegler
(d) (i) not broken down by micro-organisms; see § 34.7.1
(ii) e.g. less demand for landfill sites
(iii) See § 34.7.6. Recycling plastics makes the most efficient use of Earth's resources of crude oil.

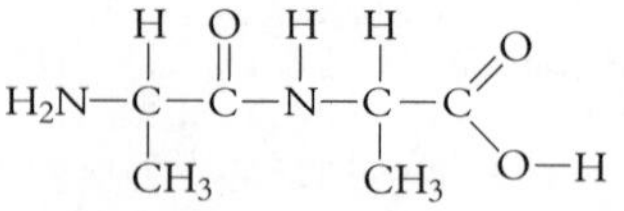

11. *(a)* (i) hydroxyl (ii) ethanediol (iii) carboxyl
(b) (i) NaOH
(ii) Fractional distillation under reduced pressure
(c) Ethene is a product of cracking in the petroleum industry. 1, 2-Dichloroethane is made from it, involving the cost of the chlorine needed.

(d) $-O-\overset{O}{\overset{\|}{C}}-C_6H_4-\overset{O}{\overset{\|}{C}}-O-CH_2-CH_2-O-\overset{O}{\overset{\|}{C}}-C_6H_4$

(e) dipole–dipole attractions; see diagram in § 34.3

(f) Flexibility results when polymer chains are not tightly packed together and have some freedom of movement. The 1, 4-dicarboxylic acid forms linear chains of polymer. The 1, 2-dicarboxylic acid forms chains which pack more closely together than in the 1, 4-isomer.

$C_6H_4-CO_2-CH_2-CH_2-O_2C-C_6H_4$ (1,2-substituted rings)

12. *(a)* (i) 1. KCN (ethanolic) 2. NaOH(aq) 5. Br_2 + NaOH(aq)

(ii) C_2H_5COCl

(b) (i) $HO_2C(CH_2)_4CO_2H$ and $H_2N(CH_2)_6NH_2$

(ii) condensation

(c) (i) $\left[-\overset{F}{\underset{H}{C}}-\overset{F}{\underset{H}{C}}-\right]_n$

(ii) e.g. non-stick pans, coating skis; see Table 27.8

(d) The polyamide is easier to break down because the —CO—NH— amide link can be hydrolysed.

13. *(a)* (i) $CH_3-C(=O)-NH_2$

(ii) $CH_3-N(CH_3)(C_2H_5)$

Heat in a 'bomb'.

(b) (i) $CH_3COCl + NH_3 \longrightarrow CH_3CONH_2 + HCl$

(ii) A 3° amine has no —H to react with —Cl.

(c) (i)

$HO_2C-C_6H_4-CO_2H + 2PCl_5 \longrightarrow$

$ClOC-C_6H_4-COCl + 2POCl_3 + 2HCl$

$n\ H_2NCH_2CH_2NH_2 + n\ ClOC-C_6H_4-COCl \longrightarrow$

$\left[-CH_2CH_2NHOC-C_6H_4-CONH-\right]_n + nHCl$

(ii) There are two different monomers forming the repeating unit, whereas in a protein the repeating unit is:

$\left[-\overset{R}{\underset{H}{C}}-\underset{O}{\overset{\|}{C}}-\overset{H}{N}-\right]$

formed from one type of monomer, an amino acid.

(d) (i) Amide hydrolysed $\longrightarrow CH_3CO_2H + (NH_4)_2SO_4$

3° amine $\longrightarrow$ salt, $[(CH_3)_2(C_2H_5)NH]^+HSO_4^-$

Amide: warm under reflux; amine: add the reactants.

(ii) Amines are basic: $R-\ddot{N}(R')H$

has a lone pair which can donate an electron pair to a H^+ ion. Amides:

$R-\overset{\delta+}{C}(=O^{\delta-})-\ddot{N}H_2$

repel H^+ by the $\delta+$ charge on the C of the CO group.

CHAPTER 35 IDENTIFYING ORGANIC COMPOUNDS

Checkpoint 35.4: Analysis

1. *(a)* Mass of C = 0.629 × 12/44 g = 0.1715 g
Mass of H = 0.257 × 2/18 g = 0.0285 g
Ratio C 0.1715/12 : H 0.0285/1
Formula is CH_2.

(b) Amount of **A** = 53.3 cm^3/22.4 $dm^3\ mol^{-1}$ = 2.38 × 10^{-3} mol
⇒ M = 0.200 g/2.38 × 10^{-3} mol = 84.0 g mol^{-1}
M of CH_2 = 14 = > molecular formula is C_6H_{12}.

2. Mass of S = 0.1322 × 32/233 = 0.018 16 g
Mass of Cl = 0.0813 × 35.5/143.5 = 0.020 11 g
Mass of C = 0.1496 × 12/44 = 0.0408 g
Mass of H = 0.0255 × 2/18 = 0.002 885 g
Mass of O = 0.1000 g – masses of
S + Cl + C + H = 0.018 055 g
Ratio of amounts in moles:
S 0.018 16/32 : Cl 0.020 11/35.5 : C 0.0408/12 :
H 0.002 89/1 : O 0.018 06/16
gives the empirical formula $C_6H_5SO_2Cl$.

3. NaOH used = 25.0 cm^3 of 0.100 mol dm^{-3}
Amount of NH_4^+ = 2.5 × 10^{-3} mol
Mass of N = 2.5 × 10^{-3} × 14 g = 3.5 × 10^{-2} g
% of N = 100 × 3.5 × 10^{-2}/0.1850 = 18.9%
Mass of C = 0.264 × 12/44 = 0.072 g
% of C = 100 × 0.072/0.146 = 49.31%
Mass of H = 0.126 × 2/18 = 0.014 g
% of H = 100 × 0.014/0.146 = 9.59%
% of O = 100% – 77.8% = 22.2%

Ratio	N	C	H	O
	18.9%/14	49.3%/12	9.6%/1	22.2%/16

gives the empirical formula C_3H_7NO.

Checkpoint 35.7: Visible-ultraviolet spectra

1. A plot of absorbance against volume of $\mathbf{M}^{2+}$(aq) or against volume of **L**(aq) gives a maximum at M^{2+}(aq) = 3.3 cm^3, **L** = 6.6 cm^3, a ratio = 1 : 2 so formula is $\mathbf{ML_2}$.

Checkpoint 35.8: Infrared spectra

1. There is a C—H aliphatic absorption at 3000 cm^{-1} and a C—Cl absorption at 765 cm^{-1}. The compound is a chloroalkane. (In fact this is the IR spectrum of $CHCl_3$.)

2. C≡N at 2250 cm^{-1} and C—H aliphatic at 3000 cm^{-1} and C—H vibrations at 1460 and 1430 cm^{-1}. The presence of C≡N and the absence of aromatic C—H and aromatic C—C indicate an aliphatic nitrile. (In fact this is propanenitrile, CH_3CH_2CN.)

3. C—H aromatic above 3000 cm^{-1}, C—H of CHO at 2700, 2800 cm^{-1}, C=O at 1700 cm^{-1}, C—C aromatic at 1600 cm^{-1} and C—H at 1200 cm^{-1}. The spectrum is that of an aromatic aldehyde. (In fact it is that of benzaldehyde.)

4. C—H aliphatic at 3000 cm^{-1}, C—H of CHO at 2720 and 2830 cm^{-1}, C=O at 1730 cm^{-1}. The compound is an aliphatic aldehyde. (In fact it is propanal.)

5. C≡N at 2200 cm^{-1}, C—H aromatic at 3050 cm^{-1}, C—C aromatic at 1480 cm^{-1}. There are indications of an aromatic ring and a nitrile group. The simplest compound possessing these structures is benzonitrile or benzenecarbonitrile, C_6H_5CN. One could identify the compound by a molar mass determination. (In fact the spectrum is that of benzenecarbonitrile.)

6. C=O at 1700 cm^{-1} and O—H with hydrogen bonding at 2600–3400 cm^{-1} suggest a carboxylic acid. Since it is a liquid, it must be an aliphatic acid. (In fact the IR spectrum is that of ethanoic acid.)

Checkpoint 35.9: Mass spectra

1. **E**: The peak at 15 corresponds to CH_3. The peak at 94 is probably the molecular peak with a side-peak at 96 suggesting chlorine or bromine. Peaks at 79 and 81 of almost equal heights indicate bromine. CH_3(15) + Br(79) = 94, and the compound is bromomethane, CH_3Br.
2. **F**: 64 is probably the molecular peak with a side-peak of 66 due to the presence of ^{37}Cl. There is a peak at 29 corresponding to the loss of ^{35}Cl from the molecular ion of **M** = 64. The peaks at 49 and 51 could correspond to the loss of CH_3 from **M** = 64 and from **M** = 66. The peaks at 29, 28 and 27 could be $C_2H_5^+$, $C_2H_4^+$ and $C_2H_3^+$. Combining C_2H_5 and Cl gives C_2H_5Cl, chloroethane.

Checkpoint 35.10: NMR

1. ethanol, C_2H_5OH. The —CH_3 1 : 2 : 1 triplet at δ1.0–1.3 and the —CH_2— 1 : 3 : 3 : 1 quartet at δ3.5–3.9 are recognisable. The peak at δ5.0–5.3 is due to —OH and is absent in ^2H_2O because the —OH proton is labile.
2. 1-amino-2, 2-dimethylpropane, $(CH_3)_3CCH_2NH_2$. The —CH_3 absorption at δ0.9 is strong. The peak at δ2.5 could be due to R—CH_2—R and that at δ1.0 to RNH_2. The ratio 9 H in CH_3 groups : 2 H in —NH_2 groups: 2 H in —CH_2— groups makes the compound $(CH_3)_3CCH_2NH_2$ a possibility.
3. propanoic acid, $CH_3CH_2CO_2H$. The —CH_3 and —CH_2 groups are recognisable – as in spectrum 1. The peak at δ11.7 could be due to —CO_2H, which does not give a peak in ^2H_2O because the H is labile. The ratio 3 H in —CH_3 : 2 H in —CH_2— : 1 H in —CO_2H identifies the compound as $CH_3CH_2CO_2H$.
4. ethylbenzene, $C_6H_5C_2H_5$. The CH_3CH_2— group is recognisable as in spectrum 1. The peak at δ7.2 is due to C_6H_5—H. The ratio 5 H in aromatic ring : 2 H in —CH_2— : 3 H in —CH_3 gives $C_6H_5C_2H_5$ as the compound.
5. ethanal, CH_3CHO. The peak at δ9.7–9.8 is due to RCHO. The peak at δ2.1 is probably due to R—$COCH_3$. The ratio 1 H in —CHO : 3 H in $RCOCH_3$ gives CH_3CHO as the formula.
6. butanone, $CH_3COCH_2CH_3$. The —CH_3 peak at δ0.9–1.1 and the —CH_2— peak at δ2.2–2.5 are identifiable. The peak at δ2.1 can be due to $RCOCH_3$. A compound with a —$COCH_3$ group and a C_2H_5— group is $CH_3COCH_2CH_3$.

Questions on Chapter 35

1. *(a)* See § 35.6.
   (b) The spectrum **A** has a peak at 2800 cm^{-1}, indicating a C—H bond and a peak at 1100 cm^{-1}, indicating a C—O bond in an alcohol, ether or ester. The spectrum **B** has a peak at 2800 cm^{-1} (C—H), a peak at 1100 cm^{-1} (C—O) and a peak at 3300 cm^{-1}, indicating the —OH group of an alcohol. **A** corresponds to an ether, e.g. $C_2H_5OC_2H_5$, $CH_3OCH(CH_3)_2$ or $CH_3OCH_2CH_2CH_3$. **B** corresponds to an alcohol, one of the isomers of C_4H_9OH.
   (c) Fragmentation patterns in the mass spectra; § 35.9.2. NMR would identify the two compounds by showing which alkyl groups were present.
2. The O—H absorption is present at 3450 cm^{-1}, and the C—O absorption at 1050 cm^{-1}, the C—H aliphatic absorption at 2900 cm^{-1}, suggesting an aliphatic chain. There is an absence of bands below 1000 cm^{-1} which would indicate an aromatic compound. It looks like an aliphatic hydrocarbon chain with the bonds C—O and O—H, that is an alcohol. (In fact this is the spectrum of dodecanol, $CH_3(CH_2)_{10}CH_2OH$.)
3. The C=O absorption at 1715 cm^{-1} and CH_2 at 1460 cm^{-1} can be seen. The absence of a big absorption band below 1000 cm^{-1} indicates an aliphatic compound. The indications are an aliphatic compound with a carbonyl group. The CO group is at the lower end of the absorption range and is probably a ketone. From M_r = 98, subtract 28 for CO, leaving 70. This could be C_5H_{10} and the compound could be $C_6H_{10}O$, cyclohexanone.
4. The C—Cl absorption is present at 750 cm^{-1}. There are aliphatic C—H vibrations at 2940 cm^{-1}. There is evidence of an aromatic ring at 800–700 cm^{-1}. This seems to be a chloroalkane. (It is in fact dichloromethane.)
5. The C = O absorption is seen at 1700 cm^{-1}, C=C at 1400 cm^{-1}, C—H at 1100–70 cm^{-1} and at 3000 cm^{-1}, O—H at 2500–2800 cm^{-1}. An aromatic compound with a C=O group and an O—H bond, e.g. an aromatic carboxylic acid. (In fact this is benzoic acid.)
6. The C=O absorption is seen at 1725 cm^{-1}, C—H aromatic at 3000 cm^{-1}, C—O—C aliphatic at 1100 cm^{-1}. An aromatic ester would fit the spectrum. (In fact this is ethyl benzoate.)
7. **A** $HCO_2CH_2CH_2CH_3$, **B** $HCO_2CH(CH_3)_2$, **C** $CH_3CO_2C_2H_5$, **D** $C_2H_5CO_2CH_3$.
   All give a molecular peak at 88.
   HCO_2^+ = 45, and this is absent, eliminating **A** and **B**.
   $CH_3CO_2^+$ = 59, and $C_2H_5^+$ = 29, and these are both present, so **C** is a possibility.
   $C_2H_5CO_2^+$ = 73, and CH_3^+ = 15, and both these are absent, so **D** is unlikely.
   The ester is **C**, $CH_3CO_2C_2H_5$.
8. The peak at m/z = 46 is the molecular peak. The peak at m/z = 47 corresponds to $^{12}C^{13}CH_5OH$. The peak at m/z = 45 is due to $C_2H_5O^+$, 31 to CH_2OH^+, 29 to $C_2H_5^+$ and 27 to $C_2H_3^+$.
9. The peak at 136 is the molecular peak. The peak at 77 corresponds to C_6H_5. The peak at 105 = 136 – 31 could be due to the loss of OCH_3, leaving C_7H_5O. The peak at 51 could be $C_4H_3^+$. Combining the benzene ring and the ability to lose OCH_3 to form $C_6H_5CO^+$ indicates $C_6H_5CO_2CH_3$, methyl benzoate.
10. 58 = molecular peak, 57 = loss of one H = $C_3H_5O^+$, 29 could be $C_2H_5^+$ or CHO^+. 28 could be $C_2H_4^+$ or CO^+. Combining C_2H_5 and CO and H gives C_2H_5CHO, propanal.
11. 102 = molecular ion, peak at 87 = $M - CH_3 = C_5H_{11}O^+$, peak at 73 = 87 – 14 = 87 – CH_2 = $C_4H_9O^+$,
    peak at 57 could be $M - C_2H_5O = C_4H_9^+$, peak at 45 could be $C_2H_5O^+$, 29 = $C_2H_5^+$.
    Combining C_2H_5O and C_4H_9O gives $C_4H_9OC_2H_5$. The isomer is in fact 2-ethoxybutane,

    $CH_3CH_2CHCH_3$
    |
    OC_2H_5

12. *(a)* There is only one type of H atom in **G**. It must be CH_3OCH_3, methoxymethane. The NMR spectrum is different from that of CH_3CH_2OH because in ethanol there are H atoms in three different environments, —OH, —CH_2— and —CH_3.
    (b) Tetramethylsilane, $(CH_3)_4Si$, has all its H atoms in identical environments and gives a single NMR line.
13. There are three types of H atom: two which are split into a quartet by three adjacent H atoms, could indicate CH_2CH_3; three which are not split; three which are split into a triplet by two adjacent H atoms, e.g. CH_2CH_3. The ester **J** could be $CH_3CO_2CH_2CH_3$.
14. **A**: $CH_3OH + CH_2—CH_2 \longrightarrow C_3H_8O_2$ (epoxide: CH_2—CH_2 bridged by O)
    (a) 4
    (b) 2 : 2 : 3 : 1

(c) 3 H of one type suggests CH_3. 1 H of another type suggests OH. 2 H and 2 H suggest CH_2 and CH_2 in different environments. The formula $CH_3CH_2CH_2OH$ fits.

15. (a) (i) C—H (ii) Compare the spectra of the two compounds with the spectra of known compounds.

(b) (i) In cyclohexane the 12 H atoms are in identical environments:

```
      CH2
     /   \
  H2C     CH2
   |       |
  H2C     CH2
     \   /
      CH2
```

In dichloromethane the 2 H atoms are in identical environments:

```
 H  Cl
  \ /
   C
  / \
 H   Cl
```

(ii) Equal amounts of cyclohexane and dichloromethane contain H atoms in a ratio 6 : 1.

(c) (i) $CH_4 + Cl_2 \longrightarrow CH_3Cl + HCl$; sunlight or heat

(ii) $Cl. + CH_4 \longrightarrow CH_3. + HCl$

$CH_3. + Cl_2 \longrightarrow CH_3Cl + Cl.$

(d) $CH_2Cl_2 : CH_2{}^{35}Cl^{35}Cl = 84$, $CH_2{}^{35}Cl^{37}Cl = 86$, $CH_2{}^{37}Cl^{37}Cl = 88$

Three peaks at 84, 86, 88

16. (a) 4 (b) 1 : 6 : 2 : 3 (c) $RCOCH_3$ (from Table 1)

(d) A peak due to n adjacent protons is split into $n + 1$ parts. The peak at δ4.8 is therefore due to a proton with 2 adjacent protons. The peak at δ2.7 is due to a proton with 1 adjacent proton.

Of 12 H atoms, 1 H of type a has 2 adjacent protons, 6 H of type b – value of δ suggests 2(—OCH_3), 2 H of type c have 1 adjacent proton, are in a —$COCH_3$ group (see (c)). 3 H of type d – value of δ suggests $RCOCH_3$.

```
                H
                |
Start with a: R—C—OR
                |
                OR

                H
                |
Add b:        R—C—OCH3
                |
                OCH3

                     H
                     |
Add d:        H3C—C—C—OCH3
                  ‖  |
                  O  OCH3
```

This contains C—O—C linkages and a >C=O group, as required. The formula adds up to $C_5H_{10}O_3$. Adding CH_2 to make it up to $C_6H_{12}O_3$ as required gives

```
          H  H
          |  |
H3C—C—C—C—OCH3
    ‖  |  |
    O  H  OCH3

          H(c) H(a)
           |    |
H(d)3C—C—C—C—O—CH(b)3
       ‖  |  |
       O H(c) O—CH(b)3
```

The H atom (a) has 2 adjacent H atoms, the two H atoms (c) each have one adjacent H atom, the six H atoms (b) and the three H atoms (d) do not have hydrogen atoms bonded to adjacent atoms.

17. (a) See § 35.9.2.

(b) $C_5H_{10}O$

B Peak at 57 corresponds to loss of C_2H_5, suggesting $C_2H_5COC_2H_5$.

C Peak at 43 corresponds to C_3H_7.

Peak at 71 corresponds to loss of CH_3.

The compound could be (1) $CH_{a3}COCH_{b2}CH_{c2}CH_{d3}$ or (2) $CH_{a3}COCH_b(CH_{c3})_3$

The NMR spectrum of (1) shows 4 peaks for 3 H_a, 2 H_b, 2 H_c, 3 H_d. The NMR spectrum of (2) shows 3 peaks for 3 H_a, 1 H_b, 9 H_c.

(c) **D** $\longrightarrow$ **E**: substitution of CH_3CO— for H—. The IR peak at 1685 cm^{-1} shows the presence of a C=O group. D could be $C_6H_5CH_3$, **E** = $CH_3C_6H_4COCH_3$ with isomers 1, 2-, 1, 3- and 1, 4-. **E** $\longrightarrow$ **F** adds 2 H; **F** is $CH_3C_6H_4CHOHCH_3$. The band at 3340 cm^{-1} shows the presence of —OH in an alcohol. Dehydration of **F** $\longrightarrow$ **G**. **G** is $CH_3C_6H_4CH{=}CH_2$. The IR band at 1630 cm^{-1} indicates a C=C bond.

E: $H_3C-C_6H_4-COCH_3$ **F**: $H_3C-C_6H_4-CHOHCH_3$

G: $H_3C-C_6H_4-CH{=}CH_2$

(ii) Acylation, reduction, dehydration

```
H   H            H   H             H
 \ /              \ /               \
  C   H    →       C   H    →        C    H
 /  \ /           / \ /               \\ /
H    C   H      H    C   H     H       C      + H⁺ + H2O
    / \ /           / \ /                \
 C6H5  O   H⁺    C6H5  O+                C6H5
                       |
                       H
```

18. (a) 4

(b) 2 : 2 : 2 : 3

(c) $RCOCH_3$ (δ2.4), RCH_3 (δ1.1)

δ2.4 peak splits into 4 therefore there are 3 adjacent protons

δ1.1 peak splits into 3 because of 2 adjacent protons

(d) δ3.8 peak: 2 adjacent protons; δ2.8 : 2 adjacent protons

(e) C_5H_9ClO

$CH_3CH_2COCH_2CH_2Cl$

2 3 2 2 Number of adjacent protons

19. (a) (i) **X** RCH_2CO, **Y** $ROCH_3$, **Z** RCH_3

(ii)

```
  H  H  O  H
  |  |  ‖  |
H—C—C—C—C—H
  |  |     |
  H  H     H
```

(iii) $CH_{a3}CH_{b2}COCH_{c3}$

There are 3 H_a protons, 2 H_b protons, 3 H_c protons.

(b) (i) See § 25.9.1.

(ii)

```
  H  H  H   H
  |  |  |  /
H—C—C—C—C
  |  |  |  \\
  H  H  H   O
```

(iii) There will be a band due to RCHO at δ9.7 but no RCH_2CO at δ2.5.

(c) (i) See § 25.9.3.

(ii)

```
    C2H5            C2H5
     |               |
     C               C
   / | \           / | \
  H  OH CH3     H3C HO  H
```

(iii) It has no asymmetric C atom (with bonds to four different groups)

CHAPTER 36 SOME GENERAL TOPICS

Checkpoint 36.2 : Synthetic routes

1. (a) Reduce by $LiAlH_4$ in ethoxyethane solution.
(b) Add NaClO (or Cl_2 + NaOH(aq) $\longrightarrow CCl_3COCH_3 \longrightarrow CHCl_3 + CH_3CO_2H$
(c) Add $NaHSO_3$ followed by KCN $\longrightarrow CH_3CH(OH)CN$ Reflux with dilute acid $\longrightarrow CH_3CH(OH)CO_2H$
(d) Oxidise part with $K_2Cr_2O_7$ + acid $\longrightarrow CH_3CH_2CO_2H$ Reduce part with $NaBH_4$(aq) $\longrightarrow CH_3CH_2CH_2OH$ Esterify the acid and alcohol, using conc. H_2SO_4 $\longrightarrow CH_3CH_2CO_2\,CH_2CH_2CH_3$
(e) Oxidise with $K_2Cr_2O_7$ + acid $\longrightarrow CH_3COCH_3$; then add $NaHSO_3$ followed by KCN $\longrightarrow (CH_3)_2C(OH)CN$
2. (a) Reduce with $LiAlH_4$ (ethoxyethane) $\longrightarrow CH_3CH(OH)CH_3$ Then heat with $Al_2O_3 \longrightarrow CH_3CH{=}CH_2$, and add $Cl_2 \longrightarrow CH_3CHClCH_2Cl$
(b) Reduce with $LiAlH_4$ (ethoxyethane) $\longrightarrow (CH_3)_2CH(OH)$ Warm the alcohol with KBr + conc. H_2SO_4 $\longrightarrow (CH_3)_2CHBr$
(c) Heat with Al_2O_3
(d) With Cl_2 in sunlight $\longrightarrow C_2H_5Cl$; then reflux with NaOH(aq) $\longrightarrow C_2H_5OH$
(e) Make C_2H_5Cl as in (d); then warm with NH_3 in a sealed container $\longrightarrow C_2H_5NH_2$
(f) $CH_3COCl + AlCl_3$, reflux at 60°C (Friedel–Crafts)
3. (a) Add $K_2Cr_2O_7$ + acid, warm, distil off CH_3CHO as it is formed (to avoid further oxidation)
(b) Reflux with PBr_3 (or red P + Br_2) $\longrightarrow C_2H_5Br$. Warm with NH_3 in a sealed container $\longrightarrow C_2H_5NH_2$
(c) Make CH_3CHO as in (a). Add $NaHSO_3$ followed by KCN $\longrightarrow CH_3CH(OH)CN$. Reduce with $LiAlH_4$(ethoxyethane) $\longrightarrow CH_3CH_2CH_2NH_2$
(d) Add $K_2Cr_2O_7$ + acid, reflux $\longrightarrow CH_3CO_2H$. Add $(NH_4)_2CO_3 \longrightarrow CH_3CO_2NH_4$. Heat with excess CH_3CO_2H above 100 °C $\longrightarrow CH_3CONH_2$.
(e) Make CH_3CO_2H as in (d). Add $SOCl_2$ (or PCl_5) $\longrightarrow CH_3COCl$
(f) Make CH_3CHO as in (a). Add $NaHSO_3$ followed by KCN $\longrightarrow CH_3CH(OH)CN$. Then reflux with conc. HCl $\longrightarrow CH_3CH(OH)CO_2H$. Heat with $Al_2O_3 \longrightarrow CH_2{=}CHCO_2H$. With H_2 + Ni catalyst $\longrightarrow CH_3CH_2CO_2H$.
4. (a) $C_6H_5CH_3$, oxidise with $KMnO_4$ + acid $\longrightarrow C_6H_5CO_2H$
(b) Boil $C_6H_5CH_3$ and pass Cl_2 through in UV or sunlight $\longrightarrow C_6H_5CH_2Cl$. With KCN $\longrightarrow C_6H_5CH_2CN$. Reflux with HCl(aq) $\longrightarrow C_6H_5CH_2CO_2H$.
(c) $C_6H_5CH_3$, oxidise with $MnO_2 \longrightarrow C_6H_5CHO$. Add $NaHSO_3$ followed by KCN $\longrightarrow C_6H_5CH(OH)CN$. With $LiAlH_4$(ethoxyethane) $\longrightarrow C_6H_5CH_2CH_2NH_2$
5. (a) With $NaNO_2$ + HCl(aq) above 10°C $\longrightarrow C_6H_5OH$
(b) Diazotise with $NaNO_2$ + HCl(aq) below 10°C $\longrightarrow C_6H_5N_2^+\,Cl^-$. Neutralise with Na_2CO_3(aq), and add KCN(aq) + CuCN(aq) $\longrightarrow C_6H_5CN$. Reflux with HCl(aq) $\longrightarrow C_6H_5CO_2H$.
(c) Make $C_6H_5CO_2H$ as in (b). Then PCl_5 or $SOCl_2 \longrightarrow C_6H_5COCl$.
(d) Make the diazonium compound as in (b). Warm with KI(aq).
6. (a) with conc. $H_2SO_4 \longrightarrow CH_3CH(CH_3)OSO_4H$. Add water, warm $\longrightarrow CH_3CH(OH)CH_3$. Then warm with $K_2Cr_2O_7$ + acid $\longrightarrow CH_3COCH_3$.
(b) With HBr $\longrightarrow CH_3CHBrCH_3$. Add KCN(ethanol), warm, distil $\longrightarrow (CH_3)_2CHCN$. Reflux with conc. HCl(aq) $\longrightarrow (CH_3)_2CHCO_2H$
(c) Make CH_3COCH_3 as in (a). Add $NaHSO_3$ followed by KCN $\longrightarrow (CH_3)_2C(OH)CN$. With $LiAlH_4$(ethoxyethane) $\longrightarrow (CH_3)_2CHCH_2NH_2$.
(d) With cold, dilute alkaline $KMnO_4$(aq) $\longrightarrow CH_3CH(OH)CH_2OH$
7. (a) Reflux with NaOH(aq) $\longrightarrow C_2H_5OH$. Warm with $K_2Cr_2O_7$ + acid, and distil off CH_3CHO as it is formed.
(b) Make C_2H_5OH as in (a). Heat with $K_2Cr_2O_7$ + acid $\longrightarrow CH_3CO_2H$. Convert part of CH_3CO_2H into CH_3CO_2Na by reaction with NaOH(aq). Convert part into CH_3COCl, using PCl_5 or $SOCl_2$. Heat $CH_3CO_2Na + CH_3COCl \longrightarrow (CH_3CO)_2O$
(c) Make C_2H_5OH as in (a). Make CH_3CO_2H as in (b). Esterify the acid and alcohol, using concentrated sulphuric acid as catalyst.
(d) Add KCN(ethanol) $\longrightarrow C_2H_5CN$. Reduce this with $LiAlH_4$(ethoxyethane) $\longrightarrow C_2H_5CH_2NH_2$. Then $NaNO_2$ + HCl(aq), warm $\longrightarrow C_2H_5CH_2OH$. Oxidise with $K_2Cr_2O_7$ + acid $\longrightarrow C_2H_5CO_2H$.
(e) Make $C_2H_5CO_2H$ as in (d). With $(NH_4)_2CO_3 \longrightarrow C_2H_5CO_2NH_4$. Heat with excess $C_2H_5CO_2H \longrightarrow C_2H_5CONH_2$
8. (a) (i) C_6H_6 + conc. HNO_3 + conc. $H_2SO_4 \longrightarrow C_6H_5NO_2$ With Sn + HCl(aq) $\longrightarrow C_6H_5NH_2$
(ii) $C_6H_5CH_3 + KMnO_4$ + acid, warm $\longrightarrow C_6H_5CO_2H$. With PCl_5 (or $SOCl_2$) $\longrightarrow C_6H_5COCl$
(iii) $C_6H_5NH_2 + C_6H_5COCl \longrightarrow C_6H_5CONHC_6H_5$
(b) $C_6H_6 + CH_3Cl + AlCl_3$ (catalyst) $\longrightarrow C_6H_5CH_3$. With Cl_2 + sunlight or UV $\longrightarrow C_6H_5CH_2Cl$. Reflux with NaOH(aq) $\longrightarrow C_6H_5CH_2OH$
(c) (i) $CH_4 + Cl_2$ in sunlight $\longrightarrow CH_3Cl$
(ii) $C_6H_6 + CH_3Cl + AlCl_3$ (catalyst) $\longrightarrow C_6H_5CH_3$ Warm with $KMnO_4$ + acid $\longrightarrow C_6H_5CO_2H$

Checkpoint 36.3: Reagents

1. (a) The reaction is a substitution, takes place in sunlight, involves free radicals. $CH_4 \longrightarrow CH_3Br \longrightarrow CH_2Br_2 \longrightarrow CHBr_3$
(b) Substitution takes place in the presence of a catalyst, $AlBr_3 \longrightarrow C_6H_5Br$, involves attack by the nucleophile $Br^+\,AlBr_4^-$. Addition takes place in sunlight by a free radical reaction to form $C_6H_6Br_6$.
(c) Substitution takes place rapidly in aqueous solution $\longrightarrow$ 2,4,6-tribromophenol $HOC_6H_2Br_3$. The $—O^{\delta-}H^{\delta+}$ group in phenol increases the electron density on the ring and facilitates attack by the electrophile Br_2 on the aromatic ring.
(d) Addition in an organic solvent $\longrightarrow CH_2BrCH_2Br$. The reaction involves attack by the electrophile $Br^{\delta+}—Br^{\delta-}$ on $CH_2{}^{\delta+}{=}CH_2{}^{\delta-}$
(e) Br_2 + NaOH(aq): Hofmann degradation $\longrightarrow CH_3NH_2 + CO_3^{2-}$
2. (a) e.g. nitrobenzene $C_6H_5NO_2 \longrightarrow$ phenylamine $C_6H_5NH_2$ (Sn + HCl(aq))
aldehyde $\longrightarrow$ 1° alcohol ($NaBH_4$(aq))
ketone $\longrightarrow$ 2° alcohol ($LiAlH_4$(ethoxyethane))
carboxylic acid $\longrightarrow$ 1° alcohol ($LiAlH_4$(ethoxyethane))
(b) addition of ozone to an alkene across the double bond $\longrightarrow$ RCH(–O–, –O–O–)CHR′ (ozonide ring) followed by reductive hydrolysis (Zn + acid) $\longrightarrow$ RCHO + R′CHO
(c) Friedel–Crafts reaction: substitution of —alkyl for —H, e.g. $C_6H_6 + CH_3Br$ ($AlBr_3$ catalyst) $\longrightarrow C_6H_5CH_3$ + HBr

(d) Friedel–Crafts reaction: substitution of —acyl for —H, e.g. $C_6H_6 + CH_3COCl$ ($AlCl_3$ catalyst) $\longrightarrow$ $C_6H_5COCl + HCl$

(e) conversion of $—CO_2H$ into —H in an aliphatic or an aromatic compound by heating with soda lime, e.g. $RCO_2Na + NaOH(s) \longrightarrow RH + Na_2CO_3$

3. (a) e.g. benzene, C_6H_6, with conc. HNO_3 + conc. $H_2SO_4 \longrightarrow$ nitrobenzene $C_6H_5NO_2$

(b) e.g. benzene, $C_6H_6 + SO_3$, in conc. H_2SO_4 (fuming sulphuric acid) $\longrightarrow$ benzenesulphonic acid, $C_6H_5SO_3H$

(c) e.g. 1° alcohol + $K_2Cr_2O_7$ + acid $\longrightarrow$ aldehyde $\longrightarrow$ carboxylic acid
e.g. 2° alcohol + $K_2Cr_2O_7$ + acid $\longrightarrow$ ketone
e.g. aromatic side-chain $\longrightarrow$ $—CO_2H$, e.g. $C_6H_5CH_3 + KMnO_4 + \text{acid} \longrightarrow C_6H_5CO_2H$

(d) hydrocarbon $\longrightarrow$ mixture of hydrocarbons with smaller molecules
e.g. propane passed over $Al_2O_3 + SiO_2$ at 450 °C:
$2CH_3CH_2CH_3 \longrightarrow CH_4 + CH_3CH{=}CH_2 + CH_2{=}CH_2 + H_2$

(e) e.g. benzene + Cl_2 ($AlCl_3$ catalyst) $\longrightarrow C_6H_5Cl + HCl$

4. (a) hydrogenation (H_2 + Ni catalyst) reduces C=C but not C=O,
e.g. $RCH{=}CHR' + H_2 \longrightarrow RCH_2CH_2R'$

(b) preparation of aromatic amines, e.g. $C_6H_5NO_2 \longrightarrow C_6H_5NH_2$

(c) $LiAlH_4$(ethoxyethane) reduces C=O, not C=C, e.g. ketone $\longrightarrow$ 2° alcohol, carboxylic acid or ester $\longrightarrow$ 1° alcohol, $RCl \longrightarrow RH$, $RCONH_2 \longrightarrow RCH_2NH_2$

(d) $NaBH_4$(aq) reduces C=O, not C=C, e.g. aldehyde $\longrightarrow$ 1° alcohol, ketone $\longrightarrow$ 2° alcohol

5. (a) Addition, e.g. $CH_2{=}CH_2 + Br_2 \longrightarrow CH_2Br{—}CH_2Br$
Substitution, e.g. $C_6H_6 + Br_2$ ($AlBr_3$ catalyst) $\longrightarrow C_6H_5Br + HBr$
With conc. NaOH(aq), Hofmann degradation: amide $RCONH_2 \longrightarrow$ amine RNH_2
$C_2H_5CONH_2 + Br_2 + 4OH^- \longrightarrow C_2H_5NH_2 + CO_3^{2-} + 2Br^- + 2H_2O$

(b) catalyst in Friedel-Crafts alkylation and acylation, e.g.
$C_6H_6 + C_2H_5Cl$ ($AlCl_3$ catalyst) $\longrightarrow C_6H_5C_2H_5 + HCl$
$C_6H_6 + CH_3COCl$ ($AlCl_3$ catalyst) $\longrightarrow C_6H_5COCH_3 + HCl$

(c) $NaNO_2$ + acid:
1° aliphatic amine > 10 °C $\longrightarrow$ 1° alcohol
1° aromatic amine < 10 °C $\longrightarrow$ diazonium compound, e.g. $C_6H_5N_2^+\,Cl^-$

(d) HCN is used to form hydroxynitriles from aldehydes and ketones. They are valuable intermediates in synthetic routes.
e.g. $RCHO + HCN \longrightarrow RCH(OH)CN$
$R_2CO + HCN \longrightarrow R_2C(OH)CN$
(In practice the route carbonyl compound $\longrightarrow$ hydrogen sulphite compound which with KCN $\longrightarrow$ cyanhydrin is preferred.

(e) Ni is used as a catalyst in addition of H_2 to the C=C bond, e.g. in the catalytic hydrogenation of liquid oils to solid fats.

(f) Decolourisation of $KMnO_4$(aq), alkaline, a weak oxidising agent, is used to test for a C=C double bond. A diol is formed, e.g. $RCH{=}CHR' \longrightarrow RCHOHCHOHR'$

(g) Ozonolysis: addition of ozone followed by reductive hydrolysis detects the position of a C=C bond, e.g.
$RCH{=}CHR'$ + (i) O_3 (ii) $Zn + CH_3CO_2H \longrightarrow RCHO + R'CHO$

6. (a) ethanol + sodium ethanoate. Reflux
$CH_3CO_2C_2H_5(l) + NaOH(aq) \longrightarrow CH_3CO_2Na(aq) + C_2H_5OH(aq)$

(b) butan-1-ol + sodium bromide. Reflux
$CH_3CH_2CH_2CH_2Br(l) + NaOH(aq) \longrightarrow CH_3CH_2CH_2CH_2OH(aq) + NaBr(aq)$

(c) sodium ethanoate + trichloromethane. Warm.
$CCl_3COCH_3(l) + NaOH(aq) \longrightarrow CHCl_3(l) + CH_3CO_2Na(aq)$

7. (a) Friedel-Crafts catalyst for alkylation and acylation of the aromatic ring. $AlCl_3$ is covalent and is a Lewis acid, able to accept a pair of electrons; see § 28.8.7.

(b) HCN forms addition compounds, hydroxynitriles, with carbonyl compounds. HCN is a weak acid partially dissociated in solution into H^+(aq) CN^-(aq). The reaction is a nucleophilic addition in which $C^{\delta+}$ of $>C^{\delta+}{=}O^{\delta-}$ is attacked by the CN^- ion.

(c) KOH(aq) is used in the hydrolysis of esters (including fats and oils), nitriles, amides and halogenoalkanes. It is completely ionised as K^+(aq) OH^-(aq). Hydrolysis involves a nucleophilic attack by OH^-(aq) on $C^{\delta+}$ of $—\overset{\delta+}{C}{=}\overset{\delta-}{O}$ (with O—R on the C) see § 33.13.1.

(d) $LiAlH_4$(in ethoxyethane solution) is a powerful reducing agent which reduces C=O but not C=C. e.g. aldehyde $\longrightarrow$ 1° alcohol, ketone $\longrightarrow$ 2° alcohol, carboxylic acid $\longrightarrow$ 1° alcohol, ester $RCO_2R' \longrightarrow$ two alcohols $RCH_2OH + R'OH$
$[AlH_4]^-$ attacks $C^{\delta+}$ of $C^{\delta+}{=}O^{\delta-}$ and adds H^- to become AlH_3.

Checkpoint 36.5 A: Functional groups and reaction mechanisms

1. (a) van der Waals forces of attraction exist between hydrocarbon molecules in petrol. Hydrogen bonds exist between H_2O molecules. No bonds form between hydrocarbon molecules and water molecules.

(b) The C—Halogen bond is polarised because halogens (excluding I) are more electronegative than carbon: $—C^{\delta+} \longrightarrow X^{\delta-}$. The δ+ C atom is attacked by nucleophiles such as OH^-.

(c) The π electrons of the $>C{=}C<$ bond interact with a Br_2 molecule, polarising the Br_2 molecule as $Br^{\delta+}—Br^{\delta-}$ (§ 27.8.5). In $—\overset{|}{C}—\overset{|}{C}—$ the electrons are σ electrons and much less easily polarised.

(d) In HO—C_6H_5 (phenol) the lone pairs of electrons on the O atom become delocalised with the π electron cloud of the ring, increasing the electron density in the ring and making it more reactive towards electrophiles, especially in the positions 2-, 4- and 6- to the —OH group. A more powerful electrophile, e.g. NO_2^+, is needed to react with benzene.

(e) In $CH_3—C^{\delta+}H_2—Cl^{\delta-}$ the C—Cl bond is polarised because Cl is more electronegative than C. The water molecule has two lone pairs: H—Ö—H which attack the δ+ C atom. In $CH_3—C^{\delta+}(=O^{\delta-})—Cl^{\delta-}$ the polar C=O group enhances the δ+ charge on the C atom, making it much more reactive towards electrophiles, e.g. H_2O.

2. (a) C_2H_5OH: addition reaction with excess alcohol at 140 °C gives ethyl hydrogensulphate, $C_2H_5OSO_3H$; elimination reaction with excess sulphuric acid at 170 °C gives ethene, C_2H_4.

C_6H_5OH: substitution reaction with conc. H_2SO_4 at r.t. gives benzenesulphonic acid, $C_6H_5SO_3H$.

(b) C_2H_5OH: PCl_5 reacts readily in the cold $\longrightarrow$ chloroethane + HCl(g)
C_6H_5OH: PCl_5 reacts slowly to give a poor yield of chlorobenzene, $C_6H_5Cl + HCl(g)$

(c) $CH_3(CH_2)_4CH_2Cl$: reflux with NaOH(aq) $\longrightarrow CH_3(CH_2)_4CH_2OH$
C_6H_5Cl: Heat with NaOH(aq), high pressure and high temperature $\longrightarrow C_6H_5ONa$

(d) $C_2H_5NH_2 + HNO_2(aq) \longrightarrow$ ethanol, $C_2H_5OH + N_2$
$C_6H_5NH_2 + HNO_2(aq) < 10\,°C \longrightarrow$ diazonium compound $C_6H_5N_2^+\,X^-$;
$>10\,° \longrightarrow$ phenol $C_6H_5OH + N_2(g)$

3. See *(a)* § 27.8.5 *(b)* § 26.4.8 *(c)* § 28.8.7 *(d)* § 29.9.1 *(e)* § 31.8.1
4. See *(a)* § 25.8.2 *(b)* § 25.8.2 *(c)* § 25.8.3 *(d)* § 31.7.5 *(e)* § 26.4.2
5. Sulphuric acid H—O, O / S / H—O, O (structure: $(HO)_2SO_2$) is a more polar reagent than H—O—H

Conc. H_2SO_4 adds to ethene to form ethyl hydrogensulphate,
CH_3-CH_2O, O / S / HO, O (structure: $CH_3CH_2OSO_2OH$)

(b) HCN is a weak acid:
$HCN(aq) \rightleftharpoons H^+(aq) + CN^-(aq)$
The addition of a base removes $H^+(aq)$ and moves the equilibrium towards the right, increasing $[CN^-(aq)]$. CN^- is the nucleophile that attacks the carbonyl group; see § 31.8.1.

(c) The ppt is CHI_3. I_2 substitutes on the C adjacent to the CO group:
$CH_3COCH_3 + I_2 \longrightarrow CI_3COCH_3$; with $OH^-(aq) \longrightarrow CHI_3 + CH_3CHO$
C_2H_5OH is oxidised by $I_2 \longrightarrow CH_3CHO$, then $\longrightarrow CI_3CHO$; with $OH^-(aq) \longrightarrow CHI_3 + HCHO$
$CH_3CH_2COCH_2CH_3$ and $CH_3CH_2CHOHCH_2CH_2OH$ cannot give CI_3CO^-.

(d) Nucleophiles, e.g. CN^-, attack the δ+ C atom in the carbonyl group. In

$$\overset{\delta+}{-C}=\overset{\delta-}{O}$$
O—H

the δ+ charge is decreased by a flow of electrons from the —OH group, and the carboxyl group is therefore not attacked by the nucleophiles which attack carbonyl compounds [see § 33.5].

6. *(a)* (i) phenolic hydroxyl group (ii) 1° alcohol group (iii) 2° aliphatic amino group
(b) (i) $Br_2(aq)$ decolourised $\longrightarrow$ white ppt of bromo-compound
(ii) with $PCl_5 \longrightarrow HCl(g)$
(c) Ar—C*(OH)(H)—C—

7. —NH_2: Diazotise ($NaNO_2 + HCl(aq) < 10\,°C$). Add phenol in NaOH(aq) $\longrightarrow$ azo dye
—CH=CH—: $Br_2(aq)$ decolourised without the evolution of HBr(g)
>CHBr: Reflux with NaOH(aq). Test the solution for $Br^-(aq)$: neutralise with $HNO_3(aq)$ and add $AgNO_3(aq)$. A yellow ppt of AgBr forms.
—CO_2H: Liberates CO_2 from Na_2CO_3.
To confirm, do a mixed melting point; find the melting point of a mixture of your product and a genuine sample of the compound. Alternatively, compare the UV or IR spectrum of your product with that of the compound.

Checkpoint 36.5 B: Draw your own conclusions

1. **A** = propanone CH_3COCH_3, **B** = propanal CH_3CH_2CHO
C = propan-1-ol $CH_3(CH_2)_2OH$, **D** = propan-2-ol $CH_3CH(OH)CH_3$,
D $\longrightarrow$ **A**: oxidation of a 2° alcohol $\longrightarrow$ ketone
C $\longrightarrow$ **B**: oxidation of 1° alcohol $\longrightarrow$ aldehyde
A and **B** are carbonyl compounds and form condensation compounds with DNP. **B**, an aldehyde, reduces $Ag^+(aq)$ to Ag, while **A**, a ketone, does not.
2. **A** is hydrolysed to **C**, which gives an acid on acidification, and **B** by refluxing with alkali. **C** is the sodium salt of the acid **E**. Since **B** reacts with KBr + conc. H_2SO_4 it must be an alcohol, and **A** must be an ester. The bromoalkane C_2H_5Br shows that **A** is an ethyl ester. The acid **E** is insoluble in water and therefore could be an aromatic acid. The $M_r = 150$ for **A** fits with ethyl benzoate. The compounds could be **A** = ethyl benzoate $C_6H_5CO_2C_2H_5$, **B** = ethanol, C_2H_5OH, **C** = sodium benzoate, $C_6H_5CO_2Na$, **D** = benzoic acid $C_6H_5CO_2H$.
3. **A** and **B** are soluble in $Na_2CO_3(aq)$; therefore they are carboxylic acids. Both **A** and **B** are reduced to the same compound therefore the isomerism arises from a C = C double bond and the isomers are *cis-trans* isomers. **A**, **B** and **C** must contain a benzene ring and a side-chain because they are oxidised to benzoic acid. **C** must be a carboxylic acid as it reacts with $Na_2CO_3(aq)$. From the formula $C_9H_8O_2$ for **A** and **B**, subtract C_6H_5 and CO_2H; this leaves C_2H_2.
A and **B** are *cis*- and *trans*-3-phenylpropenoic acid $C_6H_5CH{=}CHCO_2H$, **C** is 3-phenylpropanoic acid $C_6H_5CH_2CH_2CO_2H$, **D** is 3-phenylpropanoyl chloride $C_6H_5CH_2CH_2COCl$.
4. **P**, a crystalline solid with a fairly high melting temperature and a neutral solution, which forms salts with both acids and bases, could be an amino acid. **Q**, formed by decarboxylation, would then be an amine, as the smell and alkaline solution confirm. **R** is formed by treatment of **P** with $HNO_2(aq)$ which converts —NH_2 into —OH, therefore **R** must be a hydroxycarboxylic acid. **R** has $M_r = 76$. Subtracting 17 for —OH and 45 for —CO_2H leaves 14, allowing for CH_2. **P** is 2-aminoethanoic acid (glycine), $H_2NCH_2CO_2H$, **Q** is aminomethane/methylamine, CH_3NH_2, **R** is 2-hydroxyethanoic acid $HOCH_2CO_2H$.
5. The flame test shows that **A** is a sodium salt. The reaction with ethanoyl chloride indicates that **A** is a carboxylic acid salt and **B** is an acid anhydride, of formula $(RCO)_2O$. **B** has $M_r = 102$. Subtracting 72 for $(CO)_2O$ leaves 30, which allows for $(CH_3)_2$. **B** is ethanoic anhydride $(CH_3CO)_2O$ and **A** is sodium ethanoate CH_3CO_2Na.
C must be a base since it dissolves in acid but not in water. **D** must be the chloride of the base. Treatment of **C** with $HNO_2(aq)$ and phenol gives an azo dye, indicating that **C** is a 1° aromatic amine. **C** + $Br_2 \longrightarrow$ **E** with $M_r = 330$. Subtracting 240 for 3 Br leaves 90, allowing 16 for —NH_2 and 74 for C_6H_2—. **E** is 2,4,6-tribromophenylamine, $C_6H_2Br_3NH_2$, **C** is phenylamine, $C_6H_5NH_2$, **D** is phenylammonium chloride, $C_6H_5NH_3^+Cl^-$.
F(aq) is too weakly acidic to be a carboxylic acid because it does not react with Na_2CO_3. This suggests a phenol. Benzoylation of **F** substitutes —COC_6H_5 for —H. **G** has $M_r = 198$. Subtracting 198 for —COC_6H_5 leaves 93, indicating the phenolic group C_6H_5O—. **G** is $C_6H_5OCOC_6H_5$. **F** is C_6H_5OH.

6. **W** can be hydrolysed by alkali to give a bromide **X** – as shown by the yellow ppt of AgBr(s). **Y** gives a positive iodoform test, so it contains either CH_3CO— or CH_3CHOH— The fact that **Y** can be oxidised to **Z**, which gives a positive iodoform test, suggests that **Y** contains the group CH_3CHOH— and **Z** contains the group CH_3CO—. **Z** is an aldehyde, as shown by the DNP and $AgNO_3$ tests. If **Y** is a 2° alcohol, **W** = RR'CHBr. Subtracting 93 for CHBr from M_r = 123 leaves 30, which allows for $(CH_3)_2$; therefore **W** = $(CH_3)_2CHBr$, **X** = NaBr, **Y** = $(CH_3)_2CHOH$, **Z** = $(CH_3)_2CO$.
7. **A** seems to be an aromatic nitro compound, which is reduced to a 1° aromatic amine, e.g. $XC_6H_4NO_2 \longrightarrow XC_6H_4NH_2$. The formula $C_7H_7NO_2$ corresponds to $CH_3C_6H_4NO_2$. **B** would then be $CH_3C_6H_4NH_2$ (dissolves in acid). HNO_2(aq) converts —NH_2 into —OH, making **C** = $CH_3C_6H_4OH$ (violet colour with $FeCl_3$) and **D** = $CH_3C_6H_4OCH_3$, oxidised to **E** = $HO_2CC_6H_4OH + CH_3OH$. With soda lime, followed by acid **E** $\longrightarrow$ **F**, $C_6H_5OCH_3$.
8. **A** $\longrightarrow$ **B**, pungent-smelling gas, suggests ammonia or an amine. **A** is an ammonium salt or the salt of an amine. If **B** is an amine the reaction with HNO_2(aq) would give N_2(g) + alcohol. If **A** is the salt of an amine and it gives a white ppt with $AgNO_3$, this is a chloride and the compounds could be **A** = $C_2H_5NH_3^+ Cl^-$, **B** = $C_2H_5NH_2$.
9. *(a)* $FeCl_3 \longrightarrow$ violet colour; benzoyl chloride $\longrightarrow$ solid derivative
   (b) In $H_2NCHRCO_2H$, R = $HOI_2C_6H_2OC_6H_4CH_2$—; amino acid, forms crystals, has a zwitterion, moves towards + or – electrode in electrophoresis, depending on pH, shows reactions of —NH_2 group and reactions of —CO_2H group.
   (c) unreactive; see § 29.10
10. **H** can be oxidised to **I** and then further oxidised to **J**, suggesting alcohol $\longrightarrow$ aldehyde $\longrightarrow$ carboxylic acid. All **H**, **I** and **J** have acidic solutions and also contain a group which can be oxidised by MnO_4^-(aq); they could contain —CO_2H and also —OH. **I** is a carbonyl compound, and, since it can be oxidised, it is an aldehyde. The formulae of **H** and **I** contain 3 O atoms, therefore **H** could be HO_2CCH_2OH, **I** could be HO_2CCHO, **J** = HO_2CCO_2H.

Questions on Chapter 36

1. *(a)* (i) Add Benedict's reagent and warm. Propanal reduces Cu^{2+} to a reddish ppt of Cu_2O. Propanone does not react. (Alternatives are Fehling's solution and Tollens' reagent.)
   (ii) Add water. Propanoyl chloride fumes to give hydrogen chloride and propanoic acid, while 1-chloropropane does not react.
   (iii) Add aqueous sodium carbonate. Benzoic acid reacts with the formation of carbon dioxide. Phenol does not react.
   (iv) Add aqueous sodium hydroxide and warm. Ethanamide gives ammonia and sodium ethanoate. Ethylamine does not react.
   (b) Benzoic acid is a stronger acid than phenol. Dissolve the mixture in aqueous sodium hydroxide. Pass CO_2 through the solution to form phenol and sodium benzoate. Pour into a separating funnel. Add ethoxyethane and shake. Phenol passes into the ethoxyethane layer. Separate the layers. Dry the ethoxyethane layer and distil off the solvent (in a fume cupboard and with care because it is flammable) to leave phenol. To the aqueous layer add dilute hydrochloric acid to liberate benzoic acid. Recrystallise from water.
2. *(a)* $CH_3CHO + HCN(g) \longrightarrow CH_3CHOHCN$ (or add $NaHSO_3$ to make $CH_3CHOHSO_3Na$ and then add NaCN) Then reflux with conc. hydrochloric acid $\longrightarrow$ $CH_3CHOHCO_2H$
   (b) ethanoic acid $CH_3CO_2H + SOCl_2$ (or use PCl_5) $\longrightarrow$ ethanoyl chloride, CH_3COCl
   $C_6H_5NH_2 + CH_3COCl$ react readily at r.t. $\longrightarrow$ $CH_3CONHC_6H_5$
   (c) Boil $C_6H_5CH_3$, and pass Cl_2 through in sunlight or UV $\longrightarrow C_6H_5CH_2Cl$
   Then reflux with NaOH(aq) $\longrightarrow C_6H_5CH_2OH$
   (d) $C_6H_5NH_2$ with $NaNO_2$(aq), HCl, <5°C $\longrightarrow$ $C_6H_5N_2^+Cl^-$
   Add KI(aq) to the diazonium compound, warm $\longrightarrow C_6H_5I$
   (e) $C_6H_6 + CH_3Br + AlBr_3$ (Friedel–Crafts) $\longrightarrow C_6H_5CH_3$. Then oxidise with $KMnO_4$ + acid $\longrightarrow C_6H_5CO_2H$
   (f) $C_6H_5COCH_3 + KMnO_4$, acid $\longrightarrow C_6H_5CO_2H$
   Then add CH_3OH + conc. $H_2SO_4 \longrightarrow C_6H_5CO_2CH_3$
   (g) $CH_3CH_2CH_2OH + Al_2O_3$, heat $\longrightarrow CH_3CH{=}CH_2$
   Then conc. $H_2SO_4 \longrightarrow CH_3CH(OSO_2OH)CH_3$ and boil with water $\longrightarrow CH_3CHOHCH_3$
3. *(a)* **A**: $Cl_2 + AlCl_3$
   B: $CH_3Br + AlBr_3$ (or $CH_3Cl + AlCl_3$)
   C: Chlorine. Pass Cl_2 into methylbenzene under reflux.
   D: Chlorine. Sunlight or UV
   E: $KMnO_4$ + acid. Reflux.
   F: conc. HNO_3 + conc. H_2SO_4, 30 °C, separate from the 4-nitro compound
   (b) (i) $C_6H_5CH_2OH$ phenylmethanol (benzyl alcohol),
   (ii) $C_6H_5CH_2CN$ phenylethanenitrile
   (iii) $C_6H_5CH_2NH_2$ phenylmethylamine
4. **A** = $CH_3CHOHCH_2CO_2H$, **B** = $CH_3CH{=}CHCO_2C_2H_5$
   C = $\left(\!\!-\underset{CH_3}{\underset{|}{CH}}-\underset{CO_2C_2H_5}{\underset{|}{CH}}-\!\!\right)_n$
   D = $CH_3CHClCH_2COCl$, **E** = $CH_3CHClCH_2CO_2H$
5. (i) Add DNP to each of **A–E**; **A** and **B** give coloured ppts. Add ammoniacal silver nitrate to **A** and **B**; **A** gives a silver mirror; **B** does not.
   (ii) To each of **C–E**, add aqueous sodium hydroxide and warm. **D** gives ammonia.
   (iii) To each of **C–E**, add hydrochloric acid, warm and cool. **E** gives a white crystalline solid.
   (iv) This leaves **C** to identify. Add red litmus paper to NaOH(aq). The paper turns blue. Add **C**. The paper turns purple and then red.
6. e.g. chlorination of methane [§ 26.4.7], polymerisation of alkenes [§ 27.8.11]
7. e.g. Friedel–Crafts reactions [§ 28.8.4–7]
8. e.g. hydrolysis of halogenoalkanes [§§ 29.8.3, 29.9.1], reaction of carbonyl compounds with HCN [§ 31.8]
9. *(a)* (i) **A**: $CH_3CH_2CH_2CH_2Br$ or $CH_3CH_2CHBrCH_3$; positional isomerism
   (ii) **B**: $CH_3CH_2CH{=}CH_2$ or $CH_3CH{=}CHCH_3$; structural isomerism
   (iii) 1-bromobutane and 2-bromobutane; but-1-ene and but-2-ene
   (iv) **C**: $CH_3(CH_2)_3CN$, **D**: $CH_3(CH_2)_4NH_2$
   (v) Amount of HCl = $57.25 \times 10^{-3} \times 0.2000$ = 0.01147 mol therefore M_r = 87.2
   (vi) pH ≈ 5 (titration of a weak base against a strong acid)
   (b) I $CH_3CO(CH_2)_2CH_3$; positive iodoform test
   Add I_2 + NaOH(aq) or NaIO(aq), and warm. A yellow ppt of CHI_3 forms.
   II Add $ZnCl_2$(aq) + conc. HCl. The 2° alcohol gives a ppt in 5 minutes; the 1° alcohol takes much longer; see Table 30.1.
   III Add $NaHCO_3$. The carboxylic acid liberates CO_2. The alcohol does not react.
   IV Add $NaNO_2$ + dil. HCl(aq) < 10 °C. The aromatic amine $C_6H_5NH_2$ is diazotised. Add more $C_6H_5NH_2 \longrightarrow$ azo dye.

10. *(a)* (i) 1 KCN(ethanolic), reflux 2. NaOH(aq)
(ii) I. nucleophilic substitution, III nucleophilic addition
(b) (i) $CH_3CH_2CH_2OH$, a 1° alcohol is oxidised by acidified sodium dichromate in the cold to an aldehyde. $CH_3CHOHCH_3$ is a 2° alcohol, oxidised to a ketone. For the Lucas test see Table 30.1.
(ii) CH_3COCH_3 with DNP gives an orange crystalline ppt. $CH_2=CHCH_2OH$ decolourises Br_2 (aq) and is oxidised by $K_2Cr_2O_7$, acid.
(iii) $CH_3CH_2COCH_2CH_3$, a ketone, is not easily oxidised by $K_2Cr_2O_7$, acid. The aldehyde $CH_3(CH_2)_3CHO$ is readily oxidised by $K_2Cr_2O_7$, acid and reduces Tollens' reagent (ammoniacal silver nitrate) to silver and Fehling's solution (copper(II) sulphate etc.) to red copper(I) oxide.
(iv) $CH_3CH_2CO_2H$, an acid, liberates CO_2 from $NaHCO_3$. The ketone does not. CH_3COCH_2OH is a ketone, giving an orange ppt with DNP and also an alcohol, being oxidised by $K_2Cr_2O_7$, acid. The acid gives neither of these reactions.

11. *(a)* (i) $C_6H_5CH_2Br \xrightarrow{1} C_6H_5CH_2CN \xrightarrow{2} C_6H_5CH_2CH_2NH_2$
1. Reflux with KCN(in ethanol) 2. Reduce with $LiAlH_4$ (in ethoxyethane)
(ii) 1-bromo-1-C(CH₃)₃-cyclopentane $\xrightarrow{1}$ 1-C(CH₃)₃-cyclopentene $\xrightarrow{2}$ $OHC(CH_2)_3COC(CH_3)_3$
1. Reflux with KOH(ethanolic) 2. *either* (i) ozone (ii) Zn + ethanoic acid *or* hot conc. $KMnO_4$
(iii) $C_6H_5COCl \xrightarrow{1} C_6H_5CONH_2 \xrightarrow{2} C_6H_5NH_2$
1. NH_3, room temperature 2. Br_2 + conc. NaOH(aq)
(iv) cyclohexanol $\xrightarrow{1}$ cyclohexene $\xrightarrow{2}$ cyclohexane-1,2-diol
1. conc. H_2SO_4 2. alkaline $KMnO_4$
(b) methylenecyclohexane ($=CH_2$) + $H^{\delta+}—Br^{\delta-}$ ⟶ 1-methylcyclohexyl cation (CH_3, $^+$) Br^- ⟶ 1-bromo-1-methylcyclohexane (CH_3, Br)
(c) (i) 4-methylpentan-2-ol
(ii) 2,5,5-trimethylcyclohex-1-ene-3-one

12. *(a)* (i) Add Br_2 (in organic solvent): no reaction with benzene; decolourised by cyclohexene.
(ii) Add $NaIO_3$(aq), warm. $C_5H_9CHOHCH_3$ is oxidised to $C_5H_9COCH_3$ which gives a yellow ppt of iodoform CHI_3. The alcohol $C_4H_9CHOHCH_2CH_3$ does not react.
(iii) Add DNP. The ketone $C_2H_5COCH_2OC_2H_5$ gives a yellow ppt. The ester does not react.
(iv) Add Tollens' reagent (ammoniacal $AgNO_3$), warm. The aldehyde $CH_3(CH_2)_3CHO$ gives a silver mirror. The ketone is not oxidised.
(b) **J** = H_2NOH hydroxylamine
K = bromine water
L = $LiAlH_4$ (in ethoxyethane)
M = $CH_3CH_2CH_2CN$
N = $C_6H_5SO_3Na$

13. *(a)* (i) One group is replaced by another group. The attacking reagent has an unpaired electron, e.g. $C_2H_6 + Br_2$ in UV. The first step is $Br_2 \longrightarrow 2Br\cdot$
(ii) Again one group is replaced by another. The attacking reagent has either a negative charge or a lone pair of electrons which seek out regions of positive charge in the other reactant.
In $CH_3CH_2Br + NH_3$, $:NH_3$ attacks the $C^{\delta+}$ atom in $C_2H_5—C^{\delta+}—Br^{\delta-}$.
(iii) A small molecule is lost from a larger molecule or between two reacting molecules, e.g.
$CH_3CH_2Br \longrightarrow CH_2{=}CH_2 + HBr$
(iv) Addition of oxygen or removal of hydrogen or removal of electrons from a species, e.g.
$CH_3CH_2OH + 2[O] \longrightarrow CH_3CO_2H + H_2O$
One O atom is added and two H are removed.
(v) Reaction between an alcohol and a carboxylic acid with elimination of H_2O, e.g.
$CH_3CO_2H + CH_3CH_2OH \longrightarrow CH_3CO_2CH_2CH_3 + H_2O$
(b) Pass with H_2 over Ni catalyst.
(c) $CH_3—C(H){=}O$
(d) $CH_3CH_2CH_2OH + KBr + H_2SO_4 \longrightarrow CH_3CH_2CH_2Br$; 1-bromopropane
$CH_3CH_2CH_2Br + NH_3$, heat in sealed tube $\longrightarrow CH_3CH_2CH_2NH_2$

14. *(a)* **W** = butan-2-ol, **Y** = $CH_3CH_2COCH_3$,
Z = $CH_3CH_2C(CH_3)(CN)OH$
Z has a chiral C atom and shows optical isomerism.
(b) (i) Pass vapour over heated alumina or distil with excess conc. H_2SO_4 at 140 °C.
$CH_3CH_2CH(OH)—CH_3$ + $HO—SO_2—OH$
$CH_3CH_2CH(CH_3)—O—SO_2—OH + H_2O \longrightarrow$
$CH_3CH{=}CHCH_3 + H_2SO_4$
(ii) $CH_3CH_2CH{=}CH_2$ but-1-ene
$CH_3CH_2CH(CH_3)—O—SO_2—OH \longrightarrow CH_3CH_2CH{=}CH_2 + H_2SO_4$
(c) $LiAlH_4$ (ethoxyethane solution)
(d) Addition: two molecules react to form one. Nucleophilic addition is addition of a nucleophile, a reagent with a lone pair of electrons on one of its atoms, e.g. O, N, which it uses to form a coordinate bond to another atom.
The carbonyl group is polarised. CN^- is a nucleophile: $[:C{\equiv}N:]^-$ which bonds to the $C^{\delta+}$ atom of the carbonyl group.

$(CH_3CH_2)(CH_3)C^{\delta+}{=}O^{\delta-} + CN^- \longrightarrow (CH_3CH_2)(CH_3)C(CN)—O^- \xrightarrow{H^+} (CH_3CH_2)(CH_3)C(CN)OH$

15. *(a)* Formula = $C_4H_{10}O$. **K** is oxidised to an acid therefore it is an aldehyde or an alcohol. The formula $C_4H_{10}O$ fits an alcohol, not an aldehyde. **K** could be $CH_3(CH_2)_2CH_2OH$, butan-1-ol and **J** could be $CH_3CH_2CHOHCH_3$, butan-2-ol, which is oxidised to a ketone. Then **H**, which does not have the same functional group as **J** and **K**, must be an ether, $C_2H_5OC_2H_5$, ethoxyethane.

(b) (i) **J**, $CH_3CH_2C^*HOHCH_3$, has a chiral C atom and has optical isomers:

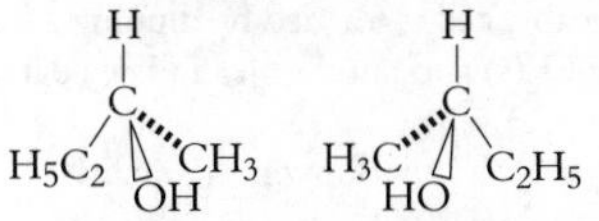

H, H_5C_2, CH_3, OH on C; H, H_3C, C_2H_5, HO on C

(ii) $CH_3CH_2CHOHCH_3 \longrightarrow CH_3CH{=}CHCH_3 + H_2O$

cis-trans isomers, **L** and **M**

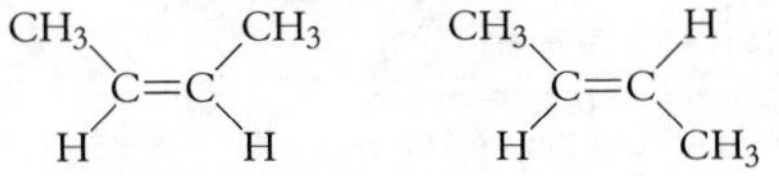

CH_3, CH_3 / C=C / H, H — *cis*-isomer

CH_3, H / C=C / H, CH_3 — *trans*-isomer

(c) With NaOH(aq), ethanol has no reaction;
phenol ⟶ sodium phenoxide, C_6H_5ONa
With diazonium compounds, ethanol has no reaction;
phenol ⟶ azo dye
Substitution in the benzene ring: phenol; substitute $—NO_2$, $—SO_3H$, —Cl, —Br, —I, —R, —COR; see § 30.11, Figure 30.11B and Table 30.2.

16. *(a)* See §§ 3.8, 3.9.

(b) M_r of $CH_2O = 30 \Rightarrow$ formulae are CH_2O, $C_2H_4O_2$ and $C_3H_6O_3$.

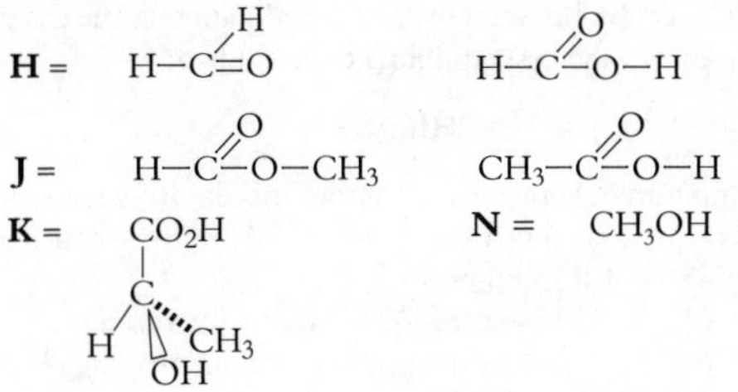

H = H–C(H)=O   H–C(=O)–O–H

J = H–C(=O)–O–CH_3 CH_3–C(=O)–O–H

K = CO_2H, H, CH_3, OH on C   **N** = CH_3OH

(c) See § 30.4.3.

SYNOPTIC QUESTIONS

PHYSICAL CHEMISTRY

1. The reaction between hydrogen and iodine in the gas phase was one of the first equilibria to be studied:

$$H_2(g) + I_2(g) \rightleftharpoons 2HI(g)$$

A mixture of known initial amounts of hydrogen and iodine was equilibrated in a sealed tube at 700 K, the mixture being rapidly cooled and then analysed.

(a) (i) Write an expression for K_c for the reaction. **1**

(ii) Explain why the reaction mixture was *rapidly* cooled. **1**

(iii) The mixture was analysed by breaking the tube before analysis in a solution of potassium iodide, in which the iodine dissolves; this can then be titrated with sodium thiosulphate solution, $Na_2S_2O_3$. The titration reaction is

$$2S_2O_3^{2-}(aq) + I_2(aq) \longrightarrow S_4O_6^{2-}(aq) + 2I^-(aq)$$

An equilibrium mixture formed from an initial mixture of hydrogen and iodine in **equal** amount in a vessel of volume 100 cm^3 was treated as above. The iodine solution produced required 20.0 cm^3 of 0.500 mol dm^{-3} sodium thiosulphate solution for complete reaction.
Given that the equilibrium constant K_c for the reaction at 700 K is 54.0, find the equilibrium concentration of hydrogen iodide in mol dm^{-3}. **5**

(b) The kinetics of the reaction between hydrogen and iodine can be investigated by reacting various known initial amounts of hydrogen and iodine, and finding the concentration of iodine at various times.

(i) The iodine concentration could be found by rapid cooling and titration as suggested earlier. Suggest why this is likely to cause errors in the determination of concentration, and outline another technique which would be more suitable in this case. **3**

(ii) The results from several experiments designed to find the rate equation for the reaction are given below. Find the order of reaction with respect to each reactant, and hence write the rate equation.

Initial $[I_2]$ /mol dm^{-3}	Initial $[H_2]$ /mol dm^{-3}	Relative initial rate
0.001	0.001	1
0.003	0.001	3
0.001	0.004	4

4

(iii) Explain why rate equations cannot be written from the stoichiometric (chemical) equation for a reaction, but have to be determined experimentally. **2**

(iv) Which molecules are involved in the rate-determining step of this reaction? Justify your answer in terms of the rate equation. **2**

18 *(L)(AL)*

2. *(a)* A lead–acid rechargeable cell is formed by dipping a lead plate coated with $PbO_2(s)$ and another lead plate coated with $PbSO_4(s)$ in $H_2SO_4(aq)$.

(i) You are provided with the following standard reduction potentials at 298 K.

	$E^\ominus$/V
$2H_2O(l) + 2e^- \rightleftharpoons H_2(g) + 2OH^-(aq)$	−0.83
$PbSO_4(s) + 2e^- \rightleftharpoons Pb(s) + SO_4^{2-}(aq)$	−0.36
$Pb^{2+}(aq) + 2e^- \rightleftharpoons Pb(s)$	−0.13
$O_2(g) + 4H^+(aq) + 4e^- \rightleftharpoons 2H_2O(l)$	+1.23
$PbO_2(s) + SO_4^{2-}(aq) + 4H^+(aq) + 2e^- \rightleftharpoons PbSO_4(s) + 2H_2O(l)$	+1.69

(I) Write half-equations for the reaction at the anode and at the cathode of the cell.

(II) Write the overall equation for the electrochemical reaction and hence determine the standard electromotive force (e.m.f.) of the cell.

(ii) Write the cell diagram in accordance with the IUPAC convention.

(iii) Explain why

(I) the voltage of the cell drops upon the discharge;

(II) the cell is rechargeable. **8**

(b) Even though the partition coefficient of ethanoic acid between water and 2-methylpropan-1-ol is 3.05 at 298 K. 2-methylpropan-1-ol is still used to extract ethanoic acid from aqueous solutions.
Calculate the efficiency of ethanoic acid extraction (in terms of %) at 298 K by shaking 100 cm^3 of a 0.50 M aqueous solution of ethanoic acid with

(i) 200 cm^3 of 2-methylpropan-1-ol;

(ii) two successive portions of 100 cm^3 of 2-methylpropan-1-ol.

Decide whether (i) or (ii) is the better extraction method. Explain your answer. **6**

(c) Sketch the expected mass spectrum for a gas sample having the composition : N_2 78%, O_2 21% and CO_2 1%.
(You only need to consider the major isotope of each element.)

3 *(HK)(AL)*

3. *(a)* The figure shows the variation of ΔG with temperature for three reactions relevant to the extraction of iron from iron oxide.

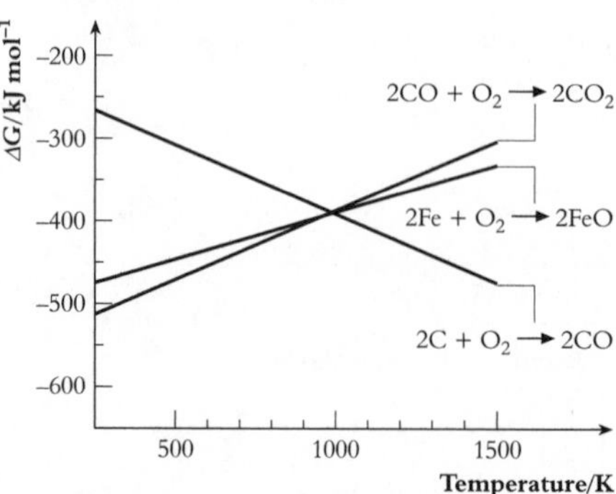

(i) Use the figure to estimate values of ΔG at 800 K for the following reactions.

$2C + O_2 \longrightarrow 2CO$
$2CO + O_2 \longrightarrow 2CO_2$
$2Fe + O_2 \longrightarrow 2FeO$ 3

(ii) Calculate the values of ΔG for the following reactions at 800 K.
$FeO + C \longrightarrow CO + Fe$
$FeO + CO \longrightarrow CO_2 + Fe$ 3

(iii) Use the values obtained in *(a)*(ii) to explain why carbon monoxide, rather than carbon, acts as the reducing agent at 800 K. 2

(iv) Use the figure to estimate the minimum temperature at which carbon becomes capable of reducing iron oxide to iron. 1

(v) Use the relevant equation given in *(a)*(ii) to explain why the reduction of iron oxide to iron using carbon as the reducing agent results in an increase in the entropy of the system. 2

(b) The table shows some values for standard electrode potentials.

Electrode reaction	$E^\ominus/V$
$Fe^{2+}(aq) + 2e^- \rightleftharpoons Fe(s)$	−0.44
$H^+(aq) + e^- \rightleftharpoons \frac{1}{2}H_2(g)$	0.00

An electrochemical cell was set up by connecting the two electrode systems whose standard electrode potential values are given in the table.

(i) Give the emf of the cell. 1
(ii) State which would be the positive electrode. 1
(iii) Write an equation to show the overall reaction in the cell. 1
(iv) Write down the cell diagram that represents the overall reaction in the cell. 2
(v) Give the name of an instrument that could be used to measure the emf of the cell. 1

17 *(AEB)(AL)* 1998

4. *(a)* Hydrogen gas and iodine vapour combine together to give hydrogen iodide in a reversible reaction. The reaction may be represented by the equation below.

$H_2(g) + I_2(g) \rightleftharpoons 2HI(g)$

(i) At equilibrium, the partial pressures of the gases at 600 K are:

Gas	Partial pressure/kPa
H_2	2.5
I_2	22.5
HI	90.0

Write the expression for the equilibrium constant, K_p, for this reaction and calculate its value at the temperature concerned. 3

(ii) At a temperature of 400 K, K_p for the reaction has a value of 200.
State what you can deduce from the value of K_p about the **position** of equilibrium at this temperature. 1

(iii) Calculate the enthalpy change for the forward reaction producing hydrogen iodide, using the bond energy values given.

Bond	Energy/kJ mol^{-1}
H—H	436
I—I	151
H—I	298

2

(b) Iodine is used in a redox titration technique to determine the percentage of sulphur dioxide, which is used as a preservative, in an orange drink. The equation for the redox reaction is given below.

$SO_2(aq) + I_2(aq) + 2H_2O(l) \longrightarrow 2HI(aq) + H_2SO_4(aq)$

Calculate the concentration in g dm^{-3} of sulphur dioxide present in the orange drink if 39.0 cm^3 of 0.050 mol dm^{-3} iodine solution reacts with 250 cm^3 of orange drink. 3

(c) Copy and complete the table, in each case state what is **observed** and give the formula of the lead compound formed when a solution containing lead(II) ions, Pb^{2+}, reacts with a solution containing iodide ions and with a separate solution containing sulphate ions.

Ion	Observation	Formula of lead compound
iodide		
sulphate		

2

11 *(WJEC)(AL)*

5. This question concerns the reaction

$H_2(g) + I_2(g) \rightleftharpoons 2HI(g)$

which, even at high temperatures, is slow.
Data: Bond energies in kJ mol^{-1}

H—H	436
H—I	299
I—I	151
Cl—Cl	242
H—Cl	431

(a) (i) Calculate ΔH for the reaction between hydrogen and iodine. 2
(ii) Sketch an energy level diagram for this reaction. 2

(b) Indicate on your sketch
(i) ΔH for the reaction
(ii) the activation energy for the forward reaction ($E_{a(F)}$)
(iii) the activation energy for the reverse reaction ($E_{a(R)}$) 3

(c) For the analogous reaction for the formation of hydrogen chloride

$H_2(g) + Cl_2(g) \longrightarrow 2HCl(g)$

suggest how you would expect the activation energy of the forward reaction to compare with that shown for the formation of HI. Give a reason for your answer. 2

(d) The reaction for the formation of hydrogen iodide does not go to completion but reaches an equilibrium.
(i) Write an expression for the equilibrium constant, K_c, for this reaction. 1
(ii) A mixture of 1.9 mol of H_2 and 1.9 mol of I_2 was prepared and allowed to reach equilibrium in a closed vessel of 250 cm^3 capacity at 700 °C. The resulting equilibrium mixture was found to contain 3.0 mol of HI.
Calculate the value of K_c at this temperature. 3

(e) The rate expression for the forward reaction between hydrogen and iodine is

Rate = $k[H_2][I_2]$

(i) What is the order of the reaction with respect to iodine? 1
(ii) When 0.10 mol of each of H_2 and I_2 were mixed at 700 °C in a vessel of 500 cm^3 capacity, the initial rate of formation of HI was found to be 1.5×10^{-5} mol dm^{-3} s^{-1}.
Calculate a value for k at 700 °C, stating the units. 3

17 *(L)(AS/AL)*

6. *(a)* (i) The decomposition of colourless dinitrogen tetroxide into brown nitrogen dioxide obeys the equation

$$N_2O_4(g) \rightleftharpoons 2NO_2(g)$$

You are provided with a sealed flask containing a mixture of N_2O_4 and NO_2. You are also given a large beaker of hot water. Using only this equipment, describe a simple experiment that might enable you to establish whether the decomposition of $N_2O_4(g)$ is exothermic or endothermic. Explain briefly the reasoning behind the experiment. **3**

(ii) 0.100 mol of pure N_2O_4 in a 1.00 dm^3 cell is completely converted into NO_2 gas at 600 K. Calculate the pressure of NO_2 in the cell.

$[R = 8.31\ J\ mol^{-1}\ K^{-1}, \quad 1\ m^3 = 10^3\ dm^3.]$ **3**

(iii) Name the nitrogen-containing species which is generated by the acid mixture in the nitration of benzene. Briefly explain why the species is referred to as an **electrophile**. **2**

(b) (i) Explain briefly how the **size** and **sign** of $E^\ominus$ for a metal ion/metal system ($M^{n+}/M(s)$) is related to the method of extraction of metal M. **2**

(ii) The following half-reactions:

$$NiO_2(s) + 2H_2O(l) + 2e^- \longrightarrow Ni(OH)_2(s) + 2OH^-(aq) \quad E^\ominus (298\ K) = +0.49\ V$$

$$Cd(OH)_2(s) + 2e^- \longrightarrow Cd(s) + 2OH^-(aq) \quad E^\ominus (298\ K) = -0.81\ V$$

are utilised in nickel oxide/cadmium batteries. Write half equations representing the reactions that occur at each electrode. Write a **balanced** equation for the overall battery reaction, and calculate the standard cell potential of the battery at 298 K. **4**

(c) (i) Explain briefly why the elements Ti-Cu possess high melting temperatures. **2**

(ii) Aqueous solutions containing Cr^{3+}, Fe^{2+}, Fe^{3+} and Cu^{2+} ions form coloured precipitates with hydroxide ions. State the colours of these precipitates, and write ionic equations for the precipitation reactions involving Cr^{3+} and Fe^{2+}. **4**

20 *(WJEC)(AL)*

7. *(a)* The reaction between nitrogen and hydrogen is given by the following equation:

$$N_2 + 3H_2 \rightleftharpoons 2NH_3$$

(i) Write an expression for the equilibrium constant, K_c, for the reaction. **1**

(ii) Nitrogen and hydrogen were mixed at 450 °C and the system allowed to reach equilibrium. The equilibrium concentrations of nitrogen, hydrogen and ammonia were 0.600, 1.80 and 0.800 mol dm^{-3} respectively. Calculate the value of the equilibrium constant, K_c, at 450 °C and state its units.

(b) When ammonia is dissolved in water the following reaction occurs:

$$NH_3(g) + H_2O(l) \rightleftharpoons NH_4^+(aq) + OH^-(aq)$$

The pH of a 0.110 mol dm^{-3} solution of ammonia is 11.1 at 25 °C. The value of the ionic product for water, K_w, is 1.00×10^{-14} $mol^2\ dm^{-6}$ at 25 °. Calculate

(i) the hydrogen ion concentration, **1**

(ii) the concentration of OH^- ions. **2**

(c) (i) Explain why it is that a solution containing ethanoic acid and sodium ethanoate acts as a buffer solution. **3**

(ii) 25.00 cm^3 of a solution of ethanoic acid required 21.20 cm^3 of aqueous sodium hydroxide for neutralisation. State how you would use this information to prepare a buffer solution containing equal concentrations (mol dm^{-3}) of ethanoic acid and sodium ethanoate. Explain your method. **3**

(d) State the reagents and conditions used to carry out the conversions (i) and (ii) below. Give the type of reaction in each case.

(i) Propan-1-ol into propanoic acid. **2**

(ii) Sodium propanoate into ethane. **2**

16 *(WJEC)(AL)*

8. *(a)* Hydrogen reacts with iodine according to the *overall* stoichiometric equation

$$H_2(g) + I_2(g) \rightleftharpoons 2HI(g) \qquad \Delta H^\ominus = -9\ kJ$$

The rate expression for the *forward* reaction is

$$Rate = k[H_2(g)][I_2(g)]$$

(i) For the forward reaction, state

I. the **order of reaction** with respect to hydrogen,

II. the **overall order** of the hydrogen/iodine reaction. **1**

(ii) State whether or not the rate expression for the forward reaction is **consistent** with the hydrogen/iodine reaction as occurring in a one step process. Briefly explain your answer. **1**

(iii) State in what way you would expect the equilibrium constant for the hydrogen/iodine reaction to change with temperature. Briefly explain your answer. **1**

(iv) **Name** the term in the rate expression for the forward reaction which is dependent upon temperature, and state its units. **1**

(b) (i) State what is meant by the term **relative atomic mass** of an element.

(ii) Explain **briefly** how mass spectrometers separate gaseous ions of different mass. **1**

(iii) A mass spectrometer in which it is suspected that air is entering through a leak, gave an intense peak at m/e = 28 and a less intense peak at m/e = 14.

I. What species are likely to have produced these peaks?

II. Write an equation showing how the species with m/e = 28 is formed in the spectrometer chamber. **2**

(c) (i) In the uranium radioactive decay series, ${}^{210}_{83}Bi$ decays by beta emission to isotope **X** which then decays by alpha emission to isotope **Y**. Write the atomic and mass numbers of isotopes **X** and **Y** in a copy of the table below. By referring to the Periodic Table, write the **symbols** for the elements possessing isotopes **X** and **Y**.

	Atomic number	Mass number	Symbol for element
X			
Y			

3

(ii) I. Explain why radioisotopes with short half-lives may be more harmful than those with long half-lives.

II. Strontium is in the same group in the Periodic Table as calcium. Why does radioactive strontium pose a hazard to the milk industry? **2**

13 *(WJEC)(AL)*

9. Consider the equilibrium

$N_2O_4(g) \rightleftharpoons 2NO_2(g)$

(a) (i) Write an expression for K_c, indicating the units. **2**

(ii) 1 mol of dinitrogen tetroxide, N_2O_4, was introduced into a vessel of volume 10.0 dm^3 at a temperature of 70 °C. At equilibrium 50% had dissociated. Calculate K_c. **4**

(iii) Using the following data calculate the enthalpy change for the forward reaction.

	$\Delta H_f^{\ominus}$ /kJ mol^{-1}
N_2O_4	+9.70
NO_2	+33.9

2

(iv) If the same experiment is carried out at 100 °C, state qualitatively, giving your reasons, how the equilibrium composition will change. **2**

(b) Explain what you would do to increase the degree of dissociation of $N_2O_4(g)$ at constant temperature. **2**

(c) What is the effect of a catalyst on the following:

(i) the value of K_c; **1**

(ii) the equilibrium position; **1**

(iii) the rate of attainment of equilibrium? **1**

(d) Suggest why the reaction

$N_2 + 2O_2 \longrightarrow 2NO_2$ **2**

is not a very useful method of making NO_2.

17 (*L*)(*AS*/*AL*)

10. The six graphs below show some general ways in which one property might vary as another is altered (as, for example, the volume of a gas which alters as the pressure changes). In answering parts (a) and (b) below, base the sketch graphs you draw on any of these general shapes that are relevant.

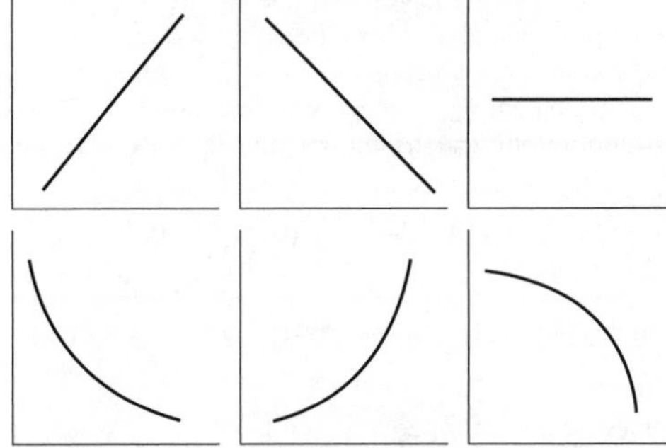

(a) In the reaction of 1 mol of hydrogen with oxygen to form steam ($\Delta H^{\ominus} = -242$ kJ mol^{-1}, $\Delta S^{\ominus} = -44$ J K^{-1} mol^{-1}), the free energy change ($\Delta G^{\ominus}$) and the equilibrium constant do not alter in the same direction when the temperature is increased.
Explain why this is so and sketch graphs with labelled axes to illustrate your answer. **5**

(b) The reaction of 1 mol of sulphur dioxide with oxygen to form sulphur trioxide ($\Delta H^{\ominus} = -100$ kJ mol^{-1}) is used in the Contact Process for the manufacture of sulphuric acid. The yield can be altered by changing the temperature or the pressure.
Using sketch graphs with labelled axes, show how separate changes in temperature and pressure affect

(i) the % yield of the process.

(ii) the equilibrium constant.

Justify the choice of graphs you make.
What other measure can be taken to improve the overall efficiency of this process? **6**

11 (*NEAB*)(*AL*)

11. *(a)* Describe the different modes of action of heterogeneous and homogeneous catalysis, giving **one** example of each type. **6**

(b) (i) Explain, in qualitative terms, the effect of ionic charge and of ionic radius on the numerical magnitude of a lattice energy.

(ii) The lattice energy of copper(II) oxide can be found using a Born Haber cycle.
Write equations, including state symbols, which correspond to

(1) the enthalpy change of formation of copper(II) oxide,

(2) the lattice energy of copper(II) oxide,

(3) the first ionisation energy of copper. **4**

(iii) Use the data below to construct a Born Haber cycle and hence calculate a value of the lattice energy of copper(II) oxide.

Enthalpy change	**/kJ mol^{-1}**
atomisation of copper	= 339
first ionisation energy of copper	= 745
second ionisation energy of copper	= 1960
atomisation of oxygen, i.e. $\frac{1}{2}O_2(g) \longrightarrow O(g)$	= 248
first electron affinity of oxygen	= −141
second electron affinity of oxygen	= 791
formation of copper(II) oxide	= −155

15

25 (*C*)(*AS*/*AL*)

12. *(a)* (i) Define the term *average bond enthalpy*. **2**

(ii) Some values of average bond enthalpies are shown in the table.

Bond	**Average bond enthalpy /kJ mol^{-1}**
C—H	412
H—H	436
O—H	463
C—O	360
C≡O (in carbon monoxide)	1077

Use these values to calculate the molar enthalpy change for the reaction:

$CO(g) + 2H_2(g) \longrightarrow CH_3OH(g)$ **3**

(b) (i) Define the term *standard molar enthalpy change of combustion*. **2**

(ii) Given that the standard molar enthalpy changes of combustion for carbon monoxide, hydrogen and methanol are −283, −286 and −715 kJ mol^{-1} respectively, calculate the standard molar enthalpy change for the reaction:

$CO(g) + 2H_2(g) \longrightarrow CH_3OH(l)$ **3**

(c) (i) Write an equation to represent the condensation of methanol vapour. **1**

(ii) Using the kinetic model of matter, give a brief qualitative description of the condensation of a gas, caused by a decrease in temperature. **2**

(iii) Suggest a brief explanation for the difference between the values obtained in *(a)*(ii) and *(b)*(ii). **2**

16 (*AEB*)(*AL*) 1998

13. Ammonia is manufactured from nitrogen and hydrogen by the Haber process. Nitrogen and hydrogen are obtained, by a multi-stage process, from methane, steam and air. The reaction between nitrogen and hydrogen is exothermic and incomplete. The ammonia formed is removed from the mixture and the unreacted gases are recycled. The process normally operates at about 500 °C and 200 atm.

(a) (i) Write an equation for the manufacture of ammonia by the Haber process. **1**

(ii) Why is the reaction carried out at a high pressure? **1**

(iii) State **one** advantage and **one** disadvantage of carrying out the reaction at high temperature. **2**

(b) (i) Write an expression for the equilibrium constant, K_p, for the ammonia synthesis. **1**

(ii) Calculate the value of K_p given the following partial pressures in Table 1 which apply at 500 °C and a total pressure of 200 atm.

Table 1

Gas	Partial pressure/atm
nitrogen	75
hydrogen	35
ammonia	90

2

(iii) State the units of K_p in *(b)* (ii). **1**

(iv) Iron is used as a catalyst in the ammonia manufacture. State its effect on the K_p value you have calculated in *(b)* (ii). **1**

(c) Urea, $CO(NH_2)_2$, is a naturally occurring substance which can be hydrolysed with water to form ammonia according to the following equation.

$$H_2O(l) + CO(NH_2)_2(aq) \longrightarrow CO_2(aq) + 2NH_3(aq)$$

The above reaction only proceeds at a detectable rate in the presence of the enzyme urease.
Explain why enzymes, when they function as biological catalysts, have such a specific activity. **2**

(d) The standard enthalpy changes of formation of water, urea, carbon dioxide and ammonia are given in Table 2. Use these data to calculate the standard enthalpy change for the hydrolysis reaction.

Table 2

Compound	$\Delta H_f^\ominus$/kJ mol^{-1}
$H_2O(l)$	−287.0
$CO(NH_2)_2(aq)$	−320.5
$CO_2(aq)$	−414.5
$NH_3(aq)$	−81.0

2

13 *(C)(AS/AL)*

14. Ammonia is made on an industrial scale by a catalysed reaction – the Haber process. This reaction is exothermic.

(a) (i) Complete a copy of the reaction pathway diagram below to show the energy changes which occur when ammonia is produced in the Haber process. Mark and label the enthalpy change, ΔH, and the activation energy, E_a, on your diagram.

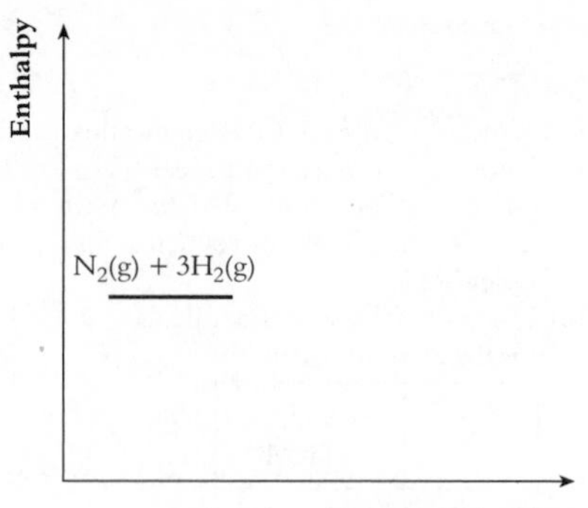

(ii) Add to your diagram a line to show the reaction pathway for the reaction if **no** catalyst had been present. Label this line 'uncatalysed'.

(iii) Using collision theory and your answers to (i) and (ii), explain how the presence of a catalyst alters the rate of a chemical reaction.

(iv) in the Haber process, a heterogeneous catalyst is used. Explain what you understand by the term *heterogeneous catalyst*.
State the catalyst used in the Haber process. **9**

(b) (i) What do you understand by the term *average bond energy*?

(ii) The synthesis of ammonia may be represented by

$$N_2(g) + 3H_2(g) \rightleftharpoons 2NH_3(g)$$

Use average bond energies/kJ mol^{-1}

N—N 163, H—H 436, N—H 388

to calculate $\Delta H^\ominus$ for the above reaction. **5**

14 *(C)(AS/AL)*

15. Acids differ in the number of hydrogen ions that can be liberated from one molecule of the undissociated acid. Hydrochloric acid is a strong monobasic, or monoprotic acid, liberating one hydrogen ion per molecule. Sulphuric acid is a dibasic, or diprotic acid, its ionisation in aqueous solution being:

I $H_2SO_4(l) + H_2O(l) \rightleftharpoons H_3O^+(aq) + HSO_4^-(aq)$ $\quad K_a$ = very large

II $HSO_4^-(aq) + H_2O(l) \rightleftharpoons H_3O^+(aq) + SO_4^{2-}(aq)$ $\quad K_a = 0.01$ mol dm^{-3}

K_a values are quoted for 25 °C.

(a) (i) State the hydrogen ion concentration in 0.01 mol dm^{-3} hydrochloric acid, which is a strong acid, and hence find the pH of this solution. **1**

(ii) State the hydrogen ion concentration of 0.1 mol dm^{-3} sulphuric acid arising from the first stage of ionisation, **I**: **1**

(iii) A solution of sodium hydrogensulphate, $NaHSO_4$, of concentration 0.1 mol dm^{-3}, which ionises according to equation **II** above has a pH of 1.57. Find the hydrogen ion concentration in this solution, and hence state what you would expect the hydrogen ion concentration in 0.1 mol dm^{-3} sulphuric acid to be. **2**

(iv) In fact the pH of 0.1 mol dm^{-3} sulphuric acid is about 0.98. This indicates a hydrogen ion concentration of 0.15 mol dm^{-3}. By considering the reactions **I** and **II** in the presence of one another explain why this is so. You are not expected to perform any further calculations. **2**

(v) If K_a for ionisation **II** has a value of 0.02 mol dm^{-3} at 80 °C, state with reasons, whether the ionisation is endothermic or exothermic. **2**

(vi) Explain the effect such an increase in temperature would have on the pH of this solution. **1**

(b) Pure sulphuric acid is a liquid, with a boiling temperature of 338 °C, which mixes with water in all proportions. Hydrogen chloride is a gas with a boiling temperature of −85 °C and is extremely soluble in water.

(i) Suggest reasons, in terms of the structure and bonding of H_2SO_4 and HCl for the large difference between their boiling temperatures. **2**

(ii) Suggest why both are very soluble in water. **1**

(iii) Magnesium sulphate and barium sulphate differ considerably in their solubility in water; use the following data to suggest why this is so.

	$MgSO_4$	$BaSO_4$
Solubility/mol dm^{-3}	1.83	9.43×10^{-6}
Hydration energy of cation/kJ mol^{-1}	−1920	−1360

3

15 *L (AL)*

INORGANIC CHEMISTRY

1. Why are elements described as s block, p block or d block? Which features are characteristic of the elements in each of these three blocks?

2. Plot a graph of ionic radius (vertical axis) against atomic number (horizontal axis) for the elements sodium to chlorine. Explain the variation in ionic radius in terms of electron configurations.

Ion	Na^+	Mg^{2+}	Al^{3+}	Si^{4+}	P^{3-}	S^{2-}	Cl^-
Radius/nm	0.095	0.065	0.050	0.041	0.212	0.184	0.181

3. Discuss the elements of the third period (Na to Ar) with reference to the following features:
(a) their reaction with oxygen
(b) their reaction with dilute sulphuric acid
(c) methods for the preparation of their chlorides
(d) the physical and chemical properties of their chlorides.

4. Explain the following statements:
(a) The atomic radii of the first series of transition elements are similar.
(b) The ionic radius of sodium is smaller than its atomic radius, but chloride ions have a larger radius than chlorine atoms.
(c) The first ionisation energy of potassium is smaller than that of sodium.
(d) The first electron affinity of chlorine is greater (more exothermic) than that of iodine.
(e) The salts NaCl and CsCl have different crystal structures.
(f) Beryllium chloride shows evidence of covalent bonding, but calcium chloride is ionic.

5. *(a)* Metallic character increases from right to left and from top to bottom in the Periodic Table. Illustrate this statement by referring to the period from sodium to chlorine and Group 4.
(b) Illustrate one of the trends in the Periodic Table by considering the properties of the oxides: Na_2O, CaO, Al_2O_3, SiO_2 and P_2O_5.

6. Distinguish between electronegativity and electron affinity. How does electronegativity vary *(a)* from carbon through nitrogen and oxygen to fluorine and *(b)* from fluorine to iodine? Explain the variations.
Which of these elements is the most powerful oxidising agent? Why?

7. Shown below are the first ionisation energies (E/kJ mol^{-1}) of the elements of the third period (Z = atomic number):

Element	**Na**	**Mg**	**Al**	**Si**	**P**	**S**	**Cl**	**Ar**
Z	11	12	13	14	15	16	17	18
E/kJ mol^{-1}	500	740	580	790	1010	1000	1260	1520

(a) State the meaning of *first ionisation energy*.
(b) Plot the ionisation energies against atomic number.
(c) Describe the shape of the plot you obtain, and explain why it has this form.
(d) Mention one way in which the behaviour of the elements mirrors the form of the graph you have plotted.

8. Explain the following statements:
(a) Aqueous solutions of sodium nitrate, aluminium sulphate and potassium cyanide have different pH values.
(b) Although silicon tetrachloride is readily hydrolysed by water, carbon tetrachloride is not.
(c) Solid beryllium chloride is soluble in ethoxyethane.
(d) Calcium oxide melts at a higher temperature than sodium chloride.
(e) Ammonium nitrate dissolves in water, although the process is endothermic.
(f) Potassium thiocyanate will detect iron(III) ions in the presence of iron(II) ions in aqueous solution.
(g) The standard enthalpy of neutralisation of hydrochloric acid by aqueous potassium hydroxide and sodium hydroxide is the same but is different from that obtained when aqueous ammonia is used.
(h) Although methane is unaffected by aqueous alkali, silane is violently hydrolysed.
(i) The shapes of the molecules BF_3 and PCl_3 are different.
(j) The standard enthalpy of solution of alkali metal fluorides changes from endothermic (e.g., LiF, NaF) to exothermic (e.g., KF, RbF, CsF).
(k) The decrease in atomic radius from scandium to zinc is very small.
(l) Tin(IV) chloride is a fuming liquid; tin(II) chloride is a solid.
(m) Silver nitrate solution is acidified with dilute nitric acid before being used to test for the presence of halide ions in solution.

9. Identify A and B and explain the reactions described.
A is a colourless, neutral liquid. It reacts as a base towards hydrogen chloride and as an acid towards ammonia. It has a very low electrolytic conductivity and high boiling and freezing temperatures compared with analogous compounds of other elements in the same group of the Periodic Table.
A reacts reversibly with red hot iron.

B is a colourless aqueous solution. It reacts with potassium manganate(VII) to give oxygen. **B** reacts with lead(II) sulphide to form a white solid and with iron(II) salts to form iron(III) salts.

10. Identify these solids, with explanations of the chemical reactions described.
C is a solid which colours a flame lilac. Its aqueous solution is yellow, changing to orange when dilute sulphuric acid is added. This orange solution reacts with ethanol when warmed, turning green and evolving a vapour with a distinctive smell.
D is a colourless solid. Its aqueous solution is neutral. When copper(II) sulphate solution is added, a white precipitate and a brown solution are formed. When lead(II) nitrate solution is added, a yellow precipitate appears. When **D** is heated with concentrated sulphuric acid, it evolves a violet vapour.
E is an orange-red crystalline solid. When heated, it forms three products, including a green solid and a colourless gas. When **E** is heated with sodium hydroxide solution, an alkaline gas is evolved, and a yellow solution is formed.
F is a white solid which gives a lilac flame test. The addition of aqueous barium chloride to a solution of **F** gives a white precipitate, which dissolves in dilute hydrochloric acid with the evolution of a gas which decolourises acidified potassium manganate(VII).

11. Identify **P**, **Q**, **R**, **S** and **T**, and give the colours of **Q**, **R**, **S** and **T**.

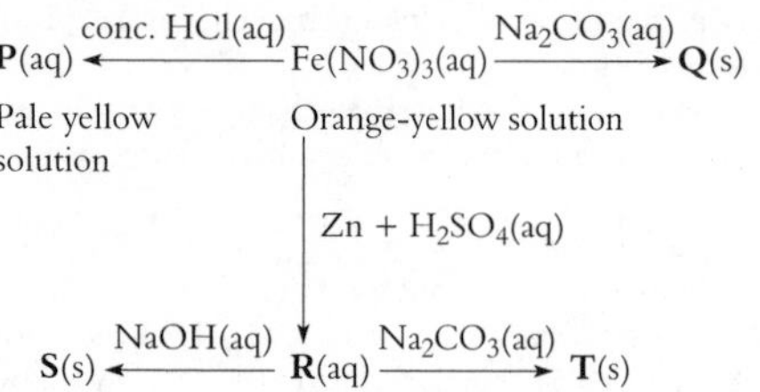

12. Describe how you could distinguish between the members of the following pairs:
(a) $Cl^-(aq)$ and $Br^-(aq)$
(b) $SO_4^{2-}(aq)$ and $SO_3^{2-}(aq)$
(c) $Ca^{2+}(aq)$ and $Ba^{2+}(aq)$
(d) $S_2O_3^{2-}(aq)$ and $SO_4^{2-}(aq)$
(e) $FeCl_3(aq)$ and $K_2Cr_2O_7(aq)$
(f) $Ag^+(aq)$ and $Zn^{2+}(aq)$.

13. *(a)* Give one example of (i) an acidic oxide (ii) a basic oxide (iii) an amphoteric oxide.
(b) Discuss (i) the chemical properties of each oxide (giving balanced equations).
(ii) the structure and bonding.

14. *(a)* Describe the bonding in and the structure of the anhydrous chlorides formed by sodium, aluminium and silicon. Explain the differences in volatility.
(b) Describe the changes that occur when sodium chloride and silicon tetrachloride are separately added to water. Describe what is observed, name the products, and comment on the pH of any solution formed.

15. Part of the Periodic Table is shown below.

Group	1	2	3	4	5	6	7
Period 2	Li	Be	B	C	N	O	F
Period 3	Na	Mg	Al	Si	P	S	Cl
Period 4	K	Ca	Ga	Ge	As	Se	Br
Period 5	Rb	Sr	In	Sn	Sb	Te	I

(a) List the symbols of the elements which react readily with cold water to form alkaline solutions. Which of these reactions do you consider to be the most vigorous? Write balanced equations for the reactions of two elements with water.
(b) For each group of the Periodic Table give the formula of the most stable hydride and state the shape of each molecule.
(c) For the elements in Period 3, give the formulae of the oxides in their highest oxidation states. State the oxidation states. Give the names and formulae of the corresponding acids or hydroxides which they form.
(d) List the symbols of the elements that form nitrates. Say what can be deduced about the nature of an element from its reactions (if any) with concentrated nitric acid and with dilute nitric acid.

16. *(a)* Define the term first ionisation energy.
(b) Discuss the relationship between the first ionisation energies of the elements listed below and their electronic configurations.

	First ionisation energy/kJ mol^{-1}		
Element	1st	2nd	3rd
Sodium	496	4561	6913
Potassium	419	3069	4400
Caesium	376	2420	3300
Magnesium	738	1450	7731
Calcium	590	1146	4942
Boron	801	2428	3660
Aluminium	578	1817	2745

17. *(a)* Sulphur dioxide, SO_2 and carbon dioxide, CO_2, both give acidic solutions when dissolved in water. Sulphur dioxide solutions gradually oxidise in air to sulphuric acid, but solutions of carbon dioxide do not oxidise in air.
(ii) The bonds in both CO_2 and SO_2 are polar, but only the SO_2 molecule has an overall dipole whereas the CO_2 molecule has no dipole. Explain this in terms of the structures of the two molecules. **3**
(ii) Explain in terms of oxidation states why only SO_2 oxidises in air. **2**
(iii) Solutions of carbon dioxide contain the following equilibrium:

$$2H_2O(l) + CO_2(aq) \rightleftharpoons H_3O^+(aq) + HCO_3^-(aq)$$

If a solution of sodium hydroxide containing phenolphthalein indicator, which is purple, is added drop by drop to a solution of carbon dioxide, the purple colour takes several seconds to disappear. What does this suggest about the position of the equilibrium and the kinetics of the reaction between carbon dioxide and water? **2**
(iv) A saturated solution of sulphur dioxide in water was left in air until it had all been converted to sulphuric acid. 25.0 cm^3 portions of this (sulphuric acid) solution required 20.8 cm^3 of 0.400 mol dm^{-3} sodium hydroxide solution. What is the solubility of SO_2 in mol dm^{-3} at the temperature and pressure of the experiment? **3**

(b) (i) Magnesium and sulphur form oxides which have different types of bonds. Explain why this is so. **3**
(ii) Explain why MgO and SO_2 react differently with water. **2**

(c) Explain why aluminium chloride is covalent and readily dimerises to Al_2Cl_6 and draw the structure of the dimer. (You are not required to show the shape of the molecule.) **3**

18 (*L*)(*AL*)

18. (a) Chemical bonding helps to explain different properties of materials.

(i) Using 'dot-and-cross' or other suitable diagrams, explain what is meant by *ionic*, *covalent* and *metallic* bonding.

(ii) Three substances, **C**, **D** and **E**, have ionic, covalent and metallic bonding respectively. Compare and explain the electrical conductivities of **C**, **D** and **E**. **14**

(b) Large quantities of nitrogen compounds are produced each year in the UK. Some, such as nitrogen fertilisers, are beneficial. Others, such as nitrogen oxides, are formed unintentionally and are far from beneficial.

(i) The nitrogen fertiliser, **F**, was shown to have the composition by mass Na, 27.1%; N, 16.5%; O, 56.4%. On heating, 3.40 g of **F** were broken down into sodium nitrite, $NaNO_2$, and oxygen gas.
Showing your working, suggest an identity for the fertiliser **F**, and calculate the volume of oxygen that was formed.
[Under the experimental conditions, 1 mole of gas molecules occupies 24 dm^3.]

(ii) The atmospheric pollutant, NO_2, is present in car exhaust gases. State **two** environmental consequences of nitrogen oxides and outline their catalytic removal from car exhaust gases. **7**

25 (*C*)(*AS/AL*)

19. (a) (i) Draw 'dot-and-cross' diagrams of an ionic oxide and a covalent oxide of your choice.

(ii) Explain how the electrical conductivity of each of your chosen compounds is related to its structure. **8**

(b) Chromium is prepared industrially by the reduction of chromium(III) oxide with aluminium:

$$Cr_2O_3(s) + 2Al(s) \longrightarrow 2Cr(s) + Al_2O_3(s) \quad \Delta H = -447 \text{ kJ mol}^{-1}$$

(i) Use oxidation numbers to show that this is a redox reaction.

(ii) Calculate the maximum mass of chromium formed, and the energy change, from the processing of 100 tonnes of chromium(III) oxide [1 tonne ≡ 10^6 g] **7**

(c) Using equations where appropriate, describe the action of water on the oxides, Na_2O, Al_2O_3 and SO_2. Interpret any reactions in terms of the structure and bonding of the oxides. **6**

25 (*C*)(*AS/AL*)

20. (a) Chloric(I) acid, HOCl, is formed as one of the products when chlorine dissolves in water. The dissociation constant of this weak acid is 3.7×10^{-8} mol dm^{-3}.

$$HOCl(aq) \rightleftharpoons H^+(aq) + ClO^-(aq)$$

(i) Calculate the pH of a 0.1 mol dm^{-3} solution of chloric(I) acid. **3**

(ii) State why an indicator colour change is generally unsuitable for monitoring the neutralisation of chloric(I) acid by sodium hydroxide. **1**

(b) Sodium chlorate(I), NaClO, is one of the products made by dissolving chlorine in cold dilute sodium hydroxide solution.

(i) Write a balanced equation to represent this reaction. **1**

(ii) The chlorate(I) ion decomposes on standing into a solution which contains chloride and chlorate(V) ions.

$$3OCl^-(aq) \rightleftharpoons 2Cl^-(aq) + ClO_3^-(aq)$$

The equilibrium constant for this reaction at room temperature is 10^{27}. Give a reason why Cl^- and ClO_3^- ions are nevertheless formed only very slowly. **2**

(iii) Give **one** large scale use for sodium chloride, and **one** large scale use for sodium chlorate(V), $NaClO_3$. **1**

(c) Silicon(IV) chloride, $SiCl_4$, is prepared by passing chlorine gas over a strongly heated mixture of carbon and silicon(IV) oxide.

$$SiO_2(s) + 2C(s) + 2Cl_2(g) \longrightarrow SiCl_4(l) + 2CO(g)$$

(i) Deduce, giving your reasoning, the type of bonding present within silicon(IV) chloride. **2**

(ii) Give the balanced equation for the reaction of silicon(IV) chloride with water. **1**

(iii) The other produce of the reaction, carbon monoxide, CO, has important uses as a reducing agent. Give details of **one** reaction where carbon monoxide acts in this way, and explain why, in terms of oxidation states, carbon monoxide is a much better reducing agent than lead(II) oxide. **3**

(iv) Give **one** reason why lead(IV) chloride cannot be made in the same way as silicon(IV) chloride. **1**

15 (*WJEC*)(*AL*)

21. (a) (i) Draw a clear diagram to show the shape of the ammonia molecule, NH_3 and the boron trifluoride molecule BF_3. State the shape of each molecule. **3**

(ii) Give an explanation for the shape of the ammonia molecule. **3**

(iii) using similar principles to those used in *(a)*(i) and (ii), predict the shape of the CH_3^+ ion by drawing a clear diagram. **1**

(b) Consider the following standard electrode potentials.

Half-reaction	$E^{\ominus}$/V
$Cl_2(aq) + 2e^- \rightleftharpoons 2Cl^-(aq)$	+1.36
$Fe^{3+}(aq) + e^- \rightleftharpoons Fe^{2+}(aq)$	+0.77
$I_2(aq) + 2e^- \rightleftharpoons 2I^-(aq)$	+0.54

(i) State what happens and what would be **observed** when

I. an aqueous solution containing Fe^{3+} ions is added to an aqueous solution of potassium iodide,

II. chlorine is bubbled through an aqueous solution containing Fe^{2+} ions. **3**

(ii) State what the results in *(b)*(i) and the electrode potentials indicate about the relative oxidising power of chlorine and iodine. **1**

(c) 25.00 cm^3 of an iron(II) salt solution was acidified and titrated with aqueous potassium manganate(VII) of concentration 0.0200 mol dm^{-3}. 22.30 cm^3 of the aqueous potassium manganate(VII) was required for exact reaction.

(i) Write an ionic equation for the reaction between iron(II) ions and manganate(VII) ions in the presence of hydrogen ions. **1**

(ii) Calculate the concentration of iron(II) ions (mol dm^{-3}) in the above solution and hence deduce the mass of iron(II) ions in 1.00 dm^3 of this solution. **3**

15 (*WJEC*)(*AL*)

22. (a) Draw the shape of each of the following molecules. Give an explanation of each shape in terms of repulsion between electron pairs.

(ii) CO_2 (ii) NH_3 (iii) SF_b **6**

(b) Explain why copper is a conductor of electricity. **2**

(c) A white copper compound, **A**, is dissolved in water to give a blue solution containing a cationic complex ion, **B**, and an anion, **C**.
On the addition of aqueous barium chloride to a sample of the blue solution, a white precipitate, **D**, is formed.
The dropwise addition of aqueous ammonia to a different sample of the blue solution causes the formation of a pale blue precipitate, **E**, followed by a deep blue solution containing the complex cation, **F**.

(i) Give the formula of each of the species **A** to **F**. **6**

(ii) Write an ionic equation to show the reaction occurring when **C** is converted into **D**. **1**

(d) Fehling's solution is a mild oxidising agent containing a copper complex ion.

(i) Describe how you would use Fehling's solution to test for a reducing sugar. What would you expect to observe in a positive test? Give the name of a reducing sugar. **3**

(ii) Give the name of and draw the structure of the functional group in a reducing sugar that reacts with Fehling's solution. **3**

(e) The water in a stream that runs close to an old copper mine is found to contain small amounts of dissolved copper ions. In an attempt to find the concentration of dissolved copper ions, 10.00 dm^3 of stream water was evaporated down to 100.00 cm^3 and was then made up to 250 cm^3 in a volumetric flask. A 25.0 cm^3 portion of this solution was titrated against EDTA solution and 20.50 cm^3 of 0.0500 mol dm^{-3} EDTA were required.

$$Cu^{2+}(aq) + EDTA^{4-}(aq) \longrightarrow [Cu(EDTA)]^{2-}(aq)$$

(i) Give the name of a suitable indicator for this titration. **1**

(ii) Calculate the concentration of Cu^{2+} in the stream water in units of g dm^{-3}. **7**

AEB (AL) 1998

23. *(a)* From the sequence of elements sodium to phosphorus in the Periodic Table name **three** chlorides, **one each** from Group I, Group IV and Group V. For each chloride state the type of bonding and give the formulae of the substances formed when the chloride reacts with water. **5**

(b) (i) Identify the Group II metal **X**, given the following information:
An aqueous solution of the nitrate of a Group II metal **X** reacts separately with aqueous sodium carbonate and aqueous sodium sulphate, giving a white precipitate in each case. When 250 cm^3 of a 0.100 mol dm^{-3} solution of the metal nitrate is treated with excess of aqueous sodium sulphate, 5.83 g of precipitate is formed.
Write a balanced equation for the reaction of the metal nitrate with sodium sulphate and calculate the relative atomic mass of **X**.
Having identified **X**, write an ionic equation for the reaction of the metal nitrate with sodium carbonate. **6**

(ii) Give a simple test, with the expected results, which would enable you to distinguish between the solids magnesium carbonate and strontium carbonate. **2**

(c) Consider the following standard electrode potentials:

Half-reaction	$E^{\ominus}/V$
$\frac{1}{2}S_2O_8^{2-} + e \rightleftharpoons SO_4^{2-}(aq)$	+2.01
$Mn^{3+}(aq) + e^- \rightleftharpoons Mn^{2+}(aq)$	+1.49
$Fe^{3+}(aq) + e^- \rightleftharpoons Fe^{2+}(aq)$	+0.77
$\frac{1}{2}I_2(aq) + e^- \rightleftharpoons I^-(aq)$	+0.54

(i) Use the relevant electrode potentials above to discuss the relative stabilities of the 2+ and 3+ ions of iron and manganese. Give also an explanation, in terms of the electronic configuration of the ions, for the conclusions you make. **4**

(ii) Peroxodisulphate(VI), $S_2O_8^{2-}$, and iodide ions react to produce iodine and sulphate(VI) ions according to the following equation:

$$\tfrac{1}{2}S_2O_8^{2-}(aq) + I^-(aq) \longrightarrow \tfrac{1}{2}I_2(aq) + SO_4^{2-}(aq)$$

Fe^{2+} ions are known to catalyse this reaction. It has been suggested that the first stage of the catalysed reaction is

$$\tfrac{1}{2}S_2O_8^{2-}(aq) + Fe^{2+}(aq) \longrightarrow Fe^{3+}(aq) + S_2O_4^{2-}(aq)$$

Write a balanced equation for the second stage and discuss both stages with respect to the relevant electrode potentials above.
State, with reasoning, whether you would expect Fe^{3+}(aq) ions to catalyse the reaction. **3**

20 *(WJEC)(AL)*

24. *(a)* Explain briefly how the lines in the emission spectrum of atomic hydrogen arise. Why do the lines converge at high frequency? **2**

(b) (i) 'The standard enthalpy change of formation, $\Delta H_f^{\ominus}$ (298 K), of $H_2O(g)$ is −241.8 kJ mol^{-1}.' State briefly the meaning of this statement and write a balanced equation to which this enthalpy change applies. **2**

(ii) Use the following bond energies and the value of $\Delta H_f^{\ominus}(H_2O(g))$ given in *(b)*(i), to calculate the bond energy of the O—H bond in the H_2O. **Show your working.**

Bond	H—H	O=O
Bond energy/kJ mol^{-1}	436	496

3

(iii) Hydrogen gas has been proposed as fuel in motor cars. State **one** advantage and **one** disadvantage of using hydrogen for this purpose. **1**

(iv) Give **one** reason why the hydrogen ion does not exist in the free state in solution. **1**

(v) Write an equation representing the catalytic hydrogenation of prop-l-ene. What property of nickel (and of transition metals in general) makes it suitable for use as a catalyst for this reaction? **3**

(vi) Calculate the volume of hydrogen at 0 °C and 1 atmosphere pressure required to react completely with 21 moles of prop-l-ene.
[Molar volume of a gas at 0 °C and 1 atm (101 kPa) is 22.4 dm^3.] **2**

(c) (i) Write an ionic equation for the reduction of the aluminium ion in the production of aluminium by electrolysis. Name the ore, solvent, and type of electrodes that are used in the manufacture of aluminium. State the approximate temperature at which reduction takes place. **3**

(ii) Sketch the shape of the complex ion $[Al(H_2O)_6]^{3+}$. Briefly describe the type of bonding between the water molecules and the central Al^{3+} ion.
[*Note:* $[Al(H_2O)_6]^{3+}$ *ions resemble* $[Cu(H_2O)_6]^{2+}$ *ions, possessing similar bonding and shape.*] **2**

(iii) If excess sodium hydroxide solution is added to aluminium nitrate solution, the $[Al(H_2O)_6]^{3+}$ ion is converted into the diaquatetrahydroxoaluminate(III) ion, $[Al(OH)_4(H_2O)_2]^-$. Write an ionic equation for this reaction. **1**

20 *(WJEC)(AL)*

25. *(a)* The electronegativities of four atoms are given below:

Electronegativity F 4.0; Cl 3.0; I 2.5; H 2.1

(i) From this list, identify the pair of atoms (which may be the same atom or different atoms) which would form a diatomic molecule with the highest degree of *ionic character*. **1**

(ii) Similarly, select a pair of atoms which would form a diatomic molecule with the maximum degree of *covalent character*. **1**

(b) The following ionic equations show the reactions of sodium oxide, Na_2O, aluminium oxide, Al_2O_3, and sulphur dioxide, SO_2, in solutions of *acids or bases:*

Sodium oxide, Na_2O

$O^{2-}(s) + 2H^+(aq) \longrightarrow H_2O(l)$;

Aluminium oxide, Al_2O_3

$Al_2O_3(s) + 6H^+(aq) \longrightarrow 2Al^{3+}(aq) + 3H_2O(l)$

$Al_2O_3(s) + 2OH^-(aq) + 3H_2O(l) \longrightarrow 2Al(OH)_4^-(aq)$;

Sulphur dioxide, SO_2

$SO_2(g) + 2OH^-(aq) \longrightarrow SO_3^{2-}(aq) + H_2O(l)$

Explain how these reactions **provide evidence** that the elements Na, Al, and S become progressively non-metallic in character. **5**

(c) The element astatine, At, is found at the foot of the halogen group in the Periodic Table. From your knowledge of the chemistry of iodine, predict the likely product(s) if sodium astatide NaAt, were mixed with concentrated sulphuric acid. State briefly the reasoning behind your prediction. **4**

(d) When chlorine gas is bubbled into water, chloric(I) acid (hypochlorous acid) is one of the initial products

$$\mathbf{Cl_2}(aq) + H_2O(l) \rightleftharpoons HOCl(aq) + Cl^-(aq) + H^+(aq)$$

Chloric(I) acid remains in equilibrium with $OCl^-(aq)$ ions

$$HOCl(aq) \rightleftharpoons H^+(aq) + \mathbf{OCl^-}(aq)$$

(i) Why is chlorine used in swimming pools? State **one** reason why highly acidic pool water is undesirable. **2**

(ii) State the oxidation number(s) of chlorine in the two species, Cl_2 and OCl^-, highlighted in bold in the two equations above. **1**

(iii) The way that the percentage of HOCl changes with pH is shown in the Figure.

Mole percentages of HOCl and OCl^- in chlorine water at 20°C

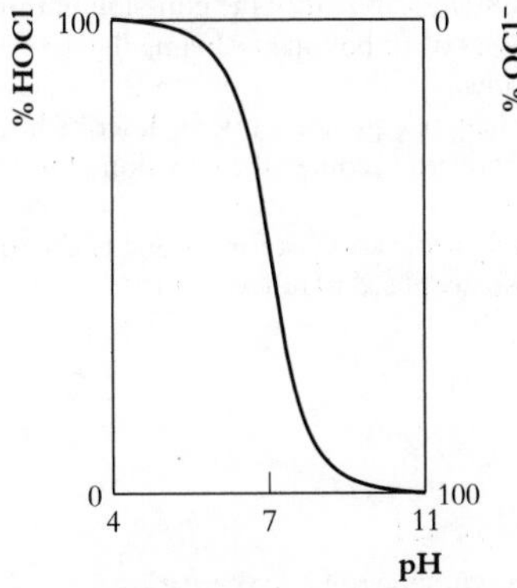

Use Le Chatelier's principle to explain the general variation in mole percentage of HOCl with increasing pH. **1**

(iv) The concentration of HOCl in a sample of pool water may be found by adding excess potassium iodide and dilute sulphuric acid and titrating the iodine produced with sodium thiosulphate. The equations representing these reactions are

$$2I^-(aq) + HOCl(aq) + H^+(aq) \longrightarrow Cl^-(aq) + \mathbf{I_2}(aq) + H_2O(l)$$

$$\mathbf{I_2}(aq) + 2S_2O_3^{2-}(aq) \longrightarrow S_4O_6^{2-}(aq) + 2I^-(aq)$$

In an experiment, excess KI and H_2SO_4 were added to 100.0 cm^3 of chlorinated pool water. When titrated, the mixture required 6.90 cm^3 of sodium thiosulphate solution (concentration 0.010 mol dm^{-3}) for complete reaction. Calculate the concentration of HOCl in the pool water in the units of

I. mol dm^{-3}, and

II. mg dm^{-3} [1 mg = 0.001 g]. **5**

20 *(WJEC)(AL)*

26. *(a)* Trends in the Periodic Table in the properties of elements and their compounds are most usefully studied when both vertical (down Group) and horizontal (across Period) comparisons are made.

(i) Give relevant examples, with formulae and equations as appropriate, to summarise and illustrate the following trends:

I. The variation of the electronegativities of the elements.

II. The occurrence of metallic or non-metallic character.

III. The occurrence of ionic or covalent bonding. **5**

(ii) Discuss similarly how you would expect the acidic or basic character of oxides to vary within the Periodic Table. **2**

(iii) Explain what you understand by amphoteric character and indicate where in the Periodic Table it is most likely to occur. Give **two** examples of elements with compounds showing marked amphotericity and describe **one** reaction of hydroxides typical of such behaviour. **4**

(b) (i) Give in outline the **chemistry** of the process by which aluminium metal is produced in industry. (Technical details and diagrams are **not** required.) **4**

(ii) State and explain what you can deduce from the nature of the process by which aluminium is extracted from its ores as regards the magnitude **and sign** of $\Delta H_f^\ominus$ for Al_2O_3 (−1676 kJ mol^{-1}) and $E^\ominus$ for Al^{3+}/Al. (−1.66 V). **2**

(iii) The species $[AlF_6]^{3-}$ is involved in the process in *(b)*(i) above.

I. Predict the shape of this anion.

II. Explain why aluminium can exhibit a coordination number of six but boron, in the same group, has a maximum coordination number of four. **3**

20 *(WJEC)(AL)*

ORGANIC CHEMISTRY

1. *(a)* Each of the following conversions can be completed in not more than *three* steps. Use equations to show how you would carry out each conversion in the laboratory and for each step, give the reagent(s), conditions, and structure of the product.

(i) $(CH_3)_3CCH{=}CH_2 \longrightarrow (CH_3)_3CC{\equiv}CH$

(ii) (cyclopentyl)–NH_2 ⟶ (cyclopentyl)–$NHCH_2$–(phenyl)

(iii)

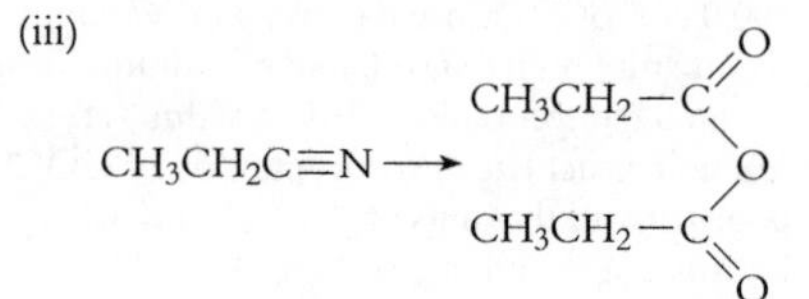

9

(b) Saponification of 1 mol of fat *G* with NaOH(aq) produces 1 mol of a triol $C_3H_8O_3$, 2 mol of $CH_3(CH_2)_{16}CO_2^-Na^+$ and 1 mol of $CH_3(CH_2)_{14}CO_2^-Na^+$.

(i) If *G* is optically active, suggest its structure. Explain.

(ii) If *G* is optically inactive, suggest its structure.

(iii) What is the *minimum* number of moles of base required for the complete saponification of 1 mol of *G*? 4

(c) Compound *H*, $C_3H_6O_2$, does not react with $NaBH_4$ and displays the following infra-red spectrum. Deduce *all* possible structures of *H*. 4

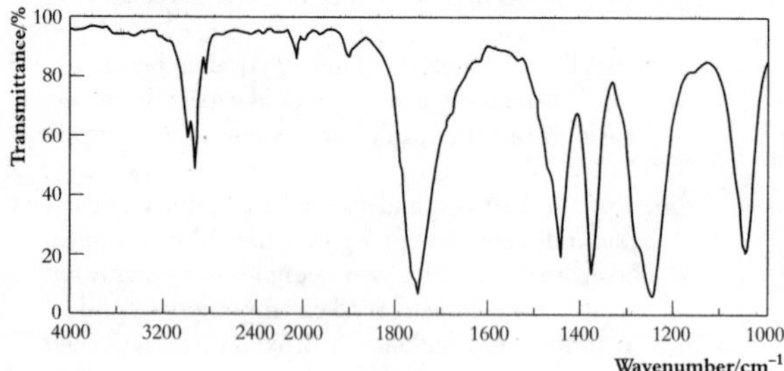

4

(HK)(AL)

2. This question concerns 2-bromo-2-methylbutane,

$$CH_3-CH_2-\overset{\displaystyle CH_3}{\underset{\displaystyle CH_3}{C}}-Br$$

which reacts with aqueous potassium hydroxide solution via an S_N1 mechanism.

(a) Show this mechanism and identify the rate determining step. 4

(b) If the conditions are altered potassium hydroxide will react to give an elimination reaction with the same halogenoalkane.

Draw the structural formula and give the name of an organic product of this elimination reaction, showing all the covalent bonds. 2

(c) The product in *(b)* can be polymerised.

(i) Write the formula for this polymer showing the structure of the repeating unit. 2

(ii) Suggest conditions under which the polymerisation could be performed. 2

(iii) Suggest why, in terms of the nature of the bonds in such polymers, they are persistent in the environment but are not particularly hazardous. 2

(d) The rate equation for the substitution reaction in part *(a)* is

rate = k[2-bromo-2-methylbutane]

(i) State the order of the reaction 1

(ii) If the same halogenoalkane is reacted with cyanide ions instead of hydroxide ions, and all other conditions remain the same, state with reasons whether the rate of the reaction would alter. 3

(e) Reaction rates generally increase with an increase in temperature for two reasons.

(i) State what these reasons are. 2

(ii) The distribution of molecular energies at a given temperature T_1 is shown below. Sketch on a copy of the axes a graph appropriate to a higher temperature T_2, and hence explain why the rate increases.

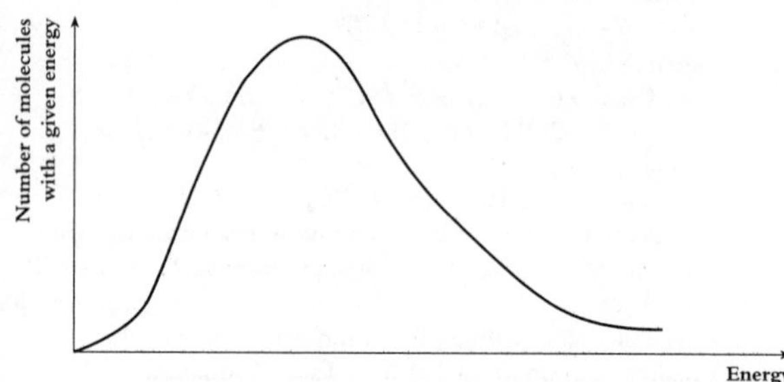

4

(iii) By using the graph, or otherwise, explain the effect of a catalyst on the rate of a reaction. 2

24 *(L)(AS/AL)*

3. *(a)* Consider the structures of the two synthetic polymers shown below.

$\text{+}CH_2CH_2\text{+}_n$ $\text{+}HN(CH_2)_6NHCO(CH_2)_4CO\text{+}_n$

Poly(ethene)   Nylon-6,6

(i) Suggest an explanation for the fact that nylon-6,6 has a higher tensile strength than poly(ethene).

(ii) Briefly explain why aqueous acids can more readily attack nylon-6,6 than poly(ethene), inducing degradation.

(iii) Apart from acidic conditions, state *one other* condition under which nylon-6,6 degrades more readily than poly(ethene). 5

(b) (i) The installation of catalytic converters onto car exhaust systems can reduce the emission of three major classes of air pollutants. Name the *three* classes of pollutants.

(ii) With the help of equations, briefly describe how a catalytic converter reduces the emission of these pollutants. 4

(c) 2-Ethanoyloxybenzoic acid (aspirin) is one of the most common substances used to relieve pain.

(benzene ring with CO_2H and, on the adjacent carbon, $OCOCH_3$)

2-Ethanoyloxybenzoic acid

(i) Outline a synthetic route for preparing 2-ethanoyloxybenzoic acid from 2-methylphenol.

(ii) Suggest how you could show the presence of the two functional groups in 2-ethanoyloxybenzoic acid. 4

(d) Identify, **J**, **K**, **L** and **M** in the following reactions.

(i)

J $\xrightarrow[\text{(2) NaOH}]{\text{(1) Sn/conc. HCl}}$ (benzene ring with NH_2 and, para to it, H_3C)

(ii) 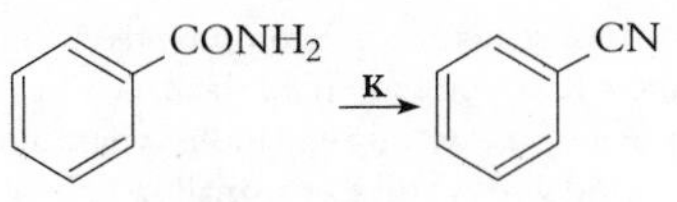 $C_6H_5CONH_2 \xrightarrow{\textbf{K}} C_6H_5CN$

(iii) $H_2C{=}CH(Cl) \xrightarrow{\textbf{L}} {+}CH_2{-}CH(Cl){+}_n$

(iv) 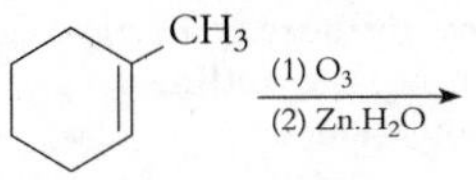 1-methylcyclohexene (CH_3) $\xrightarrow[(2)\ Zn.H_2O]{(1)\ O_3}$ **M**

4

(HK)(AL)

4. *(a)* Write an equation for the formation of ethyl ethanoate from ethanoic acid and ethanol in the presence of a strong acid catalyst.
State the type of reaction taking place. 2
(b) Write an equation for the formation of ethyl ethanoate from ethanoyl chloride and ethanol. Name and outline the mechanism of this reaction. 6
(c) Suggest two reasons why the reaction in part *(b)* is a more effective way of preparing ethyl ethanoate than that in part *(a)*. 2
(d) The proton n.m.r. spectrum of ethyl ethanoate has peaks at δ 4.1, 2.0 and 1.2.
Given that the peak at δ 2.0 is a singlet, deduce the splitting patterns of the other two peaks. You may find the data provided in the table helpful. 2

Table Proton chemical shift data

Type of proton	δ/ppm
RCH_3	0.7–1.2
R_2CH_2	1.2–1.4
R_3CH	1.4–1.6
$RCOCH_3$	2.1–2.6
$ROCH_3$	3.1–3.9
$RCOOCH_3$	3.7–4.1

12 *(NEAB)(AL)*

5. *(a)* (i) An acyclic compound *H* of molecular formula $C_4H_8O_2$ has a fruity smell. It does not produce a derivative with 2,4-dinitrophenylhydrazine nor with propanoyl chloride.
Deduce the functional group(s) of *H*. Draw **FOUR** possible structures for *H*.
(ii) On reduction with an excess of $LiAlH_4$, *H* gives **only one** product, *J*, which reacts with ethanoic anhydride. Deduce, giving equations, the structure for *H* and also the structure for *J*. 8
(b) The following compounds can exist in isomeric forms:
(i) butenedioic acid, and
(ii) 2-aminopropanoic acid.
In each case, state the type of isomerism and draw suitable representations for the isomers. 4
(c) Identify **K**, **L**, **M**, **N** and **P** in the following reactions:

(i) **K** $\xrightarrow{PCl_5}$ $(CH_3)_2CHCH_2CH_2Cl$

(ii) 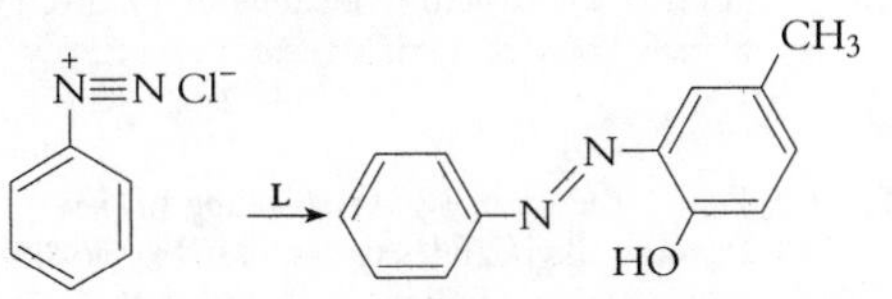 $C_6H_5\overset{+}{N}{\equiv}N\ Cl^-$ $\xrightarrow{\textbf{L}}$ $C_6H_5{-}N{=}N{-}C_6H_3(OH)(CH_3)$ (HO, CH_3)

(iii) 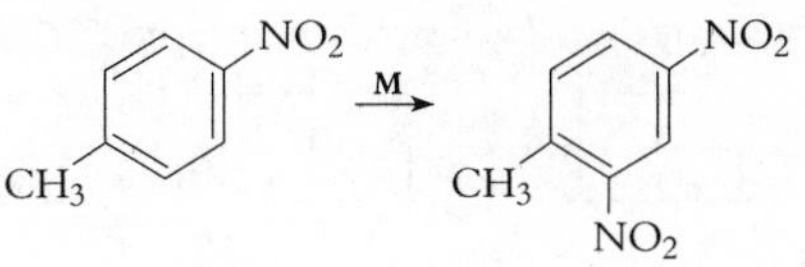 4-nitrotoluene (CH_3, NO_2) $\xrightarrow{\textbf{M}}$ 2,4-dinitrotoluene (CH_3, NO_2, NO_2)

(iv) 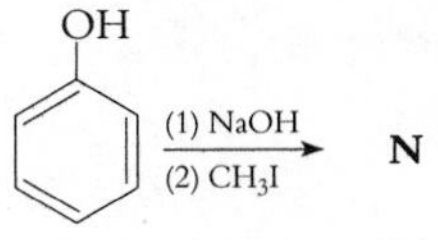 C_6H_5OH $\xrightarrow[(2)\ CH_3I]{(1)\ NaOH}$ **N**

(v) $CH_3CH_2{-}\overset{O}{\overset{\|}{C}}{-}CH_3 \xrightarrow{NaHSO_3}$ **P**

5

(HK)(AL)

6. Consider the following reaction scheme:

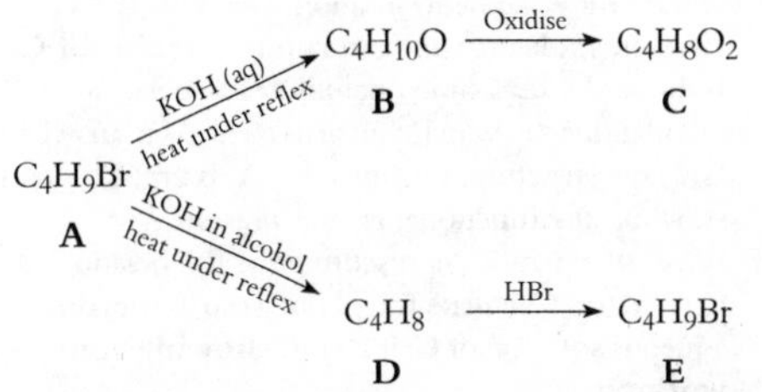

$$\underset{\textbf{A}}{C_4H_9Br} \xrightarrow[\text{heat under reflex}]{KOH\ (aq)} \underset{\textbf{B}}{C_4H_{10}O} \xrightarrow{\text{Oxidise}} \underset{\textbf{C}}{C_4H_8O_2}$$

$$\underset{\textbf{A}}{C_4H_9Br} \xrightarrow[\text{heat under reflex}]{KOH\ \text{in alcohol}} \underset{\textbf{D}}{C_4H_8} \xrightarrow{HBr} \underset{\textbf{E}}{C_4H_9Br}$$

The compound **A** is not chiral, but **E** is. **C** will liberate carbon dioxide from sodium hydrogencarbonate solution. **B** and **C** will react with one another under suitable conditions.
(a) Draw the structural formulae of **A**, **B**, **C** and **E**. 4
(b) Give a qualitative test for the functional group in **D**. 2
(c) Write the equation for the reaction of **C** with sodium hydrogencarbonate. 2
(d) Give the structure of the organic compound formed by reaction between **B** and **C**. 1
(e) Suggest suitable reagents and conditions for the conversion of **B** to **C**. 2
(f) Substance **C** has K_a value of 1.51×10^{-5} mol dm^{-3}.
(i) Find the pH of a 0.100 mol dm^{-3} solution of **C**. 3
(ii) What property is shown by a solution which contains a mixture of **C** and its sodium salt? 1
(iii) Calculate the pH of a solution formed by adding 5.5 g of the sodium salt of **C** to 500 cm^3 of a solution of **C** of concentration 0.100 mol cm^{-3}. 2

19 *(L)(AS/AL)*

7. *(a)* (i) Give the formula for
I. chlorobenzene,
II. 1-chlorobutane.
(ii) When the liquids in *(a)*(i) are heated separately with silver nitrate solution and ethanol solvent, a white precipitate is observed with l-chlorobutane only. Explain briefly the chemistry behind the experiment, and explain why the compounds react differently. 3
(b) Describe briefly how the haloalkane $CH_3CHBrCH_3$ may be prepared from propan-1-ol ($CH_3CH_2CH_2OH$). Indicate the reagents and conditions required in each stage. 3
(c) The esterification of ethanol

$$CH_3CO_2H + C_2H_5OH \xrightarrow{H^+} CH_3CO_2C_2H_5 + H_2O$$

was carried out in the laboratory. 10.0 g of ethanol was reacted with excess ethanoic acid in the presence of concentrated sulphuric acid.
(i) State the purpose of the concentrated sulphuric acid. 1
(ii) The yield of ester was found to be 15.0 g. Calculate the percentage yield of product. 2

(d) Study the following reaction sequence.

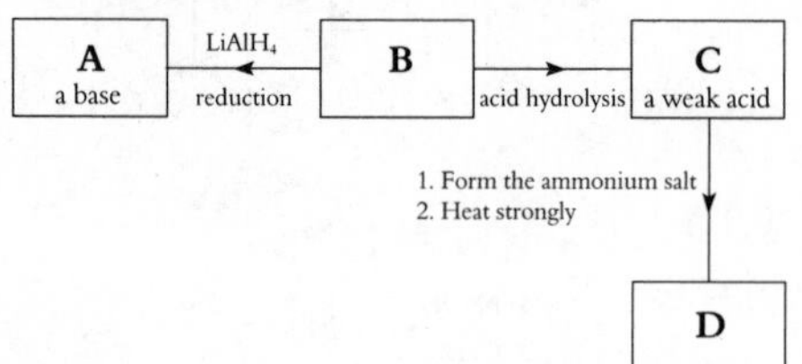

Further information

(1) **B** contains a straight carbon chain.
(2) **B** contains nitrogen but no oxygen.
(3) **C** contains only carbon, hydrogen and oxygen.
(4) One molecule of **C** contains **one** acidic hydrogen atom.
0.88 g of **C** required 100.0 cm^3 of 0.100 mol dm^{-3} NaOH for exact neutralisation.

(i) Give the molecular and structural formulae for **C**. Indicate the reasoning, including any necessary calculations, by which you arrived at your answer. **4**
(ii) Give the structural formulae for **A**, **B** and **D**, clearly showing any functional groups present. **3**
(iii) Write an equation representing the dissociation of **C** in water. Calculate the pH of a 0.010 mol dm^{-3} aqueous solution of **C** at 298 K, **showing your working**.
[K_a(C) = 1.6×10^{-5} mol dm^{-3} at 298 K.] **4**

20 *(WJEC)(AL)*

8. *(a)* Show how you would
(i) determine whether a sample of $C_2H_5CH(OH)CH_3$ is in the (+) form or (±) form.
(ii) distinguish between propan-2-ol and propanone using spectroscopy.
(iii) distinguish between C_6H_5COCl and C_6H_5COBr using a chemical test. **3**

(b) 20.0 g of 4-nitrobenzoic acid ($C_7H_5NO_4$) reacted with PCl_5, to give a product which reacted exothermically with NH_3 to give *T*. After treatment with Br_2(l) and NaOH(aq), *T* gave a solid. Crystallization of the solid from ethanol gave 9.3 g of *U* ($C_6H_6N_2O_2$).
(i) Calculate the percentage yield of *U* formed from 4-nitrobenzoic acid.
(ii) Give the structures of *T* and *U*.
(iii) Briefly give *three* reasons which could explain why the yield of *U* in the above preparation is not quantitative (i.e. 100%). **4**

(c) You are provided with a mixture of two liquids, heptanoic acid and hexan-3-one. Outline an experimental procedure, based on a solvent extraction process, to isolate pure heptanoic acid in good yield. **3**

(HK)(AL)

9. *(a)* A weakly acidic compound **A** ($C_8H_9NO_2$) gives no reaction with a mixture of sodium nitrite and hydrochloric acid at low temperature. On heating **A** under reflux with excess dilute hydrochloric acid hydrolysis occurs giving two compounds **B** (C_6H_8NClO) and **C** ($C_2H_4O_2$). After complete separation from all other components of the mixture, **C** was found to react with sodium carbonate, liberating a colourless gas.
When **B** was cooled to about 3 °C and sodium nitrite solution added at the same temperature, a colourless solution **D** ($C_6H_5ClN_2O$) was formed. Addition of phenol to this solution gave a coloured precipitate **E**.
The mass spectra of **A**, **B** and **D** all show a peak at *m/e* = 76.
(i) Deduce structures for compounds **A** to **E** inclusive. **5**
(ii) Show how you have used the data to reach your conclusions, writing equations where appropriate. **8**

(b) How would you synthesize a small sample of butan-2-ol, $CH_3CH_2CH(OH)CH_3$, from a supply of bromoethane, C_2H_5Br? No other organic material is available to you, other than for use as a solvent.
You should state clearly the reagents and conditions you would use for each step and **outline** the practical procedures you would adopt. **12**

25 *(L)(AL)*

10. *(a)* Fractional distillation and cracking are important in the petroleum industry. Explain what is involved in these processes and why they are commercially important. Include in your answer an equation to illustrate cracking and name the mechanism by which the process occurs. **15**

(b) (i) Write an equation and an outline mechanism for the reaction of 1-bromopropane with an excess of ammonia. Explain how you could distinguish between samples of 1-bromopropane and 2-bromopropane using infra-red spectroscopy and low-resolution n.m.r. spectroscopy.
(ii) O

X

Compound **X** undergoes addition reactions separately with HBr and with HCN. In each case name the type of reaction and give the structure of the product formed.
Suggest the structure of the fully saturated product formed when compound **X** reacts with an excess of hydrogen in the presence of a Ni catalyst. **15**

30 *(NEAB)(AS/AL)*

11. A carboxylic acid **A** contains 40.0% carbon, 6.70% hydrogen and 53.3% oxygen by mass. When 10.0 cm^3 of an aqueous solution of **A**, containing 7.20 g dm^{-3}, was titrated against 0.050 mol dm^{-3} sodium hydroxide, the following pH readings were obtained.

Volume NaOH/cm³	0.0	2.5	5.0	7.5	10.0	14.0	15.0	16.0	17.5	20.0	22.5
pH	2.5	3.2	3.5	3.8	4.1	4.7	5.2	9.1	11.5	11.8	12.0

(a) (i) Plot a graph of pH (on the *y* axis) against volume of NaOH (on the *x* axis).
Use a graph to determine the end point of the titration. Hence calculate the relative molecular mass of **A**. **8**
(ii) Calculate the value of K_a for **A** and state its units. **4**

(b) Calculate the molecular formula of **A**.
Given that **A** contains one asymmetric carbon atom, deduce its structure. Briefly indicate your reasoning. **4**

(c) The mass spectrum of **A** shows major peaks at *m/e* values of 15, 30, 45 and 75. Suggest a formula for the species responsible for each of these four peaks. **4**

(d) Describe a series of tests you would perform in order to confirm the structure obtained in *(b)*, given that you already know that it is an acid. **5**

25 *(L)(AL)*

12. *(a)* Define the terms (i) *heterolysis* and (ii) *homolysis*. **2**

(b) Primary alkyl halides (primary halogenoalkanes) will react with a variety of nucleophiles by an S_N2 mechanism.
(i) Outline the mechanism of the S_N2 reaction between iodoethane and potassium cyanide. **2**
(ii) Does this reaction involve heterolysis, homolysis or some other process? Name the process. **1**

(iii) Give **two** nucleophiles, other than cyanide ions or hydroxide ions, which will carry out an S_N2 reaction with iodoethane, and *name* the product obtained in each case. 4

(iv) Would you expect ethanamide to react readily with iodoethane in this way? Explain your reasoning. 2

(c) (i) Give an equation for the reaction between aqueous sodium hydroxide and the ester, ethyl ethanoate. 2

(ii) Give **one** way in which the mechanism of this reaction resembles that between hydroxide ion and iodoethane, and **one** way in which it differs from the iodoethane reaction. 4

17 *(O&C)(AL)*

13. Acid-catalysed dehydration of an optically active compound **A**. $C_4H_{10}O$, yields two isomeric products **B** and **C**. C_4H_8. Compound **B** exists in stereoisomeric forms. The reaction between **C** and hydrogen bromide produces compound **D**, C_4H_9Br, which yields **A** on hydrolysis. Oxidation of **A** gives compound **E**, C_4H_8O.
Compound **A** has a broad absorption at 3350 cm^{-1} in the infra-red, compound **E** has a strong absorption band at 1715 cm^{-1} and compounds **B** and **C** each have significant absorption bands close to 1650 cm^{-1}.
Use the data in the Table and the information provided in the question to deduce structures for compounds **A**, **B**, **C**, **D** and **E**. Name each of these compounds.

Table Infra-red absorption data

Bond	**Wavenumber/cm^{-1}**
C—H	2850–3300
C—C	750–1100
C=C	1620–1680
C=O	1680–1750
C—O	1000–1300
O—H (alcohols)	3230–3550
O—H (acids)	2500–3000

15

15*(NEAB)(AL)*

14. The substance *morphine* was first isolated from the opium poppy in 1803. It is a very effective pain killer but it is also highly addictive. Later, another substance *codeine* was extracted from the opium poppy. This is only about one-tenth as effective as a pain killer but, in small doses, it is not addictive.

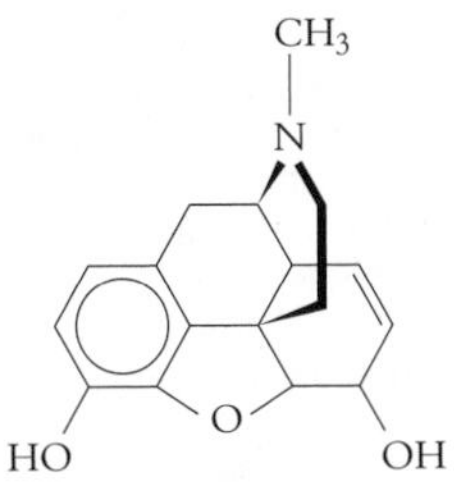

CH$_3$ N O HO OH — Morphine

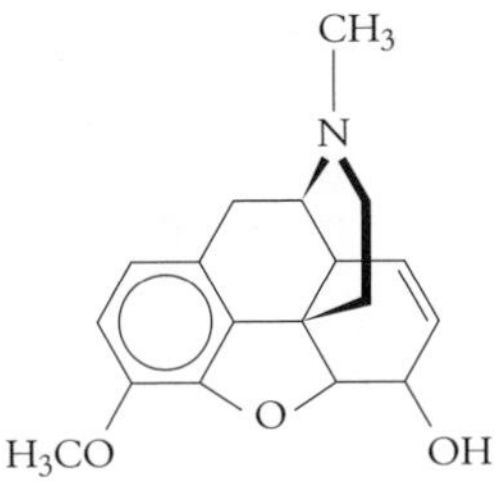

CH$_3$ N O H$_3$CO OH — Codeine

(a) For each of the cases below, describe a simple chemical test which involves a *colour change* and

(i) to which codeine and morphine would both respond in the same way, 2

(ii) to which codeine and morphine would respond differently, saying how each would behave. 3

(b) Describe, using a diagram, how it would be possible to use thin layer chromatography to show that a liquid extract from opium poppies contained various substances, among them morphine and codeine. 3

(c) Use the table of characteristic i.r. absorptions in § 35.8.2 to suggest *one* peak which morphine and codeine would have in common in their i.r. spectra. Explain your choice. 2

(d) Use the table of chemical shifts for protons in n.m.r. spectra in § 35.10 to suggest which **one** of the following chemical shift values is present in the n.m.r. spectrum of codeine but **not** morphine. Give a reason for your choice.

2.3 3.8 5.0 5.3 2

(e) Some chemists set out to esterify codeine by using ethanoic anhydride. Complete the right-hand structure to show the product they would obtain.

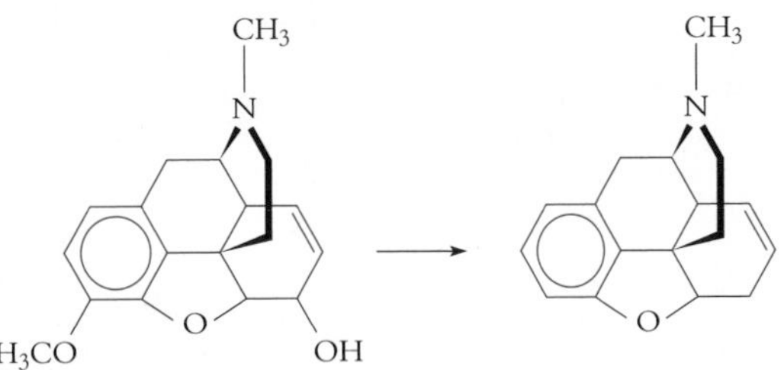

Codeine 2

(f) Having synthesised such a compound, what procedures would a pharmaceutical company have to follow before gaining approval for sale? 3

17 *(O&C)(Salters)(AL)*

15. *(a)* Draw structures of the organic product(s) when

(i) ethene reacts with bromine at room temperature, 1

(ii) benzene reacts with bromine at room temperature, in the absence of light, but in the presence of iron filings. 1

(b) (i) The benzene molecule is said to have **π-electron delocalisation**. Explain what is meant by this term. 2

(ii) Show the mechanism of the nitration of benzene. 2

(c) Five derivatives of benzene, compounds **A** to **E**, are all liquids above 35 °C and have the following structures:

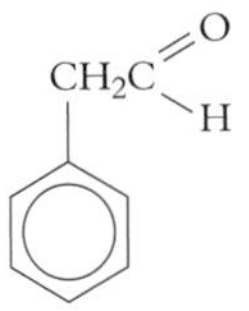

A: C_6H_5–CH$_2$CHO (CH$_2$C(=O)H)

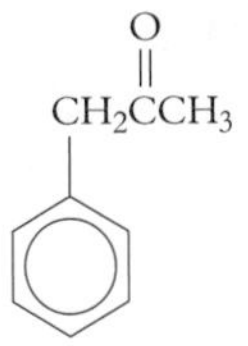

B: C_6H_5–CH$_2$COCH$_3$ (CH$_2$CCH$_3$ with C=O)

C: C_6H_5–CH$_2$CHOHCH$_3$

D: C_6H_5–CH$_2$CH$_2$OH

E: C_6H_5–C(OH)(CH$_3$)CH$_3$ (CH$_3$CCH$_3$ with OH)

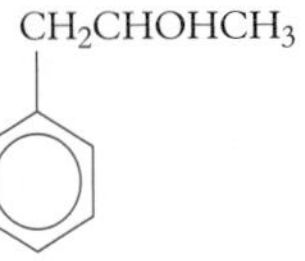

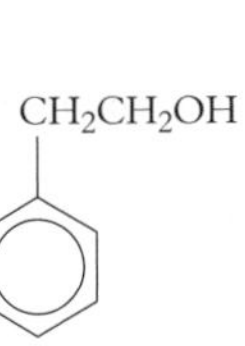

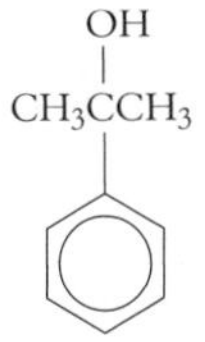

(i) Describe a simple test tube experiment to distinguish between **A** and **B** stating the reagents, conditions and the observation which enables the distinction to be made. 2

(ii) State which **one** of the five compounds, on mild oxidation, yields compound **A**. 1

(iii) State which **one** of the five compounds, on oxidation, yields compound **B**. 1

(iv) Choose **one** of the five compounds which exhibits optical isomerism. 1

(v) Choose, from the five compounds, a pair of structural isomers. 1

12 *(WJEC)(AL)*

16. Chillies are a variety of pepper which contain capsaicin, $C_{18}H_{27}O_3N$, in varying amounts. Capsaicin stimulates pain receptors in the mouth, but does not cause physical damage. Capsaicin is of the general form R′CONHR″, where R′ and R″ are organic groups. Compounds such as this can be hydrolysed by boiling them with aqueous hydrochloric acid to give a carboxylic acid and an amine salt:

$$R'CONHR'' + H_2O + HCl \longrightarrow R'CO_2H + R''NH_3^+Cl^-$$

A sample of capsaicin was hydrolysed, and gave the acid **A**, $C_{10}H_{18}O_2$, and after the amine salt solution was made alkaline, the amine **B**, $C_8H_{11}O_2N$.
Acid **A** contains a carbon–carbon double bond, which if reacted first with ozone, O_3, followed by dilute ethanoic acid solution in the presence of zinc gives carbonyl compounds which can be identified by various methods. The reaction may be represented as:

$$(a)(d)C{=}C(b)(c) \longrightarrow (a)(d)C{=}O + O{=}C(b)(c)$$

(a) Suggest a structure for **A** using the following information:
The reaction of **A** with ozone as described above gives two fragments **C** and **D**.
C, C_4H_8O, has a branched chain and reacts with ammoniacal silver nitrate solution (Tollens' Reagent) to give a silver mirror.
Compound **D**, $C_6H_{10}O_3$, similarly reacts with ammoniacal silver nitrate solution (Tollens' Reagent) and also reacts with sodium carbonate solution to give carbon dioxide. Of all the possible isomers of $C_6H_{10}O_3$, **D** has the highest melting temperature.
Compound **A** exists as two geometric isomers. **9**

(b) Suggest a structure for **B**, using the following information:
Mass spectroscopy of **B** gives a peak at $m/e = 31$.
If **B** is reacted with ice-cold sodium nitrite in the presence of concentrated hydrochloric acid and the product of this reaction is added to an alkaline solution of 2-naphthol, no coloured precipitate is formed.
If **B** is reacted with alkaline potassium manganate(VII) solution, vanillic acid is produced:

COOH
OCH_3
OH **8**

(c) Suggest a structure for capsaicin. **2**

(d) Capsaicin is a solid; describe how you would purify a sample of about 5 g of the impure material. **6**

25 *(L)(AL)*

17. *(a)* The enthalpy of hydrogenation of cyclohexene, C_6H_{10}, is -120 kJ mol^{-1} and that of benzene, C_6H_6, is -208 kJ mol^{-1}. Explain why the value for benzene is not three times that of cyclohexene and account for the difference. Hence discuss why bromine in aqueous solution will react with cyclohexene to form 1,2-dibromocyclohexane but bromine does not react with benzene under these conditions. **8**

(b) Substitution reactions in organic chemistry can involve three different mechanisms.
Name these three types of mechanism and, using the compounds methane, bromomethane and benzene, write equations to illustrate each type of mechanism. For your examples with methane and bromomethane, state the reaction conditions and outline the mechanisms involved. **17**

(c) Give the reagent and conditions needed to produce hex-1-ene from hexan-1-ol. The infra-red spectrum of one of these two compounds is shown below. Use the spectrum and the table of data to identify this compound. State **two** regions, other than the fingerprint region, where the infra-red spectrum of the other compound would be different.

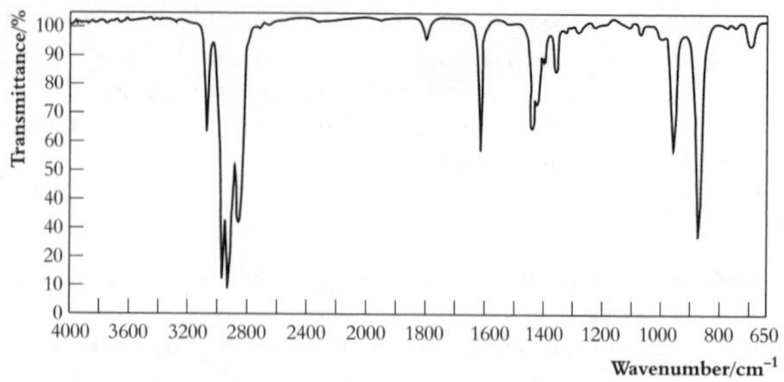

Table Infra-red absorption data

Bond	Wavenumber/cm^{-1}
C—H	2850–3300
C—C	750–1100
C=C	1620–1680
C=O	1680–1750
C—O	1000–1300
O—H (alcohols)	3230–3550
O—H (acids)	2500–3000

5

30 *(NEAB)(AL)*

18. *(a)* Write an equation for the oxidation of pentan-2-ol by acidified potassium dichromate(VI) showing clearly the structure of the organic product. You may use the symbol [O] for the oxidising agent. **2**

(b) Pent-2-ene can be formed by the dehydration of pentan-2-ol. Give the reagent and conditions used. Outline a mechanism for this reaction. **6**

(c) Alcohols **E**, **F** and **G** are branched-chain isomers of pentanol.
E cannot be oxidised by acidified potassium dichromate(VI).
F can be oxidised by acidified potassium dichromate(VI) but cannot be dehydrated.
G can be oxidised by acidified potassium dichromate(VI) and can also be dehydrated.
Draw a possible structure for each of the three alcohols. **3**

(d) Draw and name the isomer of pentene which has three peaks in its low-resolution proton n.m.r. spectrum and give the relative areas under the peaks. **4**

15 *(NEAB)(AS/AL)*

19. *(a)* Compound **W** can be converted into three different organic compounds as shown by the reaction sequence below. Give the structures of the new compounds **X**, **Y** and **Z**. **3**

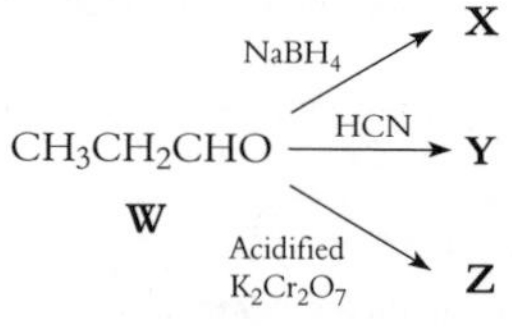

(b) Outline a mechanism for the formation of **Y**. **4**

(c) The infra-red spectra shown are those of the four compounds **W**, **X**, **Y** and **Z**. **4**

(i) Using the table of infra-red absorption data given below, identify which compound would give rise to each spectrum.

(ii) Suggest the wavenumber of the absorption caused by the C≡N bond.
(The wavenumber of this absorption is outside the fingerprint region.) **5**

Table Infra-red absorption data

Bond	Wavenumber/cm^{-1}
C—H	2850–3300
C—C	750–1100
C=C	1620–1680
C=O	1680–1750
C—O	1000–1300
O—H (alcohols)	3230–3550
O—H (acids)	2500–3000

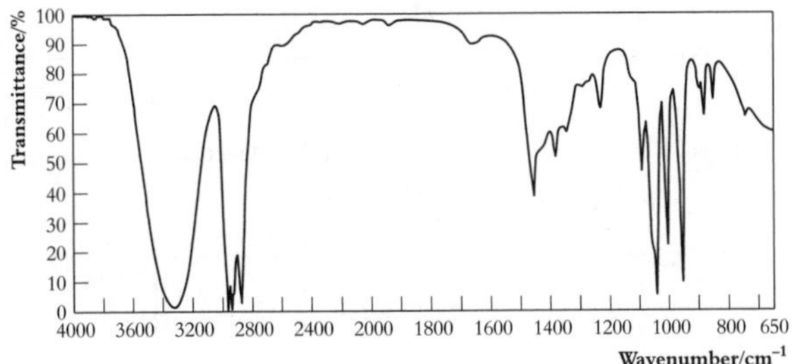

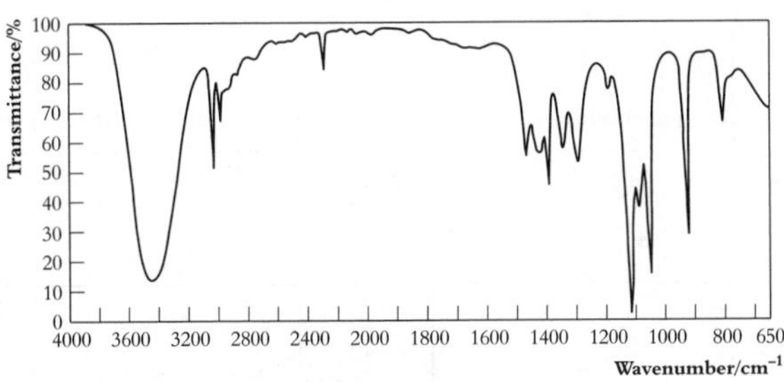

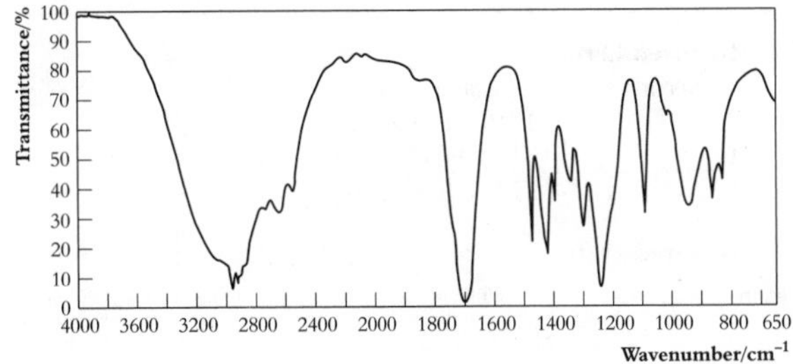

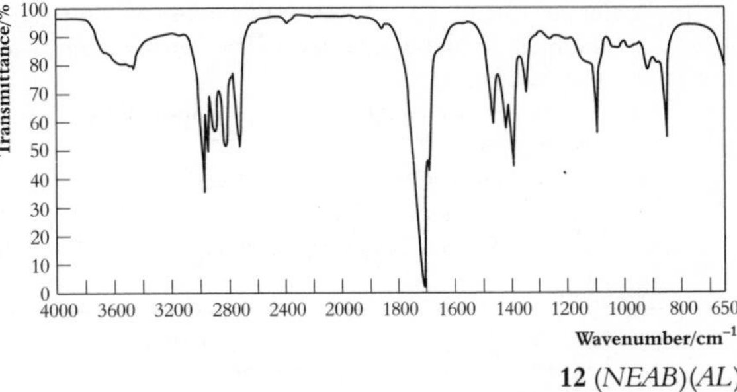

12 (*NEAB*)(*AL*)

20. A cyclic hydrocarbon **A**. C_5H_8, is converted into compound **B**, C_5H_9Br, on treatment with hydrogen bromide. When **B** is warmed with aqueous sodium hydroxide, it is converted into **C**, $C_5H_{10}O$. Mild oxidation of **C** yields compound **D**, whereas vigorous oxidation causes one of the C—C bonds to break, producing pentanedioic acid, $HOOC(CH_2)_3COOH$. The mass spectrum of compound **D** has a molecular ion peak at $m/z = 84$. Compound **A** is reformed when **B** is treated with ethanolic potassium hydroxide and also when **C** is treated with concentrated sulphuric acid.
Compound **A** has an absorption band at approximately 1650 cm^{-1} in the infra-red, compound **C** has a broad absorption at 3350 cm^{-1}, and compound **D** has a strong absorption band at 1730 cm^{-1}.
Use the data in the table, as well as the information provided in the question, to deduce structures for compounds **A**, **B**, **C** and **D**, respectively. Explain the basis for each of your deductions. For each step, name the type of reaction taking place. Outline the mechanism for the formation of compound **B**. **15**

Table Infra-red absorption data

Bond	Wavenumber/cm^{-1}
C—H	2850–3300
C—C	750–1100
C=C	1620–1680
C=O	1680–1750
C—O	1000–1300
O—H (alcohols)	3230–3550
O—H (acids)	2500–3000

15 (*NEAB*)(*AL*)

21. The table below gives some characteristic absorption frequencies in the infrared region for bonds in organic molecules.

Bond	Group	Range/cm^{-1}	Intensity
C—H	—CH_2— (alkane)	1465	medium
	methyl	1450 bend	medium
C=O	aldehyde	1740–1720	strong
	ketone	1725–1705	strong
	carboxylic acid	1725–1700	strong
O—H	alcohol (hydrogen-bonded)	3400–3200	strong and broad
	carboxylic acid (hydrogen-bonded)	3300–2500	variable and broad

(a) Using the data in the table suggest the **class** of compound for **each** of the spectra described below, giving the reasons for your choice:
(i) a medium absorption at 1450 cm^{-1} and a single strong absorption at 1730 cm^{-1};
(ii) a broad absorption between 3500 and 2500 cm^{-1} and a strong absorption at 1720 cm^{-1}. **4**

(b) The reaction scheme below represents the manufacture of aspirin.

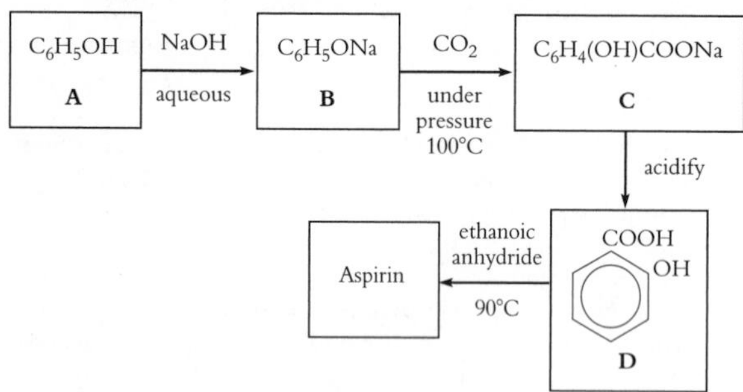

(i) Name **A** and give the systematic name for **D**. **2**
(ii) Draw the structure of a molecule of aspirin. **1**
(iii) Classify the type of compound formed when **D** is refluxed with methanol and concentrated sulphuric acid and draw its structure. **2**

(c) The pain-killer paracetamol has the structure

HO–⟨benzene ring⟩–NHCCH$_3$ (with C=O)

(i) State **two** functional groups present in the paracetamol molecule. **2**
(ii) Outline a method by which paracetamol and aspirin could be distinguished from each other. **2**

(d) The compound **D** sometimes occurs as an impurity in aspirin. It can be detected since it gives a coloration with aqueous iron(III) chloride.
The concentration of the compound responsible for the colour can be measured with an absorption spectrometer using the relationship

Absorbance = k × [concentration] where k is constant.

A standard solution of the coloured species of concentration 1.00×10^{-4} mol dm^{-3} gave an absorbance of 0.22.
A solution **X** gave the absorbance of 0.40.
Calculate the concentration of the coloured species in **X**. **2**

15 *(WJEC)(AL)*

22. (a) An organic compound **A** has a molar mass of 46 g mol^{-1} and the following elemental composition by mass:

C 52.13%; H 13.15%; O 34.72%

Determine the molecular formula of **A**. **2**

(b) The organic compound **A** has an infrared spectrum which shows the following features:

Absorption at 2900 cm^{-1}	C—H stretching frequency
Absorption at 3300 cm^{-1}	O—H stretching frequency
Absorption at 1050 cm^{-1}	C—O stretching frequency
Absorption at 1400 cm^{-1}	C—H bending frequency

The shape and position of the —OH peak indicates substantial hydrogen bonding.
(i) Explain, briefly, what is meant by the term hydrogen bonding. **1**
(ii) By reference to the infrared spectrum and your answer to *(a)* deduce the structure of **A**.
Give three reasons in support of your answer. **4**

(c) The mass spectrum of **A** is given below.

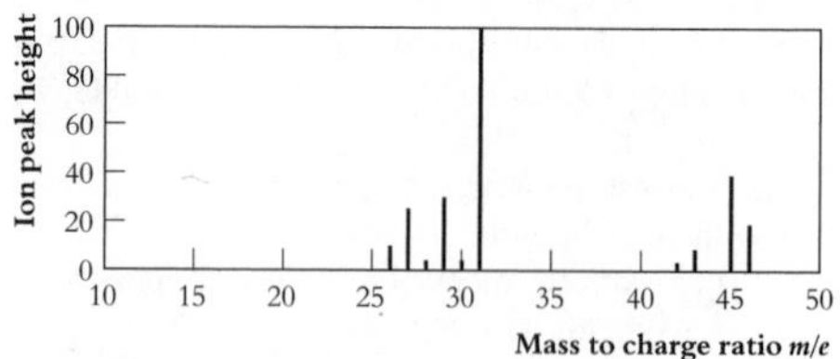

Using the structural formula of **A** deduced above, suggest formulae for the positive ions responsible for m/e peaks at 45, 31 and 29. **3**

(d) (i) When **A** is treated with ethanoyl chloride a compound **B** is formed containing 4 carbon atoms.
Give the name and structure of **B** and state to which class of organic compounds it belongs. **3**
(ii) State how you would carry out the addition of ethanoyl chloride to the compound, **A**, paying particular attention to safety. **2**

15 *(WJEC)(AL)*

23. Consider the reaction scheme summarised below, the infrared data and frequency chart and other information about compounds **A–F** which follows:

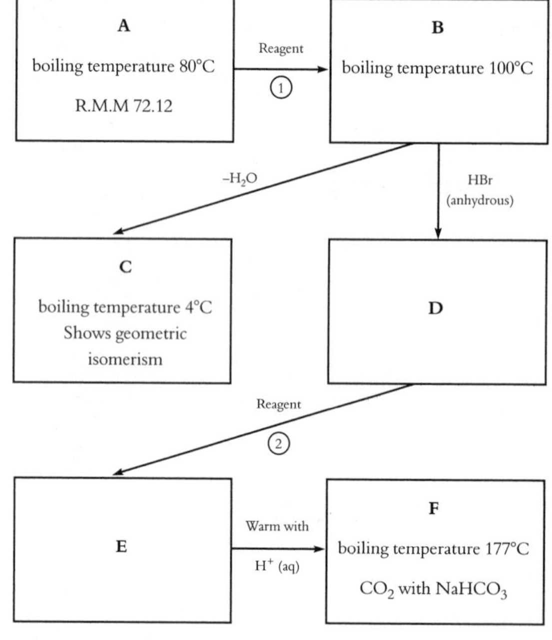

Infrared Data

Compound	i.r. wavelength/cm^{-1}
A	1710 (strong peak)
B	3300 (broad band)
E	2250 (sharp peak)

Infrared Data

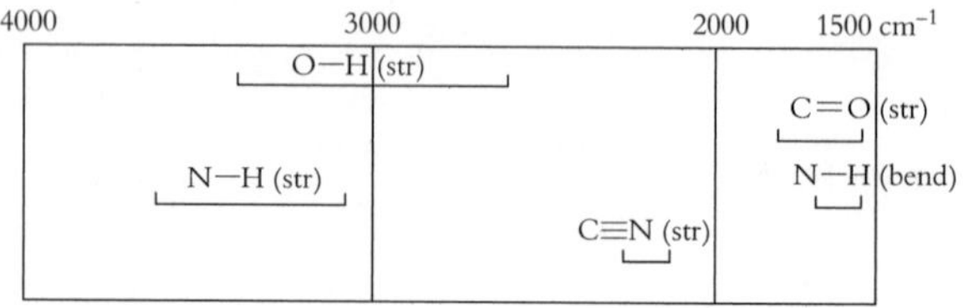

Information
1. Compound **A** gives a positive iodoform test.
2. Compounds **B** and **F** each contain one chiral centre.

3. Compound **F** (1.0000 g) titrated in aqueous solution against 0.1000 mol dm^{-3} sodium hydroxide solution required 97.90 cm^3 of the latter for complete reaction.

(a) Identify compounds **A** to **F** by writing appropriate structural formulae and give **brief** reasoning for your conclusions. 8

(b) Identify the reagents ① and ② and give the conditions appropriate for their use. 3

(c) State which of compounds **A**, **C**, **D** and **E** would also possess a chiral centre. 1

(d) Explain how geometric isomerisation arises in compound **C**. 1

(e) State the structural features in compounds **A**, **B** and **E** responsible for the observed i.r. bands 3

(f) Calculate the relative molecular mass of compound **F**. 2

(g) State the nature and approximate position of the i.r. bands you would expect to observe for compound **F**. 2

20 *(WJEC)(AL)*

24. The structural formula of the hormone adrenaline is

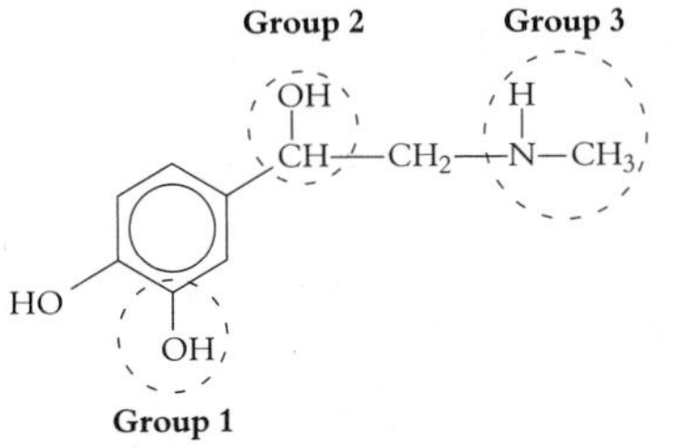

Group 2 Group 3

OH H

CH—CH$_2$—N—CH$_3$

HO OH

Group 1

(a) What is the molecular formula of adrenaline? 1

(b) Name the functional groups enclosed within the numbered dotted circles and indicate, where appropriate, whether they are primary, secondary or tertiary. 3

(c) State whether you think adrenaline is likely to dissolve in water.
Justify your answer. 2

(d) Which functional group reacts with:
(i) aqueous sodium hydroxide; 1
(ii) dilute hydrochloric acid? 1

(e) Name the reagents you would use to carry out the following reactions with adrenaline:
(i) converting functional **Group 1** from —OH into —OCOCH$_3$; 1
(ii) converting functional **Group 3** from —NHCH$_3$ into —N(CH$_3$)$_2$. 1

(f) Explain how the —NHCH$_3$ group in adrenaline and the reagent you suggested in *(e)*(ii) can react together. 2

12 *L(N)(AL)*

25. Limonene, **I**, is the substance providing the natural odour of lemons. As part of work to relate its structure to that of another important natural product, carvone, **IV**, and to establish the position of the double bonds in both of these compounds, the following sequence of reactions were carried out.
Examine this sequence of reactions carefully and answer the questions which follow it.

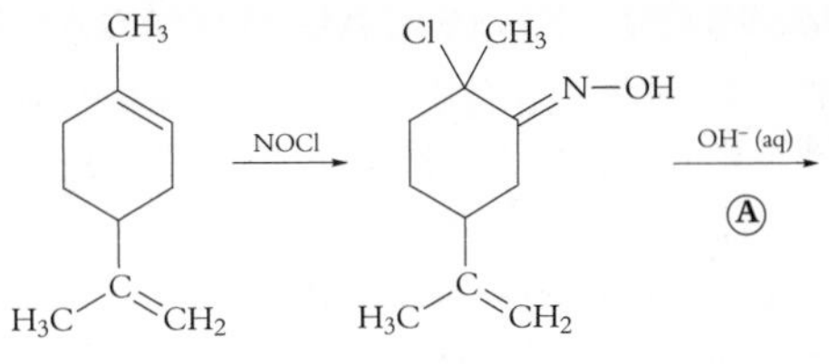

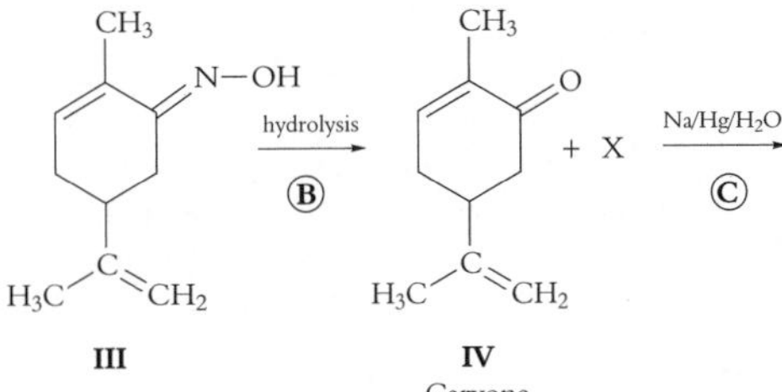

CH$_3$ N—OH H$_3$C C CH$_2$ — hydrolysis (B) → CH$_3$ O H$_3$C C CH$_2$ + X — Na/Hg/H$_2$O (C) →

III IV Carvone

CH$_3$ OH H$_3$C C CH$_2$ — (D) → CH$_3$ OH H$_3$C C O

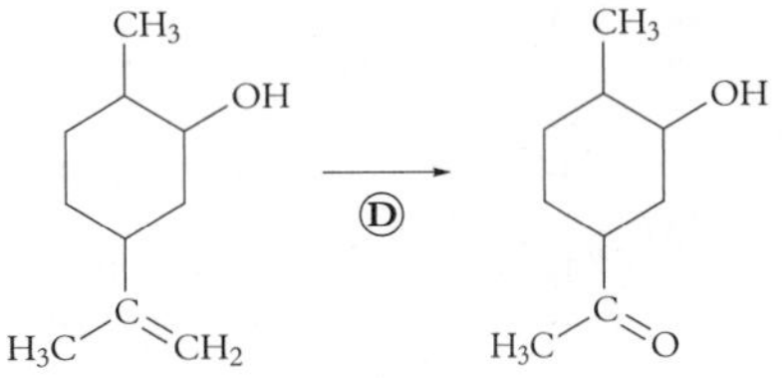

V VI

(a) What type of reaction is reaction **A**? 1

(b) Identify the **three** functional groups (not necessarily all different) in compound **IV**. 3

(c) To what classes of compound does compound **IV** belong? 3

(d) (i) What reagent would convert compound **IV** into compound **III**? 1
(ii) Considering your answer to *(d)*(i) above, suggest the identity of the unspecified product, **X**, of reaction **B**. 1

(e) What type of reaction is reaction **C**? 1

(f) At first sight, compound **V** may not be the product which you would expect to obtain from a reaction of type **C**. Give the structure of the product which you might reasonably have expected from this type of reaction. In practice, compound **V** is obtained by choosing the particular reagent given in the sequence above. 2

(g) Name a reaction which would convert compound **V** into compound **VI**, and give the other carbon-containing product which would be obtained. 2

(h) Give the structure of the products which would be obtained if compound **V** was treated with
(i) ethanoyl chloride 2
(ii) bromine in an inert solvent. 2

18 *O&C (AL)*

PHYSICAL, INORGANIC AND ORGANIC CHEMISTRY

1. (a) The free radical reaction between methane and chlorine in ultraviolet light has a mechanism whose initiation step is

$Cl_2 \longrightarrow 2Cl\cdot$

Followed by one of two possible propagation steps

$CH_4 + Cl\cdot \longrightarrow \cdot CH_3 + HCl$ I
$CH_4 + Cl\cdot \longrightarrow \cdot CH_3Cl + H\cdot$ II

(i) Use the data given below to predict which is the more likely propagation step.
bond enthalpies/kJ mol^{-1}: Cl—Cl 243; C—H 435; H—Cl 432; C—Cl 346. **4**
(ii) Identify one product you might expect from a termination step following each reaction that would not be found in the alternative reaction scheme. **2**

(b) The reaction in part *(a)* is an important industrial source of hydrochloric acid, HCl(aq). The hydrogen halides HX(aq), sometimes called the hydrohalic acids, are all Brønstead–Lowry acids.
(i) What is a Brønstead–Lowry acid? **1**
(ii) Explain why HF(aq) is the weakest of these hydrohalic acids. **2**

(c) Boron trichloride is a gaseous compound which reacts readily with water.
(i) Write an equation for this reaction. **2**
(ii) Explain why boron trichloride reacts readily with water **3**

14 *(L)(AL)*

2. You have used 1-iodobutane in some of your experiments.
(a) Construct a Hess cycle for the atomisation of 1-iodobutane, and use the data below, at 298 K, to show by calculation that the value of $\Delta H_{at}[CH_3CH_2CH_2CH_2I(g)]$ is +4987.6 kJ mol^{-1}.
$\Delta H_f[CH_3CH_2CH_2CH_2I(g)] = -52.0$ kJ mol^{-1}
$\Delta H^{\ominus}_{at}$[C(graphite)] = +716.7 kJ mol^{-1}
$\Delta H^{\ominus}_{at}[\frac{1}{2} H_2(g)] = +218.0$ kJ mol^{-1}
$\Delta H^{\ominus}_{at}[\frac{1}{2} I_2(s)] = +106.8$ kJ mol^{-1} **3**

(b) (i) Draw a 'dot-and-cross' diagram for the electronic structure of 1-iodobutane, showing outer shell electrons only. **2**
(ii) Calculate the energy of the C—I bond in 1-iodobutane.
Use the standard enthalpy change of atomisation of 1-iodobutane, and the data below:
E(C—H) = +413 kJ mol^{-1}
E(C—C) = +347 kJ mol^{-1} **3**

(c) Three drops of 1-iodobutane are added to a test tube containing 2 cm^3 of ethanol and 2 cm^3 of hot aqueous silver nitrate solution. A reaction occurs immediately.
(i) What would you observe? Write an **ionic** equation, including state symbols, for your observation. **3**
(ii) Name the **organic** product of this reaction. **1**

(d) When the experiment in *(c)* is repeated with 1-chlorobutane it is very slow. Explain why the rates of the two reactions are different. **2**

(e) The experiment in *(c)* is repeated using 2-chloro-2-methylpropane.
(i) Draw a **displayed** formula of 2-chloro-2-methylpropane. **1**
(ii) Describe what you would expect to see. **1**
(iii) Explain why this reaction is more rapid than the reaction when 1-chlorobutane is used. **2**

(L(N))(AL)

3. Parts *(a)–(c)* of this question concern the analysis of the alloy in a coin, and parts *(d)–(f)* aspects of an organic synthesis. Some modern British coins are made from an alloy, nickel-brass, which consists essentially of the metals copper, nickel and zinc. A one pound coin was completely dissolved in moderately concentrated nitric acid, in which all three metals dissolve, to give solution **A**. Dilute sodium hydroxide solution was then added carefully with stirring, until present in excess. Zinc hydroxide is amphoteric but copper and nickel hydroxides are not. A precipitate, **B**, was formed which was filtered off from the supernatant liquid, **C**.

$Ni^{2+}(aq) + 2e^- \rightleftharpoons Ni(s)$
$Zn^{2+}(aq) + 2e^- \rightleftharpoons Zn(s)$
$Cu^{2+}(aq) + 2e^- \rightleftharpoons Cu(s)$
$NO_3^-(aq) + 2H^+(aq) + e^- \rightleftharpoons NO_2(g) + H_2O(l)$

(a) (i) Using the appropriate half equations, construct an ionic equation for the reaction of copper with nitric acid. **2**
(ii) What type of reaction is taking place? **1**

(b) Identify, by giving the full formulae:
(i) the complex cations containing copper and nickel present in **A**: **2**
(ii) the precipitates in **B**; **2**
(iii) any metal-containing anion in **C**. **1**

(c) (i) Write an equation for the precipitation of any one of the metal ions in **A** with sodium hydroxide to form precipitate **B**. **2**
(ii) What type of reaction is occurring in *(c)*(i)? **1**

(d) The compound **W** (molecular formula $C_5H_8O_2$) has the structure:

$$CH_2{=}C(CH_3){-}CO_2CH_3$$

and shows no geometric isomerism.
Give the structure of an isomer of **W** which does show geometric isomerism. Explain why this structure shows such isomerism but **W** does not. **3**

(e) For the following series of changes:

$$\underset{\mathbf{W}}{CH_2{=}C(CH_3){-}CO_2CH_3} \xrightarrow{\text{Step 1}} \underset{\mathbf{X}}{C_4H_6O_2} \xrightarrow{\text{Step 2}} \underset{\mathbf{Y}}{C_4H_5OCl} \xrightarrow{\text{Step 3}} \underset{\mathbf{Z}}{C_4H_6OClBr}$$

Step 1 is brought about by boiling under reflux with dilute sulphuric acid.
(i) Deduce structures for **X** and **Y**. **2**
(ii) Give suitable reagents and conditions for each of steps 2 and 3. **4**
(iii) Give the mechanism for the reaction occurring in step 3. **3**

(f) Draw a representative length of the polymer chain which could be formed from **W**. **2**

25 *(L)(AL)*

4. Chemical reactions can be affected by homogeneous or by heterogeneous catalysts.
(a) Explain what is meant by the term *homogeneous* and suggest the most important feature in the mechanism of this type of catalysis when carried out by a transition-metal compound. **2**
(b) In aqueous solution, $S_2O_8^{2-}$ ions can be reduced to SO_4^{2-} ions by I^- ions.
(i) Write an equation for this reaction.

(ii) Suggest why the reaction has a high activation energy, making it slow in the absence of a catalyst.
(iii) Iron salts can catalyse this reaction. Write two equations to show the role of the catalyst in this reaction. **4**

(c) Below is a sketch showing typical efficiencies of transition metals from Period 5 (Rb to Xe) and Period 6 (Cs to Rn) when used in heterogeneous catalysis.

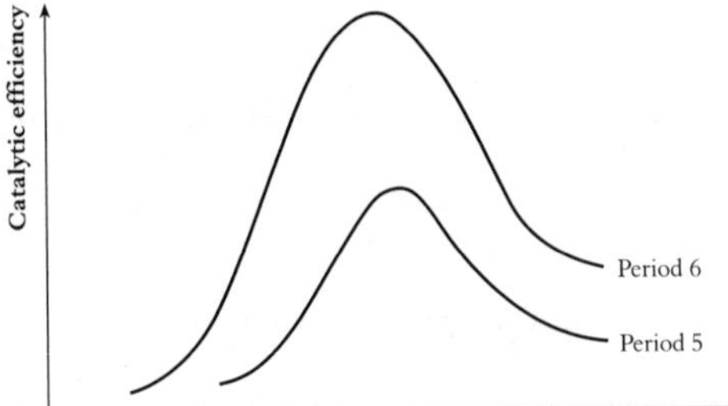

(i) Identify two metals which lie at opposite ends of these curves and explain why they show rather low catalytic efficiency.
(ii) Suggest why these curves pass through a maximum. **5**

(d) In catalytic converters which clean up petrol engine exhaust gases, a catalyst promotes the reduction of nitrogen oxides using another polluting gas as reductant. State a suitable catalyst for this task, identify the reductant, and write an equation for the reaction that results. **3**

14 (*NEAB*)(*AL*)

5. The equation for the synthesis of hydrazine by the direct combination of the elements is given below.

$$N_2(g) + 2H_2(g) \rightleftharpoons N_2H_4(g)$$

(a) Write an expression for the equilibrium constant, K_c, for this reaction. **1**
(b) Explain why the concentrations of reactants and products remain constant once a dynamic equilibrium has been established. **2**
(c) Explain why this reaction is described as *homogeneous*. **1**
(d) Predict how the addition of a catalyst will affect the position of the equilibrium and the value of K_c **2**
(e) Hydrazine, N_2H_4, and dinitrogen tetroxide, N_2O_4, react together to form nitrogen and water.
(i) Give the oxidation states of nitrogen in N_2H_4 and in N_2O_4.
(ii) Write an equation for the reaction between N_2H_4 and N_2O_4. **3**
(f) Hydrazine can be represented by the structure

```
H—N̈—N̈—H
  |  |
  H  H
```

(i) Predict the H—N—H bond angle
(ii) Write an equation for the reaction between hydrazine and an excess of hydrochloric acid.
(iii) Explain why hydrazine reacts with anhydrous cobalt(II) chloride. **3**

12 (*NEAB*)(*AS/AL*)

6. *(a)* Explain the trends in first ionisation energy and electronegativity down Group 1.
(ii) Discuss two ways in which lithium is an atypical member of Group 1.
(iii) Write equations for the reactions of sodium oxide and phosphorus(V) oxide with water and explain, in terms of the bonding present in the oxides, why the resulting solutions have different pH values. **15**

(b) The rate of reaction between compounds **C** and **D** was studied at a fixed temperature and some results obtained are shown in the table below.

Experiment	Initial concentration of **C**/mol dm^{-3}	Initial concentration of **D**/mol dm^{-3}	Initial rate r/mol dm^{-3} s^{-1}
1	0.010	0.010	1.0×10^{-6}
2	0.020	0.010	4.0×10^{-6}
3	0.030	0.020	9.0×10^{-6}
4	0.040	0.020	to be calculated

(i) Explain the meaning of the term *rate of reaction* and why rates of reaction depend on concentration. Suggest why initial rates are used in the table above.
(ii) Use the data in the table to deduce the order of reaction with respect to compound **C** and the order of reaction with respect to compound **D**. Hence calculate the initial rate of reaction in experiment 4. Write the rate equation for this reaction and hence calculate the value of the rate constant with its units. **11**

(c) Write an equation for the hydrolysis of methyl ethanoate by sodium hydroxide. When the initial concentration of both reagents was 0.020 mol dm^{-3}, the reaction was found to be first order with respect to each reagent. In a further experiment at the same temperature when the initial concentration of ester was 0.020 mol dm^{-3} and the initial concentration of hydroxide ions was 2.0 mol dm^{-3} the reaction appears to be zero order with respect to hydroxide ions. Suggest why this is so. **4**

30 (*NEAB*)(*AS/AL*)

7. (a) (i) Explain the meaning of the terms *empirical formula* and *molecular formula*. Give the three molecular formulae for organic compounds which have the empirical formula CH_2O and relative molecular masses below 100.
In fact, four compounds, **H**, **J**, **K** and **L** fit this information.
H can be oxidised to a carboxylic acid, **M**, and also reduced to a primary alcohol, **N**.
M and **N** react together, when warmed in the presence of concentrated sulphuric acid, to form **J**.
L contains a carboxylic acid group and is a structural isomer of **J**.
K contains a carboxylic acid group and shows optical isomerism.
Draw the structures of the six compounds, **H**, **J**, **K**, **L**, **M** and **N**.
(ii) Glucose (M_r = 180) also has the empirical formula CH_2O. Using its molecular formula, write an equation for the fermentation of glucose to form ethanol and give a necessary condition for fermentation to occur. **15**

(b) The table below shows the melting temperatures T_m, and the atomic radii, r, of the Period 3 elements.

Element	Na	Mg	Al	Si	P	S	Cl	Ar
T_m/K	371	923	933	1680	317	392	172	84
r/nm	0.191	0.160	0.130	0.118	0.110	0.102	0.099	0.095

(i) Explain the variation in atomic radius.
(ii) In terms of structure and bonding, explain the irregular variation in melting temperature.
(iii) Predict the variation in T_m across Period 2. Explain your answer. **15**

30 (*NEAB*)(*AS/AL*)

8. Citric acid is used in foodstuffs as an antioxidant and, together with its sodium salt, as an acidity regulator. It occurs naturally in fruit juices.

A formula of citric acid is

$$\begin{array}{c} CH_2CO_2H \\ | \\ HO-C-CO_2H \\ | \\ CH_2CO_2H \end{array}$$

(a) (i) Assuming citric acid behaves in aqueous solution as a monoprotic acid:

$$RCO_2H + H_2O \rightleftharpoons RCO_2^- + H_3O^+$$

write an expression for K_a for this acid. **1**

(ii) Calculate the pH of lemon juice which contains citric acid at a concentration of 0.200 mol dm^{-3} (K_a for citric acid = 7.4×10^{-4} mol dm^{-3}). **3**

(b) The use of citric acid together with its salt, sodium citrate, as an acidity regulator depends on the ability of this mixture to act as a buffer.

(i) What is the function of a buffer solution? **2**

(ii) Describe how the mixture of citric acid and sodium citrate achieves this buffering action. Give equations for the TWO reactions you describe. **3**

(iii) Calculate the pH of a buffer solution containing 0.200 mol dm^{-3} of citric acid and 0.400 mol dm^{-3} of sodium citrate. **2**

(c) Citric acid forms a liquid ester which has the structural formula

$$\begin{array}{c} CH_2COOC_2H_5 \\ | \\ HO-C-COOC_2H_5 \\ | \\ CH_2COOC_2H_5 \end{array}$$

(i) Describe a test you could use to show that the ester contains an —OH group. **2**

(ii) What reagent would you use to hydrolyse the ester? **1**

(iii) Treatment of the products of the reaction in *(c)*(ii) leads to the production of a pure sample of citric acid. How would you show the presence of the $-CO_2H$ group in the citric acid other than by the use of an indicator? **2**

16 *(L)(AS/AL)*

9. Sodium hydrogencarbonate, $NaHCO_3$, decomposes on heating. The decomposition products are sodium carbonate, carbon dioxide and water. The equation for the reaction is

$$2NaHCO_3(s) \longrightarrow Na_2CO_3(s) + CO_2(g) + H_2O(l)$$

The standard enthalpy changes of formation at 298 K of the four compounds are listed below

	$\Delta H_f^\ominus$ kJ mol^{-1}
$NaHCO_3(s)$	−951
$Na_2CO_3(s)$	−1131
$CO_2(g)$	−394
$H_2O(l)$	−286

(a) Copy and complete the following Hess cycle by filling in the empty box.

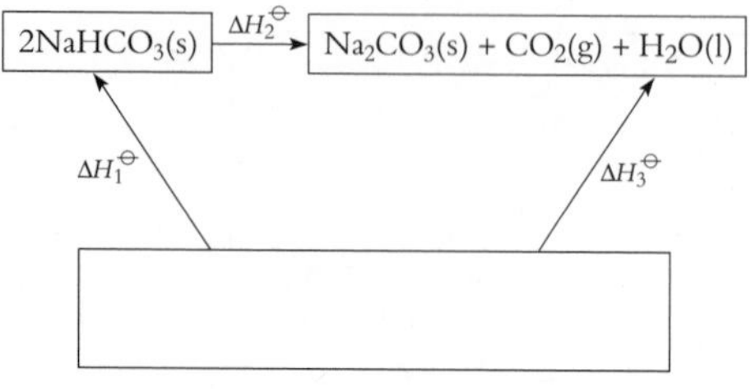

2

(b) Use your complete cycle to calculate the standard enthalpy change (in kJ) accompanying the thermal decomposition of 2 moles of sodium hydrogencarbonate.

Remember to include the appropriate sign in your answer. **2**

(c) The hydrogencarbonate ion, HCO_3^- can behave either as an acid or as a base, using the Brønsted–Lowry definitions. Write down the formula of the entity (ion or molecule) produced in each case.

(i) When acting as an acid, HCO_3^- becomes ...

(ii) When acting as a base, HCO_3^- becomes ... **2**

(d) A clean nichrome wire was moistened with concentrated hydrochloric acid, then dipped into a sample of sodium hydrogencarbonate and held in a non-luminous Bunsen flame.

What colour would the flame be? **1**

(e) Samples of sodium hydrogencarbonate to be used in baking powder must be of high purity.

How could examination of the emission spectrum of a sample be used to check that it did not contain a significant quantity of potassium? **1**

8 *(L/N)(AS/AL)*

10. This question is concerned with oxygen and ozone in the atmosphere. Read the passage, study the graphs below and then answer the questions on them.

Oxygen molecules in the stratosphere (above 100 km) undergo photodissociation by absorption of solar radiation of wavelengths (λ) less than 240 nm according to equation (B). Because the gas density at these heights is so low the free oxygen atoms have a long lifetime. At even higher levels, the more energetic solar radiation with wavelengths below 100 nm causes photoionisation of the oxygen atoms according to equation (A).

Lower down, below 70 km, any oxygen atoms formed react rapidly with oxygen molecules to form ozone.

UV radiation of wavelength greater than 240 nm is not absorbed until it reaches the ozone layer where it is absorbed by photodissociation of the ozone according to equation (C). The oxygen atoms so formed rapidly recombine with another oxygen molecule to reform ozone but, in the overall process, the incident radiation has been absorbed and so cannot reach the Earth's surface.

$$O(g) \xrightarrow{\lambda < 100\ nm} O^+(g) + e^-(g) \quad (A)$$

$$O_2(g) \xrightarrow{100\ nm < \lambda < 240\ nm} 2O(g) \quad (B)$$

$$O_3(g) \xrightarrow{\lambda > 240\ nm} O_2(g) + O(g) \quad (C)$$

It is generally accepted that chlorofluorocarbons, when they reach these high altitudes, can produce free chlorine atoms by photodissociation. These can then react with ozone according to a two-step chain reaction:

$$Cl(g) + O_3(g) \longrightarrow ClO(g) + O_2(g) \quad (D)$$

$$ClO(g) + O(g) \longrightarrow Cl(g) + O_2(g) \quad (E)$$

The net reaction is $O_3(g) + O(g) \longrightarrow 2O_2(g)$ (F)

thus removing ozone and regenerating a free chlorine atom.

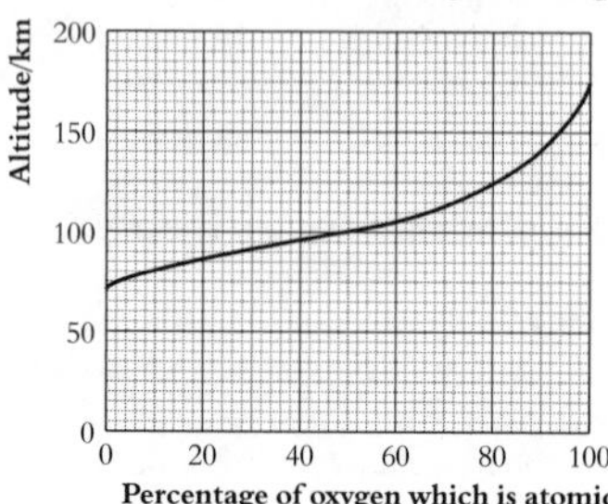

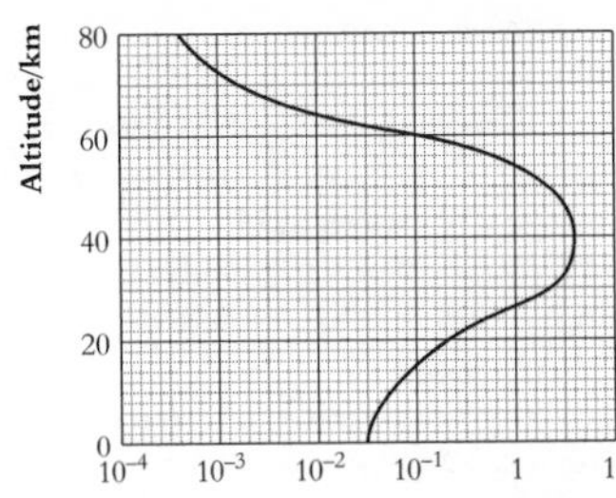

(a) Explain the difference between the terms *photodissociation* and *photoionisation*. **2**

(b) What percentage of oxygen is in the form of atoms at a height of 100 km? **1**

(c) What is the concentration of ozone at a height of 60 km? **1**

(d) At what altitude is the maximum concentration of ozone? **1**

(e) Write down an equation for the photodissociation of gaseous CF_2Cl_2. **2**

(f) In the context of chain reactions, and using the reactions A–F described above, **identify by letter** examples of *initiation*, *propagation* and *termination* reactions. **3**

(g) Why is the lifetime of oxygen atoms longer at higher altitudes? **2**

(h) Explain which type of radiation is most likely to be harmful to humans, giving your reasons. **2**

(i) Explain which type of radiation is likely to reach the Earth's surface if the ozone layer is destroyed by the CFCs. **2**

(O&C) (AL)

11. *(a)* Copper forms a compound K_3CuF_6.

(i) Give the formula and shape of the complex ion present in this compound.

(ii) What is the oxidation number of copper in this compound? Comment on the stability of this oxidation state for copper. **4**

(b) (i) Use the data below to explain why copper(I) ions disproportionate in aqueous solution, but silver(I) ions do not.

	$E^\ominus$/V
$Ag^{2+}(aq) + e^- \rightleftharpoons Ag^+(aq)$	+1.98
$Ag^+(aq) + e^- \rightleftharpoons Ag(s)$	+0.80
$Cu^+(aq) + e^- \rightleftharpoons Cu(s)$	+0.52
$Cu^{2+}(aq) + e^- \rightleftharpoons Cu^+(aq)$	+0.34

(ii) In the light of the information in *(b)*(i), suggest what you might observe when copper(I) oxide is added to excess dilute sulphuric acid. Write an equation for the reaction. **7**

(c) In an experiment to find the percentage of Cu^{2+} in a hydrated form of copper(II) sulphate, a weighed amount of $CuSO_4 \cdot xH_2O$ was dissolved in distilled water and 10 cm^3 (an excess) of potassium iodide solution added. The liberated iodine was titrated with 0.100 mol dm^{-3} sodium thiosulphate solution using starch as indicator. The equations for the reactions are:

$$2Cu^{2+}(aq) + 4I^-(aq) \longrightarrow 2CuI(s) + I_2(aq)$$

$$I_2(aq) + 2S_2O_3^{2-}(aq) \longrightarrow 2I^-(aq) + S_4O_6^{2-}(aq)$$

The experiment was performed three times in all, using different masses of the copper salt, the following results being obtained.

	A	B	C
Mass of $CuSO_4 \cdot xH_2O$/g	0.440	0.530	0.540
Volume of 0.100 mol dm^{-3} sodium thiosulphate/cm^3	24.8	29.9	24.9

(i) Calculate the titre/mass ratio for each experiment and select the values which are concordant (in good agreement).

(ii) Use the average of the concordant values from *(c)*(i) to calculate the percentage of Cu^{2+} in the hydrated copper(II) sulphate.

(iii) Why is it unnecessary to specify the volume of water in which the $CuSO_4 \cdot xH_2O$ was dissolved?

(iv) Why is a large excess of potassium iodide required in this titration?

(v) Suggest ONE advantage and ONE disadvantage of this method of performing a titration compared to the more traditional approach of making up one solution of $CuSO_4 \cdot xH_2O$ and using portions of this to perform several titrations. **14**

25 *(L)(AL)*

12. The composition of a sample of North Sea Gas is shown below:

Compound	**Percentage**
methane	94.4
higher alkanes	4.1
nitrogen	1.4
carbon dioxide	0.1

(a) Carbon dioxide may be removed from North Sea Gas using potassium hydroxide solution. Write a balanced equation for the reaction. **2**

(b) The combustion of methane is used domestically as a source of heat.

$$CH_4 + 2O_2 \longrightarrow CO_2 + 2H_2O$$

(i) Calculate the standard enthalpy of combustion of methane using the following bond energies:

Bond	**Energy/kJ mol^{-1}**
C—H	412
O═O	496
C═O	743
O—H	463

(ii) Calculate the volume of air under standard conditions needed to completely combust 5 × 10^3 moles of methane.

(iii) Write a balanced equation for the incomplete combustion of methane and explain why such combustion is dangerous to health. **9**

(c) Photochlorination of methane produces a mixture of chlorinated methanes.

(i) Name a method by which the chlorinated methanes may be separated on an industrial scale.

(ii) Write balanced equations for initiation, propagation and termination reactions in the photochlorination of methane.

(iii) Explain why light of a minimum frequency is needed in photochlorination. **7**

(CCEA) (AL)

13. Three different reactions of propan-2-ol are shown below.

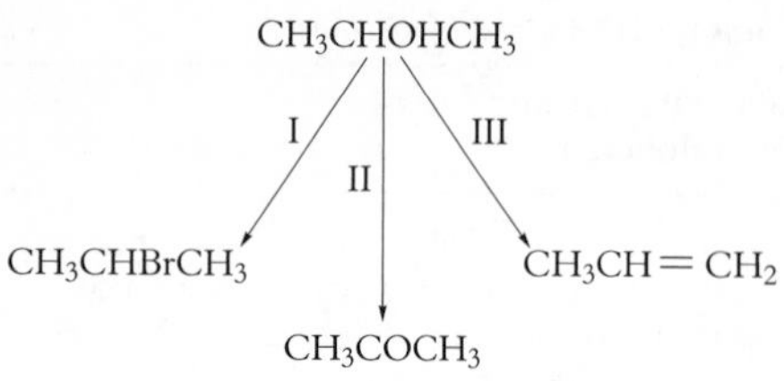

(a) For each of the reactions I, II and III, give suitable reagents and conditions. **6**

(b) If 2-methylpropan-2-ol $(CH_3)_3COH$, was used as the starting material in *(a)* instead of propan-2-ol, identify the organic products, if any, of reactions I, II and III. You should indicate if no reaction occurs. **3**

(c) Propan-2-ol and 2-methylpropan-2-ol have boiling points of 82.2 °C and 82.5 °C respectively.

(i) On a copy of the axes, draw a **fully** labelled sketch of the boiling point/composition diagram you would expect for mixtures of these two liquids. **3**

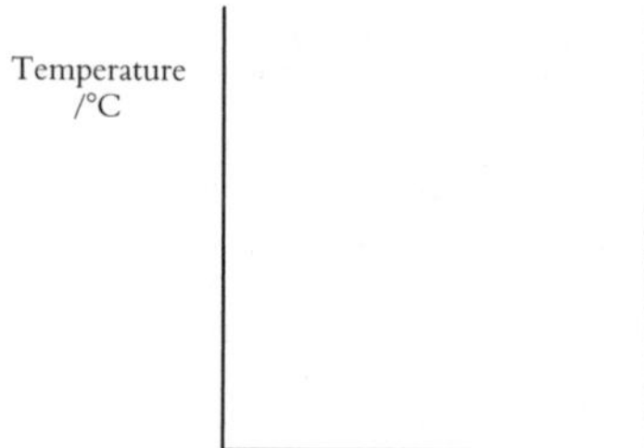

(ii) Justify the sketch in *(c)*(i) *in terms of the intermolecular forces present.* **2**

(iii) Comment on the possibility of separating this mixture by fractional distillation. **2**

16 *L (AL)*

14. This question is about ethanol and some of its reactions.

(a) A 750 cm^3 bottle of red wine is labelled as containing 12.4% of ethanol by volume.

(i) Calculate the volume of ethanol in a glass of this red wine, assuming that there are six glasses of wine in a bottle. **2**

(ii) Calculate the number of moles of ethanol in one glass of red wine.
[molar mass of ethanol = 46 g mol^{-1}; density of ethanol = 0.79 g cm^{-3}] **2**

(b) One method of analysing the amount of ethanol is to use acidified potassium dichromate(VI), $K_2Cr_2O_7$, to oxidize the ethanol. The colour change is from orange to green. The equation for the oxidation is:

$$K_2Cr_2O_7(aq) + 3C_2H_5OH(aq) + 4H_2SO_4(aq) \longrightarrow$$
$$K_2SO_4(aq) + Cr_2(SO_4)_3(aq) + 3CH_3CHO(aq) + 7H_2O(l)$$

(i) Which species in the equation is responsible for the green colour? **1**

(ii) Draw the displayed formula of the organic product, ethanal. **1**

(iii) Calculate the minimum mass of potassium dichromate(VI), $K_2Cr_2O_7$, needed to oxidize the ethanol in one glass of red wine.
Use the Periodic Table as a source of data. **3**

(c) Further oxidation of the ethanal produces ethanoic acid, CH_3CO_2H.

(i) What is the Brønsted–Lowry definition of an acid? **1**

(ii) Ethanoic acid is considered to be a weak acid. What is meant by the term **weak acid**? **1**

(iii) Write a balanced equation, including state symbols, for the neutralization of ethanoic acid by sodium hydroxide solution. **2**

(iv) The solution produced by the reaction in (iii) conducts electricity. Give the formula of the organic ion present. **1**

(v) Electrolysis of this solution produces two gases at the anode. One of the gases turns calcium hydroxide solution cloudy. The other gas is an alkane.
By considering the formula of the anion, suggest the names and formulae of these two gases. **3**

17 *L(N) (AL)*

15. *(a)* Ethanol may be manufactured from ethene and steam by the reaction

$$CH_2{=}CH_2(g) + H_2O(g) \rightleftharpoons CH_3CH_2OH(g);$$
$$\Delta H^{\ominus} = -46 \text{ kJ mol}^{-1}.$$

(i) Write down an expression for the equilibrium constant, K_p, for this reaction. **1**

(ii) If the pressure were doubled at the same temperature, state the effect, if any, on the value of the equilibrium constant, K_p. Give a reason for your answer. **1**

(b) Explain the effect on the equilibrium yield of ethanol in the reaction in *(a)* by

(i) increasing the temperature, **1**

(ii) increasing the pressure. **1**

(c) The manufacturing process in *(a)* involves the use of a **heterogeneous** catalyst.

(i) Explain the meaning of the term **heterogeneous**. **1**

(ii) Draw energy profiles for the catalysed and uncatalysed reactions. **2**

(d) (i) The standard enthalpies of formation of ethene and steam are +52.3 kJ mol^{-1} and −242 kJ mol^{-1} respectively. Using the standard enthalpy change for the reaction in *(a)*, calculate the enthalpy change of formation of gaseous ethanol. **3**

(ii) If the standard enthalpy change of formation of liquid ethanol is −248 kJ mol^{-1} then calculate the enthalpy change for the conversion of one mole of liquid ethanol to one mole of gaseous ethanol at 298 K. **1**

11 *WJEC(AL)*

16. Benzaldehyde is known as 'oil of bitter almonds' since it is found in the glucoside, amygdalin, which occurs in bitter almonds.

Benzaldehyde

Amygdalin may be hydrolysed by dilute acids, or by the enzyme emulsin, to benzaldehyde, glucose and hydrogen cyanide.

$$C_{20}H_{27}O_{11}N + 2H_2O \longrightarrow C_6H_5CHO + HCN + 2C_6H_{12}O_6$$

(a) Explain the term enzyme. **2**

(*b*) Glucose has the following structure:

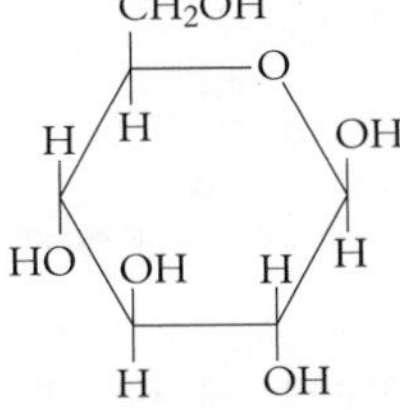

(i) How many primary, secondary and tertiary alcohol groups are there in glucose? **2**

(ii) Suggest why glucose is extremely soluble in water. **2**

(*c*) Benzaldehyde reacts with hydrogen cyanide to form a cyanohydrin called mandelonitrile.

$$C_6H_5CHO + HCN \longrightarrow C_6H_5CHOHCN$$

The reaction is speeded up by the presence of sodium hydroxide which forms cyanide ions.

(i) What type of reagent is the cyanide ion? **1**

(ii) Write an equation for the reaction of hydrogen cyanide with sodium hydroxide. **2**

(iii) In practice hydrogen cyanide is generated by the reaction of sodium cyanide with hydrochloric acid. Addition of hydrogen cyanide does not occur in the presence of excess hydrochloric acid. Suggest an explanation. **2**

(*d*) The mechanism for the formation of the cyanohydrin is shown below.

C_6H_5(H)C=O + :CN^- —step 1/slow→ C_6H_5(NC)(H)C–O^- —step 2/fast, HCN→ C_6H_5(NC)(H)C–OH + CN^-

(i) Write a rate equation for the reaction. **2**

(ii) What is the overall order of the reaction? **1**

(iii) Deduce the units of the rate constant. **2**

(*e*) Mandelonitrile is a chiral molecule but the product from the reaction of benzaldehyde with hydrogen cyanide does not rotate the plane of polarised light.

(i) Explain why mandelonitrile is a chiral molecule. **2**

(ii) Suggest why a sample of mandelonitirile prepared in the laboratory does not rotate the plane of polarised light. **2**

(*f*) Cyanohydrins are useful intermediates in synthetic organic chemistry. Name, or give the formulae of, the reagents **A**, **B**, **C** and **D** in the following flow scheme.

C_6H_5–CHOHCN —**A**→ C_6H_5–CHOHCOOH —**B**→ C_6H_5–COCOOH —**C**→ C_6H_5–CH₂CH₂OH —**D**→ C_6H_5–CH₂CH₂OOCCH

14 *(CCEA) (AL)*

17. This question concerns the compounds in the following reaction scheme:

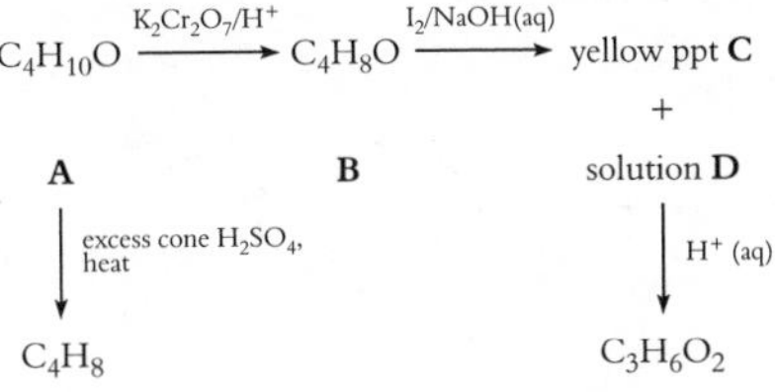

(*a*) **F** and **G** are compounds which both decolorise bromine water. **F** has two stereoisomers.

(i) What functional group is present in both **F** and **G**? **1**

(ii) Give the structural formulae of both stereoisomers of **F**. **2**

(iii) Explain how these two isomers arise. **2**

(iv) Write the structural formula of **G**. **1**

(*b*) **B** cannot be oxidised by acidified potassium dichromate(VI) solution.

(i) Write the structural formula of **B**. **1**

(ii) Draw the general structural features of molecules which can be detected by the reaction with iodine and alkali. **2**

(iii) Give the structure of the substance in solution **D**, and of the product **E**. **2**

(*c*) The mass spectrum of **A** gives peaks at *m/e* 29 and 45, amongst others. That at 45 is the largest. This spectrum shows no molecular ion peak, which would be expected at *m/e* 74. **A** is chiral.

(i) Give the structural formula for **A**. **1**

(ii) Identify the ions responsible for the peaks at *m/e* 45 and 29, and hence suggest why the molecule shows no molecular ion peak. **3**

(*d*) **A** is miscible with benzene and the mixture formed shows a positive deviation from Raoult's Law and forms an azeotrope. **3**

(i) **A** boils at 99 °C, benzene at 80 °C. Sketch a possible boiling point/composition diagram for a mixture of **A** with benzene.

(ii) Explain why a mixture of **A** with benzene shows a large positive deviation from Raoult's Law. **3**

(iii) The infra-red spectrum of **A** is shown below. The very broad peak at 3500 cm^{-1} is due to the presence of an —OH group. This peak becomes much narrower when diluted with benzene and moves to 3600 cm^{-1}.

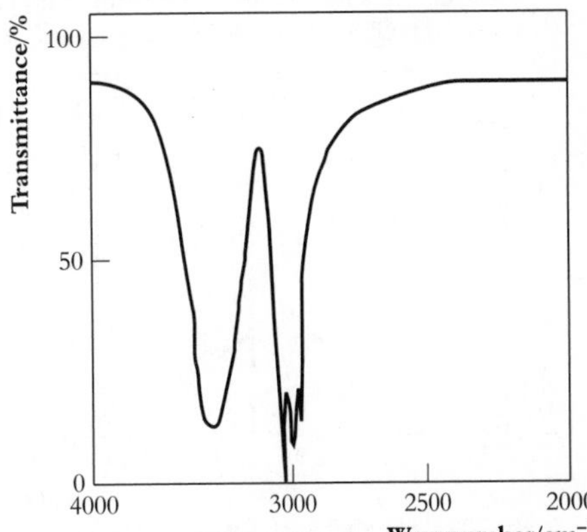

Suggest why the —OH absorption peak changes as **A** is diluted with benzene. **2**

23 *(L) (AL)*

18. *(a)* The sequence of reactions shown below may be used to convert methylbenzene into methyl 3-nitrobenzenecarboxylate.

$C_6H_5CH_3$ —Step 1→ $C_6H_5CH_2Cl$ —Step 2, KOH(aq)→ $C_6H_5CH_2OH$

$C_6H_5CH_2OH$ —Step 3→ C_6H_5COOH —Step 4→ $C_6H_5COOCH_3$ —Step 5→ $C_6H_4(NO_2)COOCH_3$ (3-nitro)

Step 5 may be carried out as a laboratory experiment to demonstrate nitration of the benzene ring. Part of the instructions for the experiment follow.

> Methyl benzenecarboxylate is dissolved in concentrated sulphuric acid and the solution cooled in ice. A cooled mixture of concentrated nitric and sulphuric acids is added to the methyl benzenecarboxylate solution. The temperature of the reaction mixture must be kept below 10 °C.

(i) Give the reagent, essential condition and type of mechanism in Step 1. **3**

(ii) Write a mechanism for Step 2. Give the name of the type of mechanism. **3**

(iii) Give the name of the type of reaction in Step 3. **1**

(iv) Give the name of the reagent and state the essential conditions for Step 4. **3**

(v) Write a balanced equation for the reaction in Step 5. **1**

(vi) Give the formula of the ion, formed from nitric and sulphuric acids in Step 5, that attacks the benzene ring and give the name of the type of mechanism involved. **2**

(vii) Suggest what other product may form in Step 5 if the temperature is allowed to rise above 10 °C during the nitration. **1**

(b) In the mass spectrometer, organic molecules may undergo fragmentation when groups of atoms break away from the parent molecular ion. These fragments are also formed as ions and may be identified from the peak pattern in a mass spectrum. A simplified mass spectrum of propenoic acid, $CH_2 = CHCOOH$, is shown in the figure.

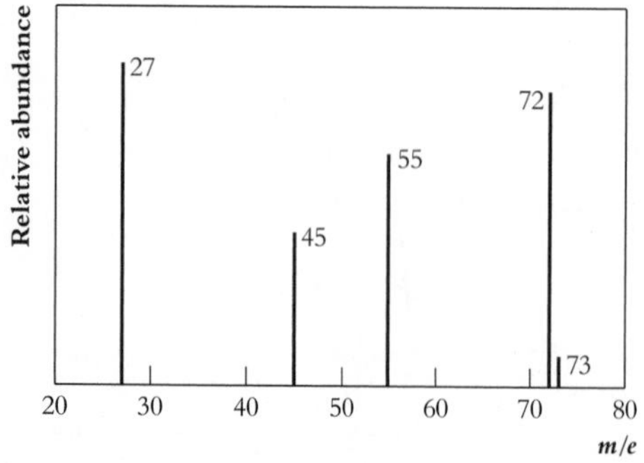

(i) Describe the process in the mass spectrometer that causes fragmentation of organic molecules. **2**

(ii) Write the formula of the molecular ion that gives a peak at m/e = 72. **1**

(iii) Write the formulae for the fragments that give peaks at m/e = 27, m/e = 45 and m/e = 55. **3**

(c) 4-hydroxyphenylazobenzene is an important dyestuff manufactured from phenylamine.

(i) Give the structural formula of 4-hydroxyphenylazobenzene. **1**

(ii) Give the reagents and essential condition for the two-stage laboratory preparation of 4-hydroxyphenylazobenzene from phenylamine. **4**

(iii) The industrial manufacture of 4-hydroxyphenylazobenzene has only a 68% yield. Calculate the amount of phenylamine required to produce 1 tonne (1000 kg) of the dyestuff. **3**

AEB (AL) 1998

19. *(a)* Give the names and structures of the two linear and three branched structural isomers of C_5H_{10} which are all alkenes. **10**

(b) Choose **one** of the branched isomers and show how it reacts with hydrogen bromide. Give the name of your product. Account for the formation of this product by reference to the mechanism of the reaction. **8**

(c) A branched alkene **B**, C_5H_{10}, reacts with hydrogen bromide to give **C**, $C_5H_{11}Br$.
Hydrolysis of **C** yields compound **D**, $C_5H_{12}O$, which produces **E**, $C_5H_{10}O$, on oxidation.
Fragmentation of the molecular ion of **E**, $[C_5H_{10}O]^+$, leads to a mass spectrum which includes a major peak at $m/z = 43$ and a minor peak at $m/z = 71$.

(i) Use Spectrum 1 and the information given in the table below, together with the mass spectral information provided above, to deduce the structure of compound **E**. Write equations to show the fragmentation of the molecular ion of **E**.

(ii) Deduce the structure of compound **D** and show how Spectrum 2, below, is in agreement with your deduction.

(iii) Deduce structures for compounds **B** and **C**. **12**

Bond	Wavenumber/cm^{-1}
C—H	2850–3300
C—C	750–1100
C=C	1620–1680
C=O	1680–1750
C—O	1000–1300
O—H (alcohols)	3230–3550
O—H (acid)	2500–3000

Spectrum 1

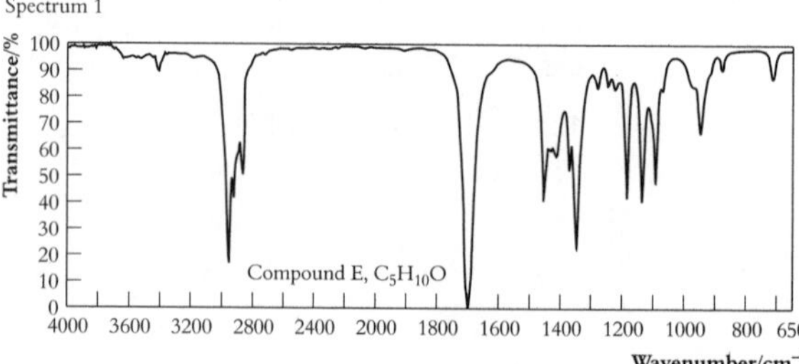

Spectrum 2

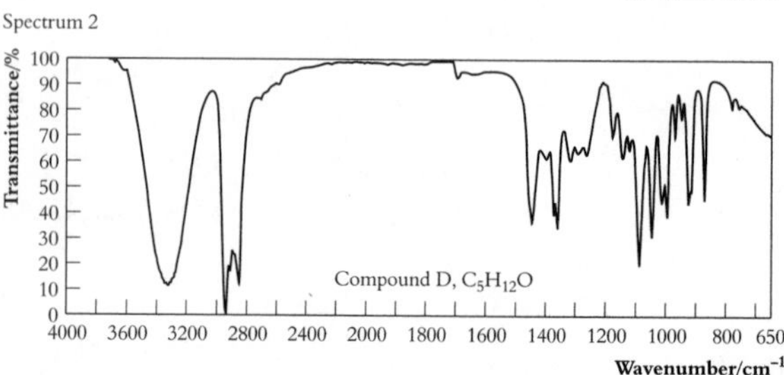

30 *NEAB (AL)*

20. Three isomeric compounds, **A**, **B** and **C**, which gave molecular ions with $m/z = 72$ in a mass spectrometer, are shown below together with the low-resolution n.m.r. spectrum of one of these isomers. The number written above each peak indicates the number of hydrogens associated with that peak.

$CH_3CH_2CH_2CHO$ (**A**)

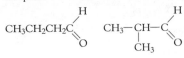

$CH_3-CH(CH_3)-CHO$ (**B**)

$CH_3-CO-CH_2CH_3$ (**C**)

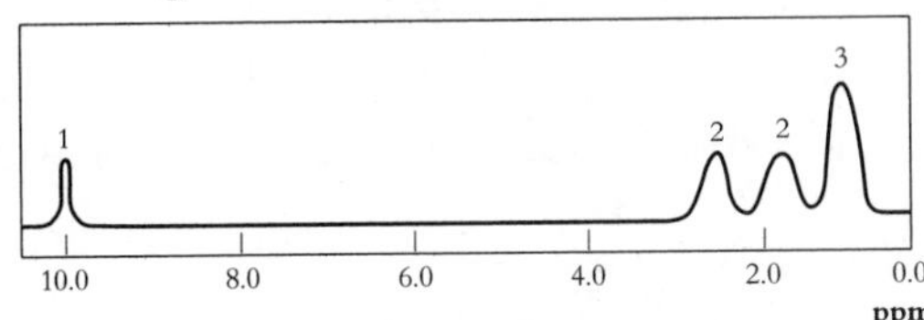

(a) (i) Identify which isomer produced the n.m.r. spectrum above and name this compound. For each of the other isomers, predict the number of peaks which would be observed in its low-resolution n.m.r. spectrum and the number of hydrogens associated with each peak. **6**

(ii) Explain how you could distinguish between isomers **A** and **C** by a chemical test. **3**

(iii) The three compounds shown above can all be prepared from alcohols by oxidation with acidified potassium dichromate(VI). Write an equation for the preparation of compound **A** by oxidation showing clearly the structure of the alcohol used. Identify a possible additional product of this reaction and explain how it is formed. **4**

(b) Compound **D** is a saturated hydrocarbon which also gives a molecular ion with $m/z = 72$ in a mass spectrometer. The n.m.r. spectrum of **D** shows only one peak. Deduce the molecular formula of **D** and draw its structure. **3**

16 *NEAB (AS/AL)*

21. *(a)* The compound, **A**, is represented by

$$ClCH_2-CH=CH-COOH.$$

(i) State what would be observed and which part, or parts, of the molecule is/are reacting when

I. **A** is treated with aqueous bromine. **2**

II. **A** is boiled with aqueous sodium hydroxide, acidified with aqueous nitric acid and then treated with aqueous silver nitrate. **2**

(ii) State which reagent(s) you would use to produce the ethyl ester of **A**. **1**

(b) The standard enthalpy changes of combustion of carbon, hydrogen and benzene are -394 kJ mol^{-1}, -286 kJ mol^{-1} and -3273 kJ mol^{-1} respectively. Determine the standard enthalpy change of formation of benzene. **2**

(c) (i) Compare the length of the carbon-carbon bonds in the benzene molecule with the lengths of the carbon-carbon bonds in ethane and ethene. **2**

(ii) Nitration of the benzene molecule is carried out using concentrated sulphuric and nitric acids.

I. Name the class of reagent reacting with the benzene molecule during nitration. **1**

II. Give the name and formula of the nitrogen-containing species involved in the initial stage of the nitration. **1**

11 *(WJEC) (AL)*

ANSWERS TO SYNOPTIC QUESTIONS

PHYSICAL CHEMISTRY

1. *(a)* (i) $K_c = [HI(g)]^2/(H_2(g)]\ [I_2(g)]$
(ii) To stop the reaction
(iii) Amount of thio = $20.0 \times 10^{-3} \times 0.500$ mol = 1.00×10^{-2} mol
Amount of $I_2 = 0.500 \times 10^{-2}$ mol = amount of H_2
$[I_2] = [H_2] = 5.00 \times 10^{-3}$ mol/0.100 dm^3
$= 5.00 \times 10^{-2}$ mol dm^{-3}
$K_c = [HI(g)]^2/(5.00 \times 10^{-2})^2 = 54.0$
$[HI(g)] = 0.367$ mol dm^{-3}
(b) (i) The reaction will continue slowly while measurements are being made. Colorimetry would measure $[I_2]$ as reaction proceeded.
(ii) From 1 and 2, order in $[I_2] = 1$
From 1 and 3, order in $[H_2] = 1$
Rate = $k\ [I_2]\ [H_2]$
(iii) The chemical equation does not give the order of reaction of each species taking part. If a species takes part in a very fast step in the reaction that species does not appear in the rate equation.
(iv) H_2 and I_2. Both appear in the rate equation.

2. *(a)* (i) I: Anode $Pb(s) + SO_4^{2-}(aq) \longrightarrow PbSO_4(s) + 2e^-$; +0.36 V
Cathode $PbO_2(s) + 4H^+(aq) + SO_4^{2-}(aq) + 2e^- \longrightarrow PbSO_4 + 2H_2O(l)$; +1.69 V
II: $Pb(s) + PbO_2(s) + 4H^+(aq) + SO_4^{2-}(aq) \longrightarrow 2PbSO_4(s) + 2H_2O(l)$
e.m.f = +1.69 – 0.36 = + 1.33 V
(ii) $Pb(s) \mid SO_4^{2-}(aq) \,\vdots\vdots\, 4H^+(aq)SO_4^{2-}(aq) \mid PbO_2(s)$
(iii) I All the PbO_2 and Pb become converted into $PbSO_4$. Then there is no difference between the plates and no e.m.f.
II In charging the cell, a direct current is passed through to reverse the reactions. $PbSO_4$ is converted into Pb at the anode and PbO_2 at the cathode. The cell then has an e.m.f.
(b) Repeated extractions are effective.
Amount of ethanoic acid = $100 \times 10^{-3} \times 0.50$ mol = 0.050 mol
(i) Let *a* mol be extracted by the solvent.

$$\frac{[\text{ethanoic acid in solvent}]}{[\text{ethanoic acid in water}]} = 3.05$$

$$\frac{a/200}{(0.050 - a)/100} = 3.05$$

$a = 0.0430$ mol
(ii) Let *b* mol be extracted by the solvent.

$$\frac{[\text{ethanoic acid in solvent}]}{[\text{ethanoic acid in water}]} = \frac{b/100}{(0.050 - b)/100} = 3.05$$

$b = 0.037\ 65$ mol

$$\frac{[\text{ethanoic acid in solvent}]}{[\text{ethanoic acid in water}]} = \frac{c/100}{(0.012\ 35 - c)/100} = 3.05$$

$c = 0.00930$ mol
Total of $b + c = 0.0470$ mol, which is more than *a*, obtained by a single extraction.

(c) Show peaks at N = 14, N_2 = 28, O = 16, O_2 = 32, C = 12, CO = 28, CO_2 = 44

3. *(a)* (i) –360 kJ mol^{-1}, –430 kJ mol^{-1}, –415 kJ mol^{-1}
(ii) 0.5 (+415 – 360) = +27.5 kJ mol^{-1}
0.5 (+415 – 430) = –7.5 kJ mol^{-1}
(iii) The reduction for which ΔG is negative is reduction by CO.
(iv) 1000 K is the temperature at which graphs intersect.
(v) 1 mole of gas is formed.
(b) (i) +0.44 V
(ii) H_2
(iii) $Fe(s) + 2H^+(aq) \longrightarrow Fe^{2+}(aq) + H_2(g)$
(iv) $Fe(s) \mid Fe^{2+}(aq) \,\vdots\vdots\, H^+(aq) \mid H_2(g)$
(v) electronic voltmeter (high resistance, takes negligible current)

4. (i) $K_p = \dfrac{p^2(HI(g))}{p(H_2(g)) \times p(I_2(g))}$
$= (90.0)^2/(2.5 \times 22.5) = 144$
(ii) K_p decreases with a fall in temperature. The position of equilibrium lies further to the right at 400 K.
(iii) Bonds broken:
(H—H) + (I—I) = 436 + 151 = 587 kJ mol^{-1}
Bonds made: 2(H—I) = 596 kJ mol^{-1}
$\Delta H_r^\ominus$ = +587 – 596 = –9 kJ mol^{-1}
(b) Amount of $I_2 = 39.0 \times 10^{-3} \times 0.050 = 1.95 \times 10^{-3}$ mol
Amount of $SO_2 = 1.95 \times 10^{-3}$ mol in 250 cm^3
$[SO_2/\text{g dm}^{-3}] = 64 \times 1.95 \times 10^{-3} \times 4$ g dm^{-3}
= 0.50 g dm^{-3}
(c) yellow ppt of $PbI_2(s)$; white ppt of $PbSO_4(s)$

5. *(a)* (i) Bonds broken:
(H—H) + (I—I) = 436 + 151 = 587 kJ mol^{-1}
Bonds made: 2(H—I) = 2 × 299 = 598 kJ mol^{-1}
ΔH = –598 + 587 = – 11 kJ mol^{-1}
(b)

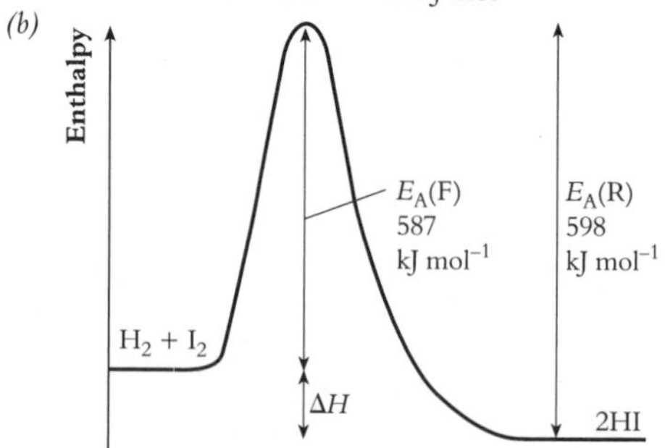

(c) E_A will be greater than for the HI reaction because Cl—Cl bond energy > I—I bond energy.
(d) (i) $K_c = [HI]^2/([H_2]\ [I_2])$
(ii)

	$H_2(g)$ +	$I_2(g)$ ⇌	2HI(g)
Initial	1.9 mol	1.9 mol	0
Equilibrium	0.4 mol/ 250 cm^3	0.4 mol/ 250 cm^3	3.0 mol/ 250 cm^3

$K_c = (3.0)^2/(0.4)^2 = 56.25$

(e) (i) 1
(ii) Rate = $k\,[H_2]\,[I_2]$
1.5×10^{-5} mol dm^{-3} s^{-1} = $k \times (0.10$ mol/0.500 dm$^3)^2$
$k = 3.75 \times 10^{-4}$ mol^{-1} dm^3 s^{-1}

6. *(a)* (i) Immerse the flask in hot water, and observe the colour.
If the brown colour deepens, the change is $N_2O_4 \longrightarrow 2NO_2$, showing that the change is endothermic. If the colour fades, the change is $2NO_2 \longrightarrow N_2O_4$, showing that the change from N_2O_4 to NO_2 is exothermic.
(ii) 0.200 mol NO_2
$PV = nRT$
$P = 0.200$ mol $\times$ 8.31 J K^{-1} mol^{-1} $\times$ 600 K/1.00 $\times 10^{-3}$ m^3
$= 9.97 \times 10^5$ Pa
(iii) nitryl cation; see § 28.8.2
Being positively charged NO_2^+ attacks a region of high electron density in a molecule.
(b) (i) A metal with a high negative value of $E^\ominus$ is a powerful reducing agent, that is, the tendency is for $M \longrightarrow M^{n+} + ne^-$. Extracting the metal from its ore is therefore difficult because this involves reducing M^{n+} to M.
(ii) $Cd(OH)_2(s) + 2e^- \longrightarrow Cd(s) + 2OH^-(aq)$; −0.81 V
$NiO_2(s) + 2H_2O(l) + 2e^- \longrightarrow Ni(OH)_2(s) + 2OH^-(aq)$; 0.49 V
To give a positive value of $E^\ominus$,
$E^\ominus = +0.49 - (-0.81) = 1.30$ V
NiO_2 is the oxidant (the cathode) and Cd is the reductant (the cathode)
$NiO_2(s) + Cd(s) + 2H_2O(l) \longrightarrow Ni(OH)_2(s) + Cd(OH)_2(s)$
(c) (i) The number of electrons in the valence shell is high and the metallic bond is strong.
(ii) $Cr^{3+}(aq) + 3OH^-(aq) \longrightarrow Cr(OH)_3(s)$
$Fe^{2+}(aq) + 2OH^-(aq) \longrightarrow Fe(OH)_2(s)$
$Cr(OH)_3$ blue-green, $Fe(OH)_2$ green, $Fe(OH)_3$ rust, $Cu(OH)_2$ blue; see § 24.12.3

7. *(a)* (i) $K_c = [NH_3]^2/([N_2]\,[H_2]^3)$
(ii)

	N_2	H_2	NH_3
Amount/mol	0.600	1.80	0.800

$K_c = (0.800)^2/\{0.600 \times (1.80)^3\} = 0.183$ mol^{-2} dm^6
(b) (i) $[H^+]$ = antilg (−11.1) = 7.94×10^{-12} mol dm^{-3}
$[OH^-] = 1.00 \times 10^{-14}/[H^+] = 1.26 \times 10^{-3}$ mol dm^{-3}
(c) (i) See § 12.8.
(ii) Take 25.00 cm^3 of aqueous ethanoic acid. Add 10.60 cm^3 of aqueous NaOH; then half the acid has been neutralised and [ethanoic acid] = [sodium ethanoate]
(d) (i) Acidified potassium dichromate(VI), heat; oxidation (§ 30.7.2)
(ii) Distil with soda lime (§ 33.8.6); decarboxylation

8. *(a)* (i) I. 1, II. 2
(ii) Yes, it could involve collision between H_2 and I_2 molecules.
(iii) It will decrease because the reaction $L \longrightarrow R$ is exothermic.
(iv) rate constant, mol dm^3 s^{-1}
(b) (i) See § 3.4.
(ii) See § 1.9.
(iii) I. N_2 and N
II. $N_2 \longrightarrow N_2^+ + e^-$
(c) (i) **X** is $^{210}_{84}Po$, **Y** is $^{206}_{82}Pb$
(ii) I. People may receive a high dose of radiation in a short time.
II. Radioactive strontium is built into bones and teeth in the same way as calcium. They are both in Group 2.

9. *(a)* (i) $K_c = [NO_2(g)]^2/[N_2O_4(g)]$ mol dm^{-3}
(ii)

	N_2O_4	$2NO_2$
Initial	1 mol	0
Equilibrium	0.5 mol	1.0 mol

$K_c = (1.0/10.0)^2/(0.5/10.0) = 0.2$ mol dm^{-3}
(iii) $\Delta H^\ominus = 2\Delta H_f^\ominus(NO_2) - \Delta H_f^\ominus(N_2O_4)$
$= 2(+33.9) - 9.70 = +58.1$ kJ mol^{-1}
(iv) Rise in temperature favours the endothermic reaction. The equilibrium mixture contains more NO_2.
(b) Decrease the pressure. The dissociation increases the amount of gas present, causing expansion.
(c) (i) none (ii) none (iii) increased
(d) $\Delta H = +67.8$ kJ mol^{-1}
The reaction is endothermic: energy must be supplied. NO is formed also.

10. *(a)* $2H_2(g) + O_2(g) \rightleftharpoons 2H_2O(g)$;
$\Delta H^\ominus = -242$ kJ mol^{-1}, $\Delta S^\ominus = -44$ J mol^{-1}
The reaction is exothermic therefore K_p decreases with a rise in temperature:
$\Delta G = -RT \ln K$ means that ln K decreases linearly with T.
$\Delta G^\ominus = \Delta H^\ominus - T\Delta S^\ominus$
$= -242$ kJ $- T(-44$ J)
The term $-T\Delta S^\ominus$ is positive. It becomes larger as T increases, therefore $\Delta G^\ominus$ becomes less negative as T increases.

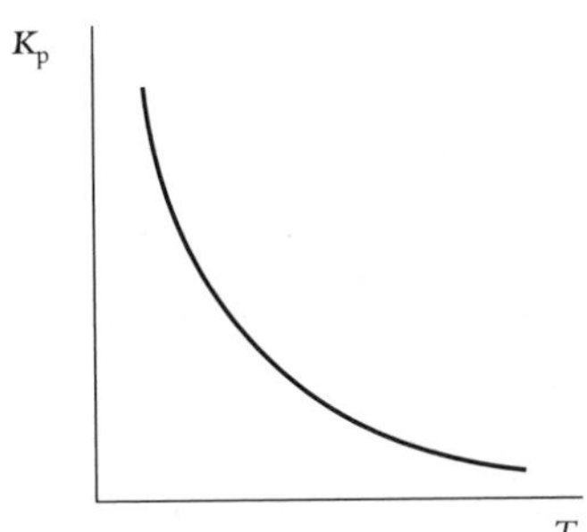

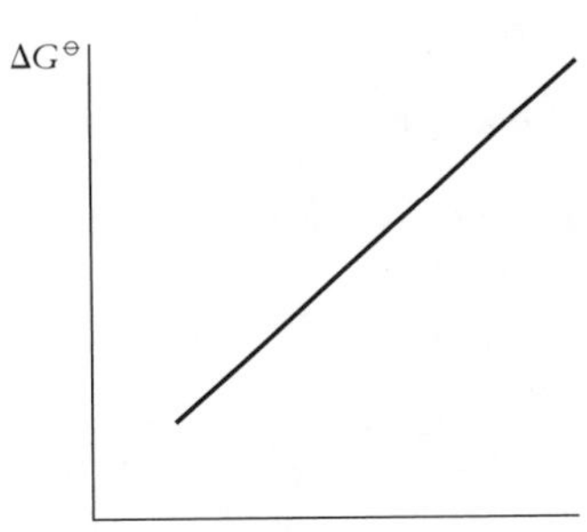

(b) $2SO_2(g) + O_2(g) \rightleftharpoons 2SO_3(g)$; $\Delta H^\ominus = -100$ kJ mol^{-1}
(i) % yield decreases with T because the reaction is exothermic and increases with pressure because the reaction involves a decrease in volume.
(ii) K_p decreases with T (see above). K_p remains constant as pressure changes. Use a catalyst.
(i)

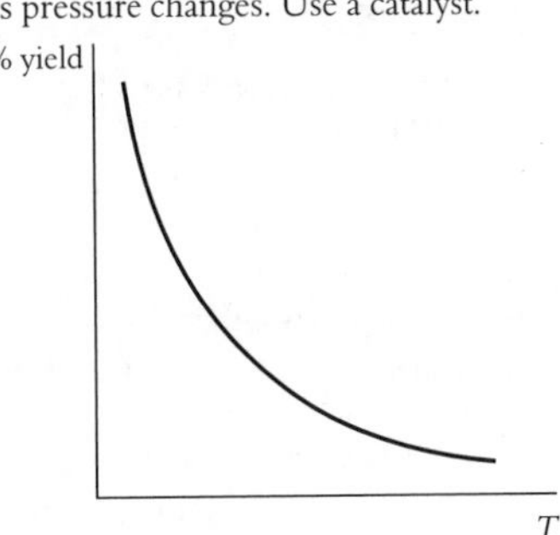

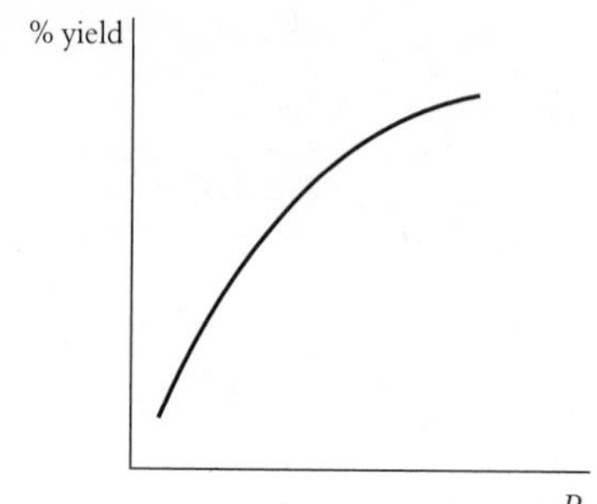

(ii)

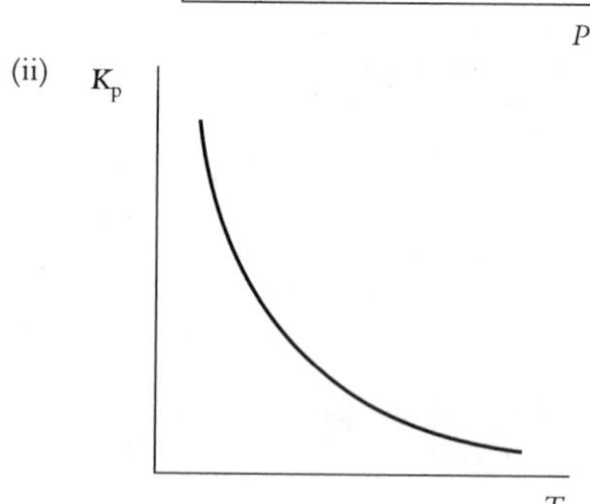

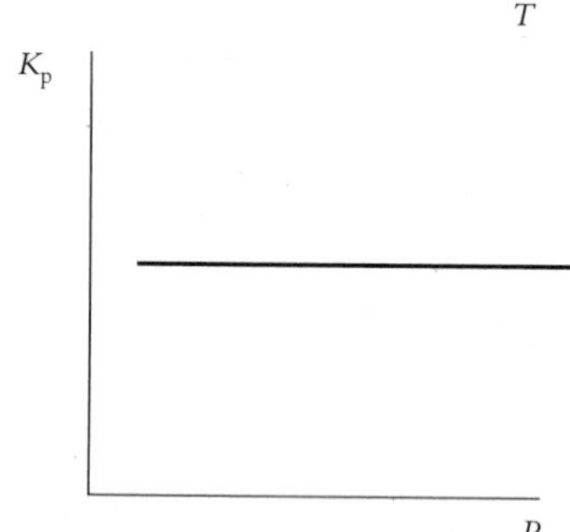

11. *(a)* See §§ 14.4, 14.5, 14.6.

(b) (i) Lattice enthalpy is highest for ions of small size and multiple charge; see § 10.13

(ii) **1.** $Cu(s) + \frac{1}{2}O_2(g) \longrightarrow CuO(s)$

2. $Cu^{2+}(g) + O^{2-}(g) \longrightarrow CuO(s)$

3. $Cu(g) \longrightarrow Cu^+(g) + e^-$

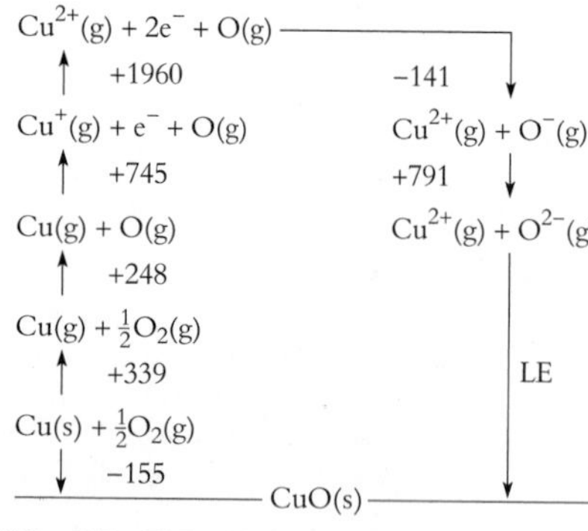

$+339 + 248 + 745 + 1960 - 141 + 791 + LE = -155$

$LE = -4097\ kJ\ mol^{-1}$

12. *(a)* (i) See § 10.11.

(ii) Bonds broken:
$(C{=}O) + 2(H{-}H) = 1077 + 2(436) = 1949\ kJ\ mol^{-1}$
Bonds made: $3(C{-}H) + (C{-}O) + (O{-}H) =$
$3(412) + 360 + 463 = 2059\ kJ\ mol^{-1}$
$\Delta H_r^\ominus = +1949 - 2059 = -110\ kJ\ mol^{-1}$

(b) (i) See § 10.7.1.

(ii)

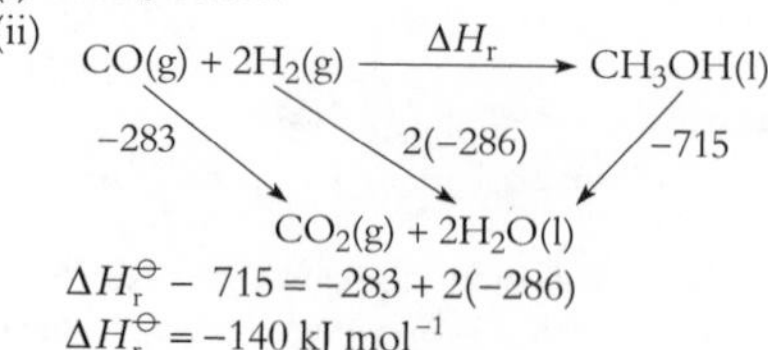

$\Delta H_r^\ominus - 715 = -283 + 2(-286)$

$\Delta H_r^\ominus = -140\ kJ\ mol^{-1}$

(c) (i) $CH_3OH(g) \longrightarrow CH_3OH(l)$

(ii) Molecules have less kinetic energy, move less rapidly and intermolecular forces become important; see § 10.7.2.
In *(a)*(ii) CH_3OH*(g)* is formed; in *(b)*(ii) $CH_3OH(l)$ is formed. The difference is ΔH for vaporisation of methanol, $+30\ kJ\ mol^{-1}$

13. *(a)* (i) $N_2(g) + 3H_2(g) \rightleftharpoons 2NH_3(g)$

(ii) The reaction involves a decrease in the number of moles of gas and therefore a decrease in volume, so the forward reaction is favoured by high pressure (Le Chatelier's Principle, § 11.5.1).

(iii) The yield is less because the forward reaction is exothermic. The rate of attainment of equilibrium is low at low temperature.

(b) (i) $K_p = p^2(NH_3(g))/\{p^3(H_2(g)) \times p(N_2(g))\}$
$= (90)^2/\{(35)^3 \times 75\} = 2.52 \times 10^{-3}\ atm^{-2}$

(iii) atm^{-2}

(iv) none

(c) See § 14.5.2.

(d) $H_2O(l) + CO(NH_2)_2(aq) \longrightarrow CO_2(aq) + 2NH_3(aq)$
−287 −320.5 −414.5 2(−810)
$\Delta H = -414.5 - 162.0 + 287 + 320.5 = +31\ kJ\ mol^{-1}$

14. *(a)* (i) (ii)

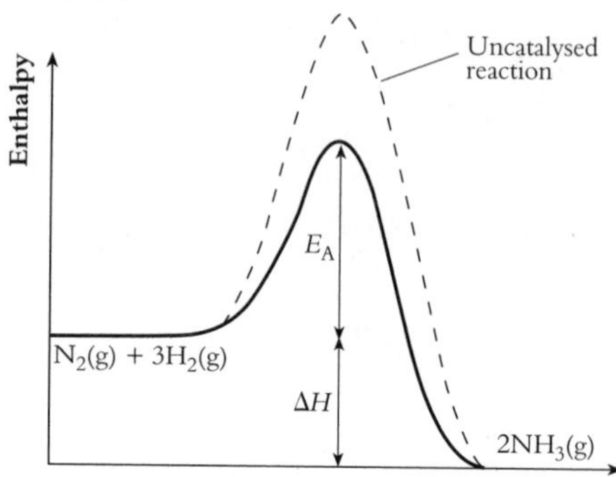

(iii) A catalyst provides an alternative reaction route of lower activation energy. Therefore a higher fraction of collisions results in reaction; see § 14.4.

(iv) The catalyst is in a different phase from the reactants, e.g. a solid catalyst in a reaction between gases. Iron

(b) (i) See § 10.11.
Bonds broken: $(N{-}N) + 3(H{-}H) =$
$163 + (3 \times 436) = +1471\ kJ\ mol^{-1}$
Bonds made: $6(N{-}H) = 6 \times 388 = -2328\ kJ\ mol^{-1}$
$\Delta H = -857\ kJ\ mol^{-1}$ of the equation

15. *(a)* (i) $0.01\ mol\ dm^{-3}$; pH = 2

(ii) $0.10\ mol\ dm^{-3}$

(iii) $[H^+(aq)] = 0.0269\ mol\ dm^{-3}$
Total $[H^+(aq)] = 0.127\ mol\ dm^{-3}$

(iv) Equilibrium (ii) removes HSO_4^- ions from equilibrium (i) and increases the dissociation of H_2SO_4 to form H^+ ions. The $[H^+]$ is therefore greater than predicted from (i).

(v) If K_a increases with temperature ionisation is endothermic.

(vi) $[H^+]$ increases and pH decreases.

(*b*) (i) Hydrogen bonding in H_2SO_4 makes the T_b higher than that of HCl.
(ii) hydration of the ions H^+, SO_4^{2-}, Cl^-

(iii) Energy is required to separate the ions in the crystal structure. This is compensated for by the energy given out when the ions are hydrated.
$M^{2+} + aq \longrightarrow Mg^{2+}(aq)$ gives out more energy than
$Ba^{2+} + aq \longrightarrow Ba^{2+}(aq)$.

INORGANIC CHEMISTRY

1. See § 15.3 and Table 15.3.
2. The graph is shown as part of Figure 15.2C. As the nuclear charge increases from left to right and as more electrons are added in the same shell, the electrons are held closer to the nucleus and atomic radius decreases.
3. (*a*) See § 15.4.
   (*b*), (*c*) See Table 15.4.
   (*d*) See § 15.5.2.
4. (*a*) The electrons added from left to right across the transition elements go into the inner d subshell, and atomic radius is determined mainly by the outer s subshell.
   (*b*) Na loses an electron in forming Na^+ so the remaining electrons are more tightly held by the nucleus. Cl gains an electron in forming Cl^- so the electrons are less tightly held by the nucleus.
   (*c*) The electron removed from K is in the $n = 4$ shell; the electron removed from Na is in the $n = 3$ shell, closer to the nucleus.
   (*d*) The electron added to Cl is closer to the nucleus than that added to I, so more energy is released when $Cl + e^- \longrightarrow Cl^-$.
   (*e*) Cs^+ is larger than Na^+; see Figures 6.4A and B.
   (*f*) Be^{2+}, being small and doubly charged, can polarise Cl^- to form a bond with partial covalent character; Ca^{2+} is too large to polarise Cl^-; see § 4.6.3.
5. Period 3:
   Na: electrical conductor, forms cations, basic oxide, powerful reductant
   Mg: electrical conductor, forms cations, basic oxide, powerful reductant
   Al: electrical conductor, forms cations and oxoanions, amphoteric oxide, powerful reductant
   Si: semiconductor, forms oxoanions, weakly acidic oxide, very weak reductant
   P: non-conductor, forms oxoanions, strongly acidic oxides, weak reductant and weak oxidant
   S: non-conductor, forms anions and oxoanions, strongly acidic oxides, weak reductant and weak oxidant
   Cl: non-conductor, forms anions and oxoanions, unstable oxides, powerful oxidant
   Group 4:

Element	Electrical conductor?	Reaction with dilute acids	Bonds	Oxides
C	diamond non-conductor; graphite conductor	none	covalent	CO_2 weak acid CO very weak acid
Si	semiconductor	none	covalent	acidic
Ge	semiconductor	none	covalent	amphoteric
Sn	conductor	reacts	Sn(IV) covalent Sn(II) ionic	SnO_2 acidic SnO basic
Pb	conductor	very slow	Pb(II) ionic	PbO basic

   (*b*) See § 15.5.1, Figures 15.6A, C and D.
6. For electronegativity see § 4.6.3; electron affinity § 10.12. Electronegativity increases C ⟶ F because the nuclear charge increases [see § 15.2] and decreases F ⟶ I because the electrons in the outer shell in I are further from the nucleus than those in F.
   F has the greatest tendency to accept an electron to form F^- because the electron enters a shell close to the nucleus. The nearer the electron is to the positive nucleus the more energy is given out.
7. (*a*) See § 10.12.
   (*b*) See Figure 15.2E.
   (*c*) From Na to Mg, IE increases because of the increase in nuclear charge. From Mg to Al, IE falls owing to the stability of Al^+, (Ne)$3s^2$ with its full s subshell. From Al to Si to P, IE increases as the nuclear charge increases. From P to S, IE falls owing to the stability of S^+ (Ne)$3p^3$, with its half-full p subshell. From S to Cl to Ar, IE increases owing to the increase in nuclear charge.
   (*d*) Na, Mg, Al form positive ions. The other elements do not owing to the high value of IE.
8. (*a*) $NaNO_3$, salt of strong acid and weak base, neutral, pH 7; $Al_2(SO_4)_3$, hydrolysed [see § 19.4.1], pH <7; KCN salt of weak acid and strong base, hydrolysed [§ 12.9], pH > 7.
   (*b*) See § 23.5.2.
   (*c*) $BeCl_2$ has a high degree of covalent character and therefore dissolves in covalent solvents.
   (*d*) The ions Ca^{2+} and O^{2-}, being doubly charged, have a stronger electrostatic attraction between them than Na^+ and Cl^-.
   (*e*) increase in entropy; see § 10.15.
   (*f*) red colour with Fe^{3+} due to $Fe(CNS)_3$; see Table 24.17C
   (*g*) see § 12.9.1.
   (*h*) SiH_4 has the empty d orbitals of Si into which H_2O can coordinate as the first step in hydrolysis; see § 23.5.2.
   (*i*) B has 3 electrons in the valence shell, therefore BF_3 is trigonal planar (like BCl_3 in Figure 5.2A). P has 5 electrons in its valence shell, therefore PCl_3 is pyramidal, with the lone pair of electrons occupying one apex (similar to NH_3 in Figure 5.2F).
   (*j*) $\Delta H^{\ominus}_{solution}$ depends on the difference between $\Delta H^{\ominus}_{lattice\ dissociation}$ (positive) and $\Delta H^{\ominus}_{solvation}$ (negative). In LiF and NaF the ions are small and the forces of attraction between them are strong. $\Delta H^{\ominus}_{lattice\ dissociation}$ is highly endothermic and not outweighed by the exothermic $\Delta H^{\ominus}_{solution}$. In KF, RbF, CsF less energy is required to dissociate the lattice, the $\Delta H^{\ominus}_{solvation}$ is exothermic and the net result is an exothermic process.
   (*k*) The electrons added from Sc to Zn enter the 3d subshell, while the atomic radius is determined mainly by the outer 4s subshell.
   (*l*) Sn^{4+} has a high polarising power due to its multiple charge and $SnCl_4$ is a covalent liquid. It is hydrolysed as H_2O coordinates into empty d orbitals of Sn. Sn^{2+} has less polarising power than Sn^{4+}, and $SnCl_2$ is an ionic compound.
   (*m*) This is to prevent precipitation of AgOH(s).
9. **A** is water. It accepts a proton from HCl ⟶ H_3O^+ and gives a proton to $NH_3 \longrightarrow NH_4^+$. It is very slightly ionised. The high T_b and T_m are due to hydrogen bonding. The reaction with hot iron ⟶ $Fe_3O_4 + H_2$.
   B is hydrogen peroxide. It is oxidised by $KMnO_4$ to O_2. It oxidises PbS to $PbSO_4$ and Fe^{2+} to Fe^{3+}.

10. **C** is K_2CrO_4. The lilac flame shows K. The colour change is due to $CrO_4^{2-} \longrightarrow Cr_2O_7^{2-}$. $K_2Cr_2O_7$ + acid oxidise ethanol to ethanoic acid, with the smell of vinegar.
D is KI. With $CuSO_4$(aq) it gives white CuI(s) + I_2. With $Pb(NO_3)_2$(aq) it gives yellow PbI_2(s). With conc. H_2SO_4, it gives violet I_2(g).
E is $(NH_4)_2Cr_2O_7$. On heating it forms Cr_2O_3(s) and NH_3(g). With NaOH(aq) it gives NH_3(g) and Na_2CrO_4.
F is K_2SO_3. The lilac flame shows **K**. The ppt is $BaSO_3$ (not $BaSO_4$(s) because it reacts with HCl(aq)). The gas is SO_2(g).

11. **P** = $FeCl_4^-$(aq), **Q** = $Fe(OH)_3$(s), rust-red, **R** = $Fe(NO_3)_2$, green, **S** = $Fe(OH)_2$(s), green, **T** = $FeCO_3$(s), white

12. *(a)* Add $AgNO_3$(aq) + HNO_3(aq); AgCl(s) is white, AgBr(s) is pale yellow.
(b) Add $BaCl_2$(aq) + HCl(aq).
$SO_4^{2-}(aq) \longrightarrow$ ppt, and $SO_3^{2-}(aq) \longrightarrow SO_2(g)$
(c) flame test: Ca red, Ba apple green
(d) Add HCl(aq); $S_2O_3^{2-} \longrightarrow S(s)$
(e) Add NaOH(aq): $K_2Cr_2O_7 \longrightarrow$ yellow K_2CrO_4(aq), $FeCl_3 \longrightarrow Fe(OH)_3$(s), rust-coloured,
(f) with aldehyde $Ag^+ \longrightarrow$ Ag(s) mirror, with Cl^-(aq) $\longrightarrow$ white AgCl(s), with Br^-(aq) $\longrightarrow$ primrose AgBr(s), with I^-(aq) $\longrightarrow$ deep yellow AgI(s)

13. *(a)* (i), (ii), (iii) many examples in § 15.5.1.
(b) For chemical properties see § 15.5.1 and Figure 15.6D; for structure see Figure 15.6C; for bonding see Figure 15.6A.

14. *(a)* See § 15.5.2. NaCl ionic, crystalline solid; $AlCl_3$ dimer, covalent see § 19.4.2; $SiCl_4$ covalent liquid
NaCl is involatile because the ions are held together by electrostatic forces of attraction. Al_2Cl_6 is a volatile solid, and $SiCl_4$ is a volatile liquid because they consist of small molecules with weak forces of attraction between molecules.
(b) NaCl dissolves as Na^+(aq) Cl^-(aq) to form a neutral solution. $SiCl_4$ is hydrolysed to $Si(OH)_4$(s) + HCl(aq) and is acidic.

15. *(a)* Li, Na, K, Rb, Ca, Sr; Rb most vigorous
e.g. $2Na(s) + 2H_2O(l) \longrightarrow 2NaOH(aq) + H_2(g)$
e.g. $Ca(s) + 2H_2O(l) \longrightarrow Ca(OH)_2(aq) + H_2(g)$
(b) $Li^+ H^-$ ionic structure, BeH_2 linear, BH_3 trigonal planar, CH_4 tetrahedral, NH_3 trigonal pyramid, H_2O bent line, HF linear
(c) Na_2O (+1), MgO (+2), Al_2O_3(+3), SiO_2(+4), P_2O_5,(+5), SO_3(+6), C I_2O_7 (+7) sodium hydroxide NaOH, magnesium hydroxide $Mg(OH)_2$, aluminium hydroxide, $Al(OH)_3$, silicon(IV) hydroxide $Si(OH)_4$, phosphoric(V) acid H_3PO_4, sulphuric acid H_2SO_4, chloric(VII) acid $HClO_4$

16. *(a)* See § 10.12.
(b) IE decreases Na $\longrightarrow$ K $\longrightarrow$ Cs as the electron to be removed is further from the nucleus and less energy is required to remove it.
IE for Mg > IE for Na because Mg has one more proton than Na and a greater nuclear charge to resist ionisation.
Mg $\longrightarrow$ Ca and B $\longrightarrow$ Al: IE decreases as the electron to be removed is further from the nucleus
Mg $\longrightarrow$ Al: IE decreases because Al loses an electron from the 3p subshell while Mg loses an electron from the 3s subshell, which is nearer to the nucleus.

17. *(a)* (i) As the molecule CO_2 is linear the dipoles cancel.

$$O^{\delta-}{=}C^{\delta+}{=}O^{\delta-}$$

The molecule SO_2 is bent so there is a resultant dipole.

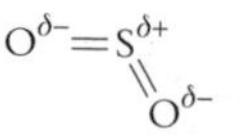

$$O^{\delta-}{=}S^{\delta+}{=}O^{\delta-}$$

(ii) C is restricted to the $n = 2$ shell with an oxidation state of +4. S has 6 electrons in the outer shell so it can form

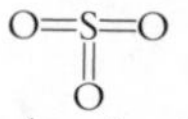

O=S(=O)=O

therefore SO_2 is oxidised to SO_3 or H_2SO_4.
(iii) Suggests the position of equilibrium lies to the LHS so that $[HCO_3^-]$ is low and also that the reaction L $\longrightarrow$ R is slow so that the HCO_3^- neutralised is not instantly replaced.
(iv) Amount of NaOH = $20.8 \times 10^{-3} \times 0.400$ mol
= 8.32×10^{-3} mol
Amount of H_2SO_4 in 25.0 cm^3 = 4.16×10^{-3} mol
= amount of SO_2 in 25.0 cm^3
Solubility of SO_2 = 0.166 mol dm^{-3}

(b) (i) Mg forms ionic bonds by donating the 2 electrons in its $3s^2$ subshell to a non-metallic element which accepts electrons to form an anion. S forms ionic compounds containing S^{2-} with metals and covalent compounds with e.g. O by sharing electrons.
(ii) The lone pair on the O^{2-} anion transfers to $H^{\delta+}$ of H_2O leading to the formation of $2OH^-$

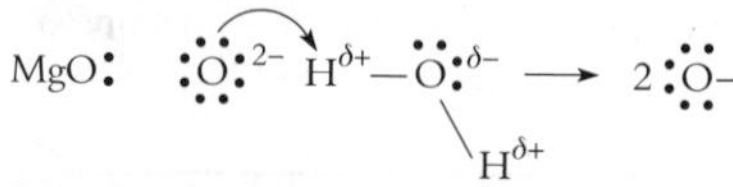

MgO: $:\ddot{O}:^{2-}$ $H^{\delta+}$—$\ddot{O}:^{\delta-}$ (—$H^{\delta+}$) $\longrightarrow$ $2:\ddot{O}$—H^-

SO_2: An electron pair on O of H_2O transfers to S of SO_2. A H atom rearranges on to the negatively charged O in the intermediate to form H_2SO_3, which ionises as an acid.

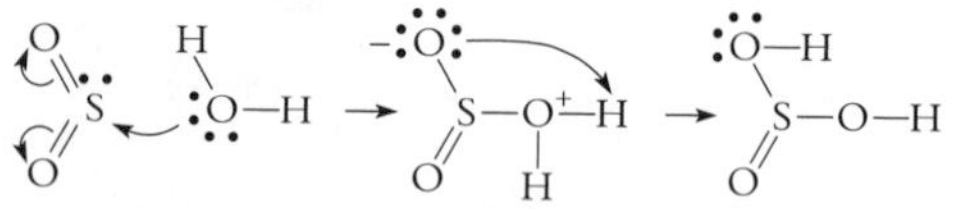

O=S=O + H—Ö—H → ⁻:Ö:—S(=O)—O⁺(H)—H → :Ö—H—S(=O)—O—H

(c) The enthalpy required to form Al^{3+} is so high that it is not compensated for by the formation of $Al^{3+}\ 3Cl^-$ in the anhydrous state. In $AlCl_3$, Al has 6 electrons in the valence shell and can accept 2 more by coordination from Cl^-:

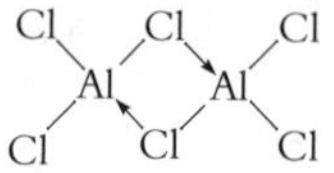

$Cl_2Al(\mu\text{-}Cl)_2AlCl_2$

18. *(a)* ionic: see § 4.3; covalent: see § 4.4; metallic: see § 6.3
(ii) **C** conducts when molten or in aqueous solution, not as the solid. **E** conducts when solid. **D** does not conduct.
(b) (i) Ratio is Na 27.1/23 : N 16.5/14 : O 56.4/16
= Na : N : 3 O, giving F the formula $NaNO_3$
Heating $2NaNO_3(s) \longrightarrow 2NaNO_2(s) + O_2(g)$
Since M_r ($NaNO_3$) = 85,
3.40 g F $\longrightarrow$ $0.5 \times 3.40/85$ mol O_2
= 24 $dm^3 \times 0.5 \times 3.40/85$ = 0.48 dm^3
(ii) For acid rain see § 21.10, ozone layer § 21.5, catalytic converters § 26.6

19. *(a)* (i) For ionic oxide see § 4.3.4, covalent oxide Figure 4.4F
(ii) When sufficient heat is supplied to melt the ionic oxide the ions can move independently to the electrodes where the anions release electrons and the cations gain electrons, enabling electrons to flow through an external circuit. The covalent oxide does not consist of charged particles which move towards electrodes and cannot conduct electricity.
(b) (i) $Cr_2O_3(s) + 2Al(s) \longrightarrow 2Cr(s) + Al_2O_3(s)$
Cr(+3) Al(0) Cr(0) Al(+3)
(ii) M_r of Cr_2O_3 = 152
ΔH for 100 tonnes = $447 \times 100 \times 10^6/152$ kJ
= 294×10^6 kJ
(c) (i) $Na_2O(s) + H_2O(l) \longrightarrow 2NaOH(aq)$
Na_2O is ionic, and O^{2-} can donate electrons to H of H_2O (see answer to Question 19(b)
(ii) Al_2O_3: no reaction

SO_2: The S atom of SO_2 accepts a lone pair of electrons from O of H_2O (see answer to Question 19(b)(ii))

20. *(a)* (i) $K_a = [H^+(aq)][ClO^-(aq)]/[HOCl(aq)]$
$[H^+(aq)]^2 = 3.7 \times 10^{-8}$ mol dm$^{-3} \times 0.100$ mol dm^{-3}
pH = 4.2
(ii) Chloric(I) acid bleaches indicators.

(b) $Cl_2(g) + NaOH(aq) \longrightarrow NaClO(aq) + NaCl(aq)$
(ii) The energy of activation is high.
(iii) NaCl; e.g. food preservation and flavouring and many other uses. $NaClO_3$ e.g. weed killer

(c) (i) liquid therefore covalent
(ii) $SiCl_4(l) + 4H_2O(l) \longrightarrow Si(OH)_4(s) + 4HCl(aq)$
(iii) e.g. reduction of oxides of iron; see § 24.17.1
The most stable oxidation state of C is +4, whereas the most stable oxidation state of Pb is +2.
(iv) The CO produced in the reaction would reduce $PbCl_4$ to $PbCl_2$. Also $PbCl_4$ dissociates above room temperature into $PbCl_2 + Cl_2$.

21. *(a)* (i) NH_3: pyramidal; see Figure 5.2F
BF_3: trigonal planar; similar to Figure 5.2B.
(ii) Three bonding pairs and one lone pair of electrons occupy the corners of a tetrahedron with N at the centre; see § 5.2.3.
(iii) trigonal planar

(b) (i) I Fe^{3+} is a stronger oxidant than I_2 (has a higher $E^\ominus$) therefore Fe^{3+} oxidises I^- to I_2. The yellow colour of Fe^{3+} is replaced by the dark brown colour of I_2.
II Cl_2 oxidises Fe^{2+} (because Cl_2 has a higher $E^\ominus$). The green colour of Fe^{2+} is replaced by the yellow colour of Fe^{3+}.
(ii) $Cl_2 > I_2$ as oxidant

(c) (i) $MnO_4^-(aq) + 8H^+(aq) + 5Fe^{2+}(aq) \longrightarrow Mn^{2+}(aq) + 4H_2O(l) + 5Fe^{3+}(aq)$
(ii) Amount of $MnO_4^- = 22.3 \times 10^{-3} \times 0.200$
$= 4.46 \times 10^{-4}$ mol
Amount of Fe^{2+} in 25.00 cm$^3 = 4.46 \times 10^{-4}/5$ mol
$= 8.92 \times 10^{-5}$ mol
$[Fe^{2+}(aq)] = 3.57 \times 10^{-3}$ mol dm^{-3}
Mass of Fe^{2+} ions/dm^{-3} =
3.57×10^{-3} mol dm$^{-3} \times 56$ g mol^{-1} = 0.200 g dm^{-3}

22. *(a)* (i) linear; O=C=O
(ii) pyramidal; see Figure 5.2F
(iii) octahedral; see Figure 5.2L

(b) See metallic bond, § 6.3.

(c) (i) **A** is $CuSO_4$, anhydrous, **B** is $[Cu(H_2O)_6]^{2+}(aq)$, **C** is $SO_4^{2-}(aq)$, **D** is $BaSO_4(s)$, **E** is $Cu(OH)_2(s)$, **F** is $[Cu(NH_3)_4]^{2+}(aq)$
(ii) $SO_4^{2-}(aq) + Ba^{2+}(aq) \longrightarrow BaSO_4(s)$

(d) (i) Add Fehling's solution (**A** and **B**) or Benedict's reagent to a solution of the sugar. Warm in a water bath. After a few minutes a reducing sugar gives a red ppt of Cu_2O. e.g. glucose
(ii) —CHO, aldehyde

(e) (i) eriochrome black
(ii) Amount of EDTA = $20.50 \times 10^{-3} \times 0.0500$ mol
$= 1.025 \times 10^{-3}$ mol
Amount of Cu in 10 dm$^3 = 1.025 \times 10^{-2}$ mol
Mass of Cu in 10 dm$^3 = 1.025 \times 10^{-2} \times 0.1 \times 63.5$ g
= 0.0651 g

23. *(a)* See § 15.5.2.

(b) $\mathbf{X}(NO_3)_2(aq) + Na_2CO_3(aq) \longrightarrow \mathbf{X}CO_3(s) + 2NaNO_3(aq)$
$\mathbf{X}(NO_3)_2(aq) + Na_2SO_4(aq) \longrightarrow \mathbf{X}SO_4(s) + 2NaNO_3(aq)$
Amount of **X** = $250 \times 10^{-3} \times 0.100 = 25.0 \times 10^{-3}$ mol
= Amount of $\mathbf{X}SO_4$
Mass of $\mathbf{X}SO_4$ = 5.83 g
$M = 5.83$ g$/25.0 \times 10^{-3}$ mol = 233 g mol^{-1}
M of $SO_4 = 96 \Rightarrow M$ of **X** = 233 − 96 = 137 g mol^{-1}
X is Ba.
$Ba^{2+}(aq) + CO_3^{2-}(aq) \longrightarrow BaCO_3(s)$
(ii) flame test: Mg bright white light, Ba apple green

(c) (i) Mn^{3+} is a powerful oxidant (high $E^\ominus$); that is, the Mn^{2+} ion is more stable than the Mn^{3+} ion. Fe^{3+} is an oxidant but has a lower $E^\ominus$ value, so the difference in stability between the two ions is less than in the case of Mn.
Mn^{2+} (Ar)3d^5 has the stability associated with a half-full d subshell, compared with Mn^{3+} (Ar)3d^4.
Fe^{3+} (Ar)3d^5 has the stability associated with a half-full d subshell, compared with Fe^{2+} (Ar)3d^6.
(ii) $Fe^{3+}(aq) + I^-(aq) \longrightarrow Fe^{2+}(aq) + \frac{1}{2}I_2(aq)$
Fe^{3+} is a stronger oxidant (has a higher $E^\ominus$) than I_2.
$S_2O_8^{2-}$ is a stronger oxidant (has a higher $E^\ominus$) than Fe^{3+}.
Both reactions involve collisions between oppositely charged ions, whereas the equation for the overall reaction would involve a collision between two negatively charged ions, which repel one another.
Fe^{2+} is reformed in the reaction so Fe^{2+} acts as a catalyst.

24. *(a)* See § 2.2 and Figure 2.2C.

(b) (i) See § 10.7.1.
$H_2(g) + \frac{1}{2}O_2(g) \longrightarrow H_2O(g)$;
$\Delta H^\ominus = -241.8$ kJ mol^{-1}
This is the standard enthalpy of formation of water vapour.
(ii) $H{-}H + \frac{1}{2}O{=}O \longrightarrow H{-}O{-}H$;
$\Delta H^\ominus = -241.8$ kJ mol^{-1}
$-241.8 = 2(H{-}O) - 436 - 248$
$\Rightarrow (H{-}O) = 221$ kJ mol^{-1}
(iii) The combustion products are non-polluting. Hydrogen forms an explosive mixture with air.
(iv) It is the smallest ion, and the high ratio (charge/size) makes it attract a molecule of water to form H_3O^+.

H^+ + :Ö—H (with H below O) → $[H{-}\ddot{O}{-}H]^+$ (with H below O)

(v) $CH_3CH{=}CH_2(g) + H_2(g) \longrightarrow CH_3CH_2CH_3(g)$
variable oxidation state
(vi) 21 mol propene require 21 mol H_2
$= 21 \times 22.4$ dm^3 = 470 dm^3

(c) (i) $Al^{3+} + 3e^- \longrightarrow Al$; see § 19.3.2.
(ii) Octahedral. Lone pairs of electrons on the O atoms of H_2O molecules form coordinate bonds to the Al^{3+} ion.
(iii) $[Al(H_2O)_6]^{3+}(aq) + 4OH^-(aq) \longrightarrow [Al(H_2O)_2(OH)_4]^-(aq) + 4H_2O(l)$

25. *(a)* (i) HF (ii) HI

(b) The oxide of Na is ionic and basic, the O^{2-} ion accepting protons from H_2O to form $OH^-(aq)$. This is typical of a metal oxide.

$(Na^+)_2O^{2-}(s) + H_2O(l) \longrightarrow 2Na^+(aq) + 2OH^-(aq)$

The oxide of Al can react as a base:

$Al_2O_3(s) + 6H^+(aq) \longrightarrow 2Al^{3+}(aq) + 3H_2O(l)$

In addition Al_2O_3 can react as an acid to form aluminate ions.

$Al_2O_3(s) + 2OH^-(aq) + 3H_2O(l) \longrightarrow 2[Al(OH)_4]^{2-}$

This behaviour is shared with non-metallic elements, which react to form compounds with the element in the anion.
SO_2 reacts as an acid, abstracting OH^- from water to form sulphite ions and hydrogen ions.

$SO_2(g) + H_2O(l) \longrightarrow 2H^+(aq)SO_3^{2-}(aq)$

(c) At_2 mixed with HAt. Conc. H_2SO_4 will displace HAt from NaAt. It will also oxidise HAt to At_2. The extent of oxidation will be greater than with HI.

(d) (i) To kill bacteria. Acid attacks e.g. concrete surrounds and grouting between tiles.

(ii) Cl_2 (0), ClO^- (+1)

(iii) As pH increases, $[H^+]$ decreases and the position of the equilibrium

$$Cl_2(aq) + H_2O(l) \rightleftharpoons HClO(aq) + Cl^-(aq) + H^+(aq)$$

moves from left to right. As $[H^+]$ decreases and [HClO] increases, the position of the equilibrium

$$HClO(aq) \rightleftharpoons H^+(aq) + ClO^-(aq)$$

is driven more rapidly by these two factors from left to right.

(iv) Amount of thio $= 6.90 \times 10^{-3} \times 0.010$ mol
$= 6.90 \times 10^{-5}$ mol
Amount of I_2 in 100 $cm^3 = 3.45 \times 10^{-5}$ mol
= Amount of HClO in 100 cm^3
$[HClO] = 3.45 \times 10^{-4}$ mol dm^{-3} = 18.1 mg dm^{-3}

26. *(a)* (i) I. See Figure15.2F.
II. See § 15.3 III. See §§ 15.3, 15.4, Figure 15.6A.

(ii) See § 15.5.1, Figure 15.6D.

(iii) The ability to act as an acid and as a base in different reactions. Groups 3 and 4, e.g. Al and Sn.

$$Al(OH)_3(s) + 3HCl(aq) \longrightarrow AlCl_3(aq) + 3H_2O(l)$$
$$Al(OH)_3(s) + NaOH(aq) \longrightarrow NaAl(OH)_4(aq)$$

(b) (i) See § 19.3.2.

(ii) The high negative value of $\Delta H^\ominus$ shows that a large quantity of energy must be supplied to split Al_2O_3 into its elements. The high negative value of $E^\ominus$ shows that Al is a reducing agent with a strong tendency to form Al^{3+} ions, therefore a high electric potential is needed to reverse the process and discharge Al^{3+} ions.

(iii) I octahedral II B, $(He)2s^23p$, is limited to the $n = 2$ shell; Al, $(Ne)3s^23p$, has d orbitals in the $n = 3$ shell available for the formation of coordinate bonds.

ORGANIC CHEMISTRY

1. *(a)* (i) $(CH_3)_3C—CH{=}CH_2 \xrightarrow{Br_2}$
$(CH_3)_3C—CHBrCH_2Br \xrightarrow{\text{KOH(ethanol), reflux}} (CH_3)_3C—C{\equiv}CH$

(ii) $C_5H_9—NH_2 + C_6H_5COCl \longrightarrow C_5H_9—NHCO—C_6H_5$

(iii)

$$CH_3CH_2C{\equiv}N \xrightarrow{H_2O} CH_3CH_2CO_2H \xrightarrow{PCl_5} CH_3CH_2COCl \longrightarrow (CH_3CH_2CO)_2O$$

$CH_3CH_2CO_2H \downarrow CH_3CH_2CO_2Na$; CH_3CH_2COCl + $CH_3CH_2CO_2Na$ — Distil → $(CH_3CH_2CO)_2O$

(b) If **G** is optically active, the structure is:

$CH_2OCOC_{17}H_{35}$
|
$C^{\star}HOCOC_{17}H_{35}$
|
$CH_2OCOC_{15}H_{31}$

If **G** is optically inactive, the structure is:

$CH_2OCOC_{17}H_{35}$
|
$CHOCOC_{15}H_{31}$
|
$CH_2OCOC_{17}H_{35}$

(c) $C_3H_6O_2$ is not reduced by $NaBH_4$, suggesting carboxylic acid or ester. The peak at 1750 cm^{-1} suggests >C=O. The peaks at 3000 cm^{-1} suggest —OH, hydrogen-bonded in carboxylic acids and C—H, aliphatic. The compound could be $C_2H_5CO_2H$ or $CH_3CO_2CH_3$ or $HCO_2C_2H_5$.

2. *(a)* See § 29.9.1.

(b) $CH_3—CH{=}C(CH_3)—CH_3$ 2-methylbut-2-ene

(c) (i) $-\!\!\left[C(CH_3)(H)—C(CH_3)(CH_3)\right]\!\!-_n$

(ii) An initiator is needed; see § 27.8.11.

(iii) The C—C bond is not very reactive and is not attacked by organisms in the soil. These compounds are not inhaled because of their low vapour pressure and are not absorbed if swallowed.

(d) (ii) 1 (ii) No change. Rate ∝ [RBr] The rds is the ionisation of RBr $\longrightarrow R^+ + Br^-$ for reaction of a 3° halogenoalkane.

(e) (i) Average kinetic energy of molecules increases; [see § 14.2.3] and distribution of molecular energies changes [see § 14.3].

(ii) See Figure 14.3C.

(iii) See Figure 14.4A.

3. *(a)* (i) The polymer chains in nylon are cross-linked by hydrogen bonds; see § 34.3.

(ii) The —NHCO— amide group is attacked by $H^+(aq)$.
$RNHCOR'(s) + H^+(aq) \longrightarrow RNH_4^+(aq) + R'CO_2H(aq)$

(iii) Hydrolysis by alkalis
$RNHCOR'(s) + OH^-(aq) \longrightarrow RNH_2(l) + RCO_2^-(aq)$

(b) Hydrocarbons, oxides of nitrogen, carbon monoxide; see § 26.6

(c) (i) 2-methylphenol ($C_6H_4(CH_3)OH$) $\xrightarrow{CrO_3}$ 2-hydroxybenzoic acid ($C_6H_4(CO_2H)OH$) $\xrightarrow{CH_3COCl}$ $C_6H_4(CO_2H)OCOCH_3$

(ii) $—CO_2H$ liberates CO_2 from $NaHCO_3$
$—OCOCH_3$ hydrolyse $\longrightarrow CH_3CO_2H$ with smell of vinegar

(d) (i) $J = H_3C—C_6H_4—NO_2$

(ii) $\mathbf{K} = P_2O_5$

(iii) **L** = free radical initiator, e.g. benzoyl peroxide

(iv) **M** = cyclohexane ring chain with $COCH_3$ and CHO ends

4. *(a)* $CH_3CO_2H(l) + C_2H_5OH(l) \rightleftharpoons CH_3CO_2C_2H_5(l) + H_2O(l)$, esterification

(b) $CH_3COCl(l) + C_2H_5OH(l) \rightleftharpoons CH_3CO_2C_2H_5(l) + HCl(g)$
nucleophilic substitution; see § 33.10.2

(c) 1. In $CH_3—C^{\delta+}(=O^{\delta-})\rightarrow Cl$ the $C^{\delta+}$ has a larger positive charge than the $C^{\delta+}$ in $CH_3—C^{\delta+}(=O^{\delta-})\rightarrow O—H$ because Cl is more electronegative than O.

2. The HCl formed leaves the reaction mixture, driving the equilibrium from left to right.

(d)

```
     Ha  O        Hb  Hc
     |   ||       |   |
Ha—C—C—O—C—C—Hc
     |            |   |
     Ha           Hb  Hc
```

The line at $\delta 4.1$ is due to RCO_2CH_2—; $\delta 1.2$ is due to —CH_3 of —$CO_2CH_2CH_3$

Three H_a have no adjacent protons, therefore the line is not split. Two H_b have three adjacent protons, therefore the line at δ 4.1 is split into four. Three H_c have two adjacent protons, therefore the line at δ 1.2 is split into three.

5. *(a)* (i) Not a carbonyl compound (DNP), not an alcohol (propanoyl chloride). Fruity smell suggests ester. $HCO_2CH_2CH_2CH_3$, $HCO_2CH(CH_3)_2$, $CH_3CO_2C_2H_5$, $C_2H_5CO_2CH_3$

(ii) Reduction gives one product, therefore **H** is $CH_3CO_2C_2H_5$, **J** is C_2H_5OH.

(b) (i) *cis-* H_3C(H)C=C(H)CH_3 and *trans-*

(ii) optical NH_2—C(H)(CO_2H)(CH_3)

(c) (i) **K** = $(CH_3)_2CHCH_2CH_2OH$,

(ii) **L** = 1, 4-$HOC_6H_4CH_3$,

(iii) **M** = conc. H_2SO_4 + conc. HNO_3

(iv) **N** = $C_6H_5OCH_3$

(v) **P** = C_2H_5(OH)C(CH_3)(SO_3Na)

6. *(a)* **A** = $CH_3(CH_2)_2\,CH_2Br$

B = $CH_3(CH_2)_2CH_2OH$

C = $CH_3(CH_2)_2CO_2H$

D = $CH_3CH_2CH=CH_2$

E = $C_2H_5CHBrCH_3$

(b) Bromine water is decolourised.

(c) $CH_3(CH_2)_2CO_2H(aq) + NaHCO_3(s) \longrightarrow CH_3(CH_2)_2CO_2Na(aq) + CO_2(g) + H_2O(l)$

(d) $CH_3(CH_2)_2CO_2(CH_2)_3CH_3$

(e) $K_2Cr_2O_7$, acid, heat

(f) (i) $K_a = [H^+(aq)]^2/[HA(aq)]$

$1.51 \times 10^{-5} = [H^+(aq)]^2/0.100 \Rightarrow pH = 2.91$

(ii) buffer action

(iii) 5.5 g $CH_3(CH_2)_2CO_2Na$ = 5.5/110 mol = 0.050 mol

500 cm^3 of 0.100 mol dm^{-3} C = 0.0500 mol

$pH = pK_a + \lg\{[Salt]/[Acid]\} = 4.82 + \lg 1 = 4.82$

7. *(a)* (i) 1. C_6H_5Cl 2. $CH_3(CH_2)_3Cl$

(ii) Chlorobutane reacts with water. See § 29.10 for lack of reactivity of halogenoarenes.

$CH_3(CH_2)_3Cl(l) + H_2O(l) \longrightarrow CH_3(CH_2)_3OH(aq) + HCl(aq)$

The Cl^- (aq) formed gives a white ppt of AgCl(s).

(b) $CH_3CH_2CH_2OH \xrightarrow{P_2O_5} CH_3CH{=}CH_2 \xrightarrow{HBr} CH_3CHBrCH_3$

(c) (ii) catalyst

(ii) C_2H_5OH (M_r = 46) $\longrightarrow$ $CH_3CO_2C_2H_5$ (M_r = 88)

10.0 g $C_2H_5OH \longrightarrow 88 \times 10/46$ g = 19.13 g ester

% yield = 100 × 15.0/19.1 = 78%

(d) Amount of NaOH = amount of H^+

= amount of **C** = 1.0×10^{-2} mol

M_r of **C** = 88

C, like **B**, has an unbranched carbon chain. M_r of —CO_2H = 45 and 88 – 45 = 43 = C_3H_7

C could be $CH_3(CH_2)_2CO_2H$, and **B** could be $CH_3(CH_2)_2CN$. **A** would then be $CH_3(CH_2)_3NH_2$, and **D** would be $CH_3(CH_2)_2CONH_2$.

$C_3H_7CO_2H(aq) + H_2O(l) \rightleftharpoons C_3H_7CO_2^-(aq) + H_3O^+(aq)$

$K_a = [H^+(aq)][C_3H_7CO_2^-(aq)]/[C_3H_7CO_2H(aq)]$

$1.6 \times 10^{-5} = [H^+(aq)]^2/0.010 \Longrightarrow pH = 3.40$

8. *(a)* (i) The (+) enantiomer rotates the plane of polarised light; the (±) racemic mixture does not.

(ii) $CH_3CHOHCH_3$ and CH_3COCH_3 The IR spectrum of the carbonyl compound has a large absorption peak at 1800 cm^{-1}. The IR spectrum of the alcohol has a peak for hydrogen bonded —OH in alcohols at 3230–3500 cm^{-1}.

(iii) Hydrolyse by warming with NaOH(aq). Test for Cl^- and Br^-. Add $HNO_3(aq) + AgNO_3(aq) \longrightarrow$ white ppt of AgCl(s) or pale yellow ppt of AgBr(s).

(b) 4-$NO_2C_6H_4CO_2H$ $\xrightarrow{PCl_5}$ 4-$NO_2C_6H_4COCl$ $\xrightarrow{NH_3}$ 4-$NO_2C_6H_4CONH_2$ (T)

$\xrightarrow{Br_2,\ NaOH(aq)}$ 4-$NO_2C_6H_4NH_2$ (U)

$C_7H_5NO_4$ (M_r 167) $\longrightarrow$ $C_6H_6N_2O_4$ (M_r = 138)

20.0 g $\longrightarrow$ 20.0 g × 138/167 = 16.5 g

In the reaction with PCl_5 some of the acid chloride formed is hydrolysed back to the starting material. In reaction 2 equilibrium is reached as some of the amide and HCl formed react to reform the acid chloride. In reaction 3, the yield is good but recrystallisation leaves some product in solution.

(c) Dissolve the mixture in e.g. ethoxyethane, and add NaOH(aq). Pour into a separating funnel and shake. Heptanoic acid passes into the NaOH(aq) layer as its sodium salt. Separate. Add HCl(aq) to the aqueous layer. Heptanoic acid comes out of solution. Extract the heptanoic acid from the aqueous layer with ethoxyethane, dry with e.g. anhydrous calcium chloride, and distil in a fume cupboard.

9. **A** is not a 1° amine. **C** could be CH_3CO_2H, which liberates CO_2 from $NaHCO_3$. Then **A** is $C_6H_5NOCOCH_3$ e.g. $HOC_6H_4NHCOCH_3$. **B** reacts with $NaNO_2$, presumably in diazotisation. **D** = $HOC_6H_4N_2^+Cl^-$, which gives an azo dye with phenol.

A: 4-$HOC_6H_4NHCOCH_3$ **B**: 4-$HOC_6H_4NH_3^+Cl^-$

C: CH_3CO_2H **D**: 4-$HOC_6H_4N_2^+Cl^-$

E = HO—C_6H_4—N = N—C_6H_4—OH

$m/e = 76$, $C_6H_4 = 76$. All contain the group C_6H_4,

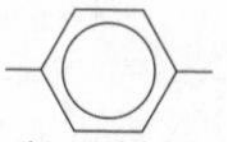

(b) Add Mg turnings to a dry solution of C_2H_5Br in ethoxyethane. A Grignard reagent is formed [see § 29.11]. Add (i) ethanal, CH_3CHO (ii) dilute acid

$$C_2H_5Br \xrightarrow{\text{Mg(ethoxyethane)}} C_2H_5Mg^+Br^- \xrightarrow{\text{(i) }CH_3CHO\text{ (ii) }H^+(aq)} C_2H_5CH(OH)CH_3$$

10. (a) See §§ 26.2.1, 26.4.2.

(b) (i) $CH_3(CH_2)_2Br(l) + NH_3(g) \longrightarrow CH_3(CH_2)_2NH_2(g) + HBr(g)$

The $C^{\delta+} \longrightarrow Br^{\delta-}$ bond is polarised. The lone pair on N of $\ddot{N}H_3$ attacks the $C^{\delta+}$ atom, weakening the C—Br bond so that Br^- splits off, followed by H^+.

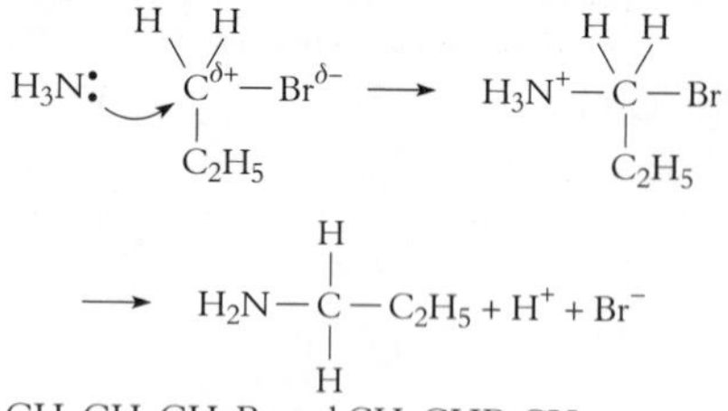

$CH_3CH_2CH_2Br$ and $CH_3CHBrCH_3$

IR: Compare the spectra with known samples.

NMR: Compare peak heights.

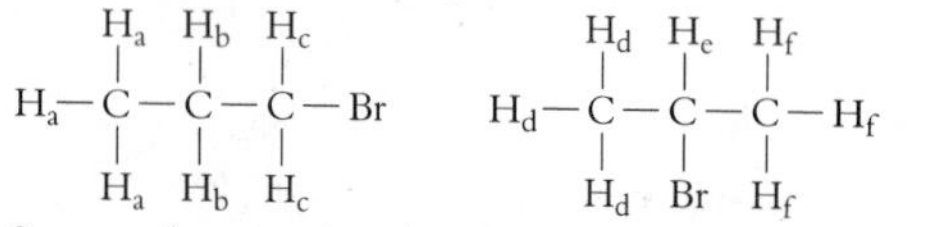

3 types of proton, 3 peaks	3 types of proton, 3 peaks
Ratio of peak heights	Ratio of peak heights
$3H_a : 2H_b : 2H_c$	$3H_d : 1H_e : 3H_f$

(ii) I. HBr electrophilic addition

II. HCN nucleophilic addition III. H_2, Ni, reduction

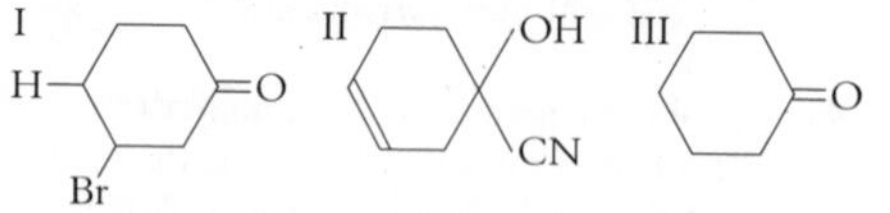

11. (a) (i) The graph shows the end point at 16.0 cm^3 of NaOH(aq)

Amount of NaOH $= 16.0 \times 10^{-3} \times 0.050$ mol $= 8.0 \times 10^{-4}$ mol

Mass of **A** $= 10.0 \times 10^{-3} \times 7.2$ g $= 0.072$ g

Since **A** is monoprotic, M_r of **A** $= 0.072/8.0 \times 10^{-4} = 90$. Since M_r of $CH_2O = 30 \Longrightarrow$ molecular formula is $C_3H_6O_3$

(ii) From the graph, pH at end point = 9.1

$[NaA] = 8.0 \times 10^{-4}$ mol/(10.0 + 16.0) cm^3 $= 3.077 \times 10^{-2}$ mol dm^{-3}

When the acid is half-neutralised, when 8.0 cm^3 of NaOH(aq) have been added, pH = 4.0 (from the graph). At this point [salt formed] = [acid remaining], that is, $[A^-(aq)] = [HA(aq)]$

$K_a = [H^+(aq)][A^-(aq)]/[HA(aq)] = [H^+(aq)]$

and $pK_a = pH = 4.0$. From $C_3H_6O_3$ subtract CO_2H. This leaves C_2H_5O which could be C + CH_3 + OH + H. Four different groups are attached to one C atom, which is asymmetric.

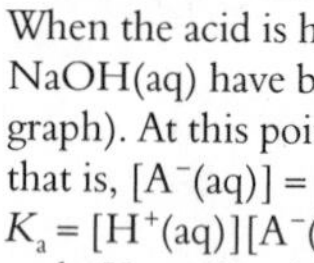

(c) $m/e = 15 = CH_3^+$, $m/e = 30 = CHOH^+$, $m/e\ 45 = CO_2H^+$, $m/e = 75 = CHOHCO_2H^+$

(d) 2° alcohol, oxidised to a ketone by $K_2Cr_2O_7$, acid. A ketone gives a ppt with DNP but does not reduce Fehling's solution. Having the group CH_3CHOH—, it gives iodoform, a yellow ppt, with NaIO.

12. (a) See § 25.8.2.

(b) (i) similar to $OH^- + RX$; see §§ 29.8.3, 29.9.1

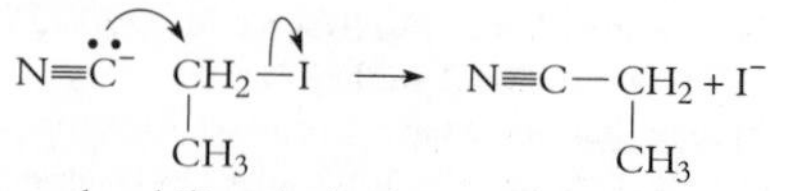

(ii) nucleophilic substitution

(iii) $C_2H_5O^- \longrightarrow C_2H_5OC_2H_5$, ethoxyethane

$H_3N: \longrightarrow H_2NCH_2CH_3$ ethylamine/aminoethane

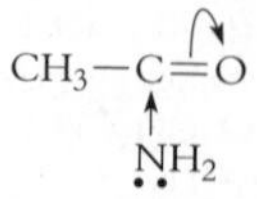

No, the C=O group draws electrons away from $—NH_2$ and CH_3CONH_2 is much less basic than CH_3NH_2 and a much poorer nucleophile.

(c) (i) $CH_3CO_2C_2H_5(l) + NaOH(aq) \longrightarrow CH_3CO_2Na(aq) + C_2H_5OH(aq)$

(ii) OH^- is a nucleophile. In ester hydrolysis equilibrium is set up:

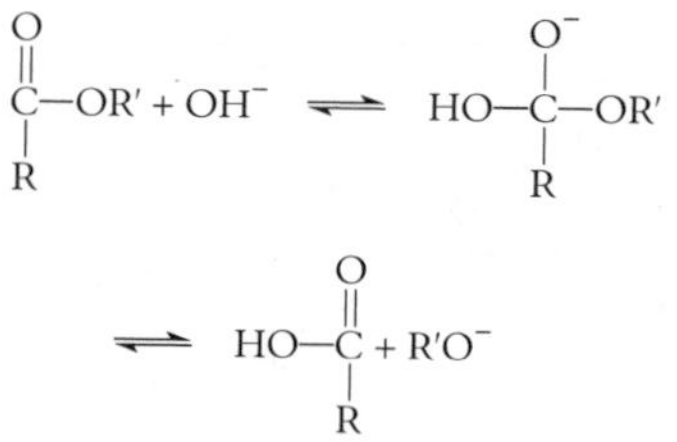

13. $$\mathbf{A}: C_4H_{10}O \xrightarrow{-H_2O} \mathbf{B} + \mathbf{C}: C_4H_8 \xrightarrow{HBr} \mathbf{D}: C_4H_9Br \xrightarrow{\text{Hydrolyse}} \mathbf{A}$$

A ↓ Oxidise

E: C_4H_8O

B and **C** are $CH_3CH_2CH{=}CH_2$ and $CH_3CH = CHCH_3$

B has *cis*- and *trans*-isomers; **B** is $CH_3CH{=}CHCH_3$ and **C** is $CH_3CH_2CH{=}CH_2$

D is $CH_3CH_2CHBrCH_3$, **A** is $CH_3CH_2CHOHCH_3$, **E** is $CH_3CH_2COCH_3$

The absorption in the IR at 1715 cm^{-1} confirms the presence of a C=O group in **E**. The IR absorption at 1650 cm^{-1} confirms the >C=C< group in **B** and **C**. The IR absorption at 3350 cm^{-1} is due to —OH in an alcohol, confirming the presence of —OH in **A**.

A butan-2-ol, **B** *cis*- and *trans*-but-2-ene, **C** but-1-ene, **D** 2-bromobutane, **E** butanone

14. (a) (ii) Test for 2° alcohol: oxidise with $K_2Cr_2O_7$, acid $\longrightarrow$ ketone. Add DNP $\longrightarrow$ orange ppt. Test for C=C: bromine (in solvent) decolourised.

(ii) Add $FeCl_3$(aq). Morphine, a phenol, gives a violet colour with $FeCl_3$(aq) and a ppt with Br_2(aq) of the 1-bromo-derivative. Codeine does not.

(b) See § 8.7.4.

(c) >CHOH at 3230–3550 cm^{-1} >C=C< at 1680–1610 cm^{-1}, 3° amine at 3600–3100 cm^{-1}

(d) δ 3.8 shows $ROCH_3$.

(e) Replace —OH by $—OCOCH_3$.

(f) Tests on animals, applications to the Medicines Control Agency for licence, controlled clinical trials

15. (a) (i)

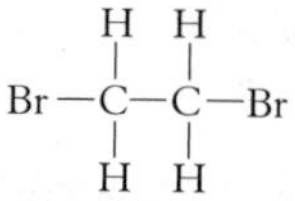

(ii)

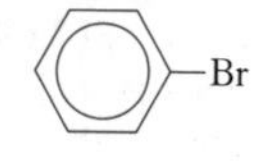

(b) (i) See § 28.6.
(ii) See § 28.8.2.
(c) (i) Add Tollens' reagent (ammoniacal $AgNO_3$), warm: **A** gives a silver mirror, while **B** does not react.
(ii) **D** (iii) **C** (iv) **C** (v) **C** and **E**

16. **A**: $C_{10}H_{18}O_2 \xrightarrow{O_3}$ **C**: C_4H_8O + **D**: $C_6H_{10}O_3$
C has a —CHO group and a branched chain; it could be C_3H_7CHO, that is, $(CH_3)_2CHCHO$.
D has —CHO and —CO_2H: $C_4H_8CHOCO_2H$.
The functional groups can be in positions 1,2- or 1,3- or 1,4-.
The highest T_b belongs to the isomer with an unbranched chain and the functional groups in the 1,4-positions, $CHOCH_2CH_2CH_2CH_2CO_2H$.
A = $(CH_3)_2CHCH=CH(CH_2)_4CO_2H$, *cis-* and *trans-* isomers
(b) **B**: $m/e = 31$ could be OCH_3^+.
B is not a 1° aromatic amine.
A side chain is oxidised to —CO_2H.
B – vanillic acid + $CO_2H = C_8H_{11}O_2N - C_8H_8O_4 + CO_2H = CH_4N$
The CH_4N could be —CH_2NH_2. This would not give a diazonium compound.
B = [benzene ring with CH_2NH_2, OCH_3, OH]
(c) [benzene ring with $CH_2NHCO(CH_2)_4CH=CHCH(CH_3)_2$, OCH_3, OH]
(d) It seems to be soluble in water or it would not 'stimulate pain receptors in the mouth'. Dissolve in hot distilled water. Filter. Warm the filtrate to redissolve any solid. Allow to cool. Filter. Dry the residue.

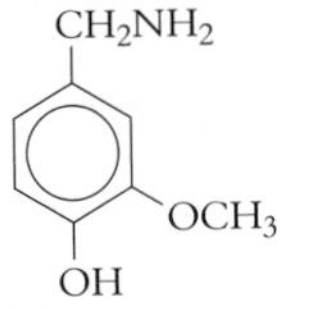

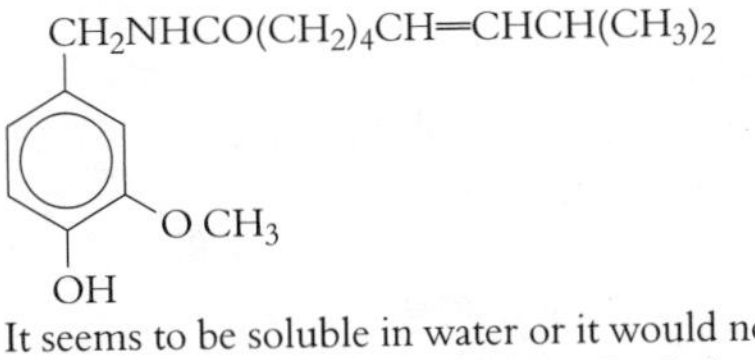

17. *(a)* See §§ 5.4.1, 10.11.2, 28.6.
The reaction of Br_2 with cyclohexene is an addition reaction. If benzene were to add a molecule of Br_2, it would lose the energy of delocalisation, and this is why the reaction is not feasible.
(b) 1. free radical substitution $CH_4 + Cl_2 \longrightarrow CH_3Cl + HCl$
2. nucleophilic substitution
$CH_3Br + OH^- \longrightarrow CH_3OH + Br^-$
3. electrophilic substitution
$C_6H_6 + CH_3Br \longrightarrow C_6H_5CH_3 + HBr$
For mechanisms see (1) § 26.4.7, (2) §§ 29.8.3, 29.9.1 (3) § 28.8.7.
(c) $CH_3(CH_2)_4CH_2OH \longrightarrow CH_3(CH_2)_3CH=CH_2$
E.g. pass the vapour over heated Al_2O_3. There is a peak at 1650 cm^{-1} corresponding to C=C, a peak at 2850–3000 cm^{-1} corresponding to C—H, and no peak at 3230–3550 cm^{-1} for O—H. This is the IR spectrum of hex-1-ene.

18. *(a)* $CH_3CH_2CH_2CHOHCH_3 + [O] \longrightarrow CH_3CH_2CH_2COCH_3 + H_2O$
(b) conc. H_2SO_4, 170 °C; mechanism: § 30.7.2
(c) **E** = $CH_3—CH_2—C(CH_3)_2—O—H$ **F** = $H—C(CH_3)_2—C(CH_3)(H)—O—H$ [F: upper C bears H_3C and H_3C; lower-right C bears CH_3 and H]
G = $CH_3CH_2—CH(CH_3)—CH_2OH$
(d) $(H_{a3}C)_2C=C(H_b)(CH_{c3})$
1 : 3 : 6, 2-methylbut-2-ene

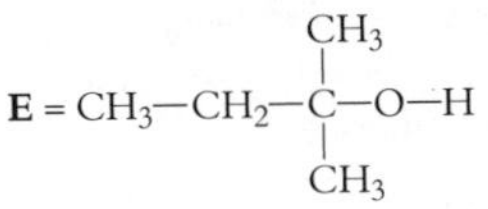

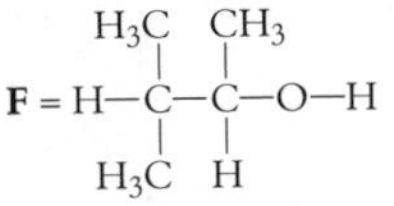

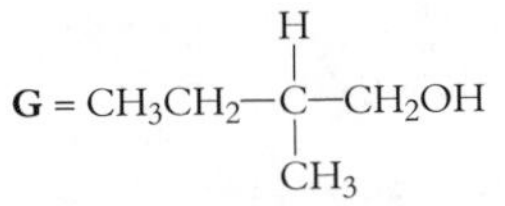

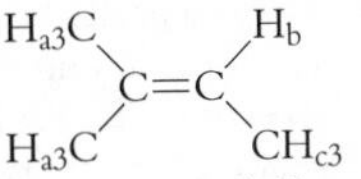

19. *(a)* **X** = $CH_3CH_2CH_2OH$, **Y** = $CH_3CH_2CHOHCN$.
Z = $CH_3CH_2CO_2H$
(b) See § 31.8.1.
W: Spectrum 4 has the C=O band at 1700 cm^{-1}.
X: Spectrum 2 has the —OH in alcohols band at 3500 cm^{-1}
Y: Spectrum 1 has the —OH peak and also a second large peak, probably due to —CN, at 2900–3000 cm^{-1}.
Z: Spectrum 3 has the —OH in acids peak at 2500–2900 cm^{-1} and the C=O peak at 1700 cm^{-1}.

20. **A** could be cyclopentene [ring: CH_2, CH_2, CH=CH, $CH_2—CH$]
B [cyclopentane ring with CHBr] **C** [cyclopentane ring with CHOH] **D** [cyclopentanone ring with C=O]
With KOH(ethanol) **B** ⟶ **A** by loss of HBr. With conc. H_2SO_4, **C** ⟶ **A** by loss of H_2O. The IR spectra show: **A** the >C=C< bond, **C** the —OH in alcohols, **D** the >C=O peak.

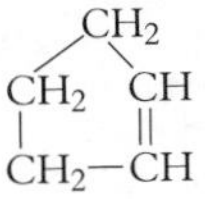

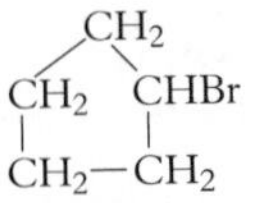

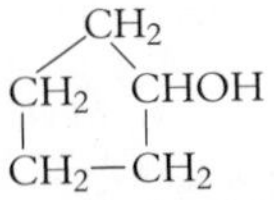

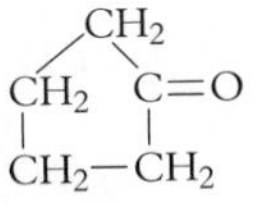

21. *(a)* (i) The absorption at 1450 cm^{-1} could be due to —CH_3 and that at 1730 cm^{-1} could be due to —CHO, suggesting an aliphatic aldehyde, e.g. CH_3CHO.
(ii) The absorption at 3500–2500 cm^{-1} could be due to —CO_2H and that at 1720 cm^{-1} could be due to —CHO or >C=O or —CO_2H, suggesting a carboxylic acid.
(b) (i) **A** = phenol, **D** = 2-hydroxybenzenecarboxylic acid
(ii) CO_2H $OCOCH_3$
(iii) [benzene ring with CO_2CH_3 and OH] an ester
(c) (i) phenolic group —OH, amide group —$NHCOCH_3$.
(ii) The two substances have different IR spectra.
Aspirin: —OH in CO_2H, 3300–2500 cm^{-1}
—CO_2R ester, 1750–1700 cm^{-1}
Paracetamol: —NH in 2° amine, 3600–3100 cm^{-1}
—OH in phenol, 3550–3230 cm^{-1}
Also paracetamol, a phenol, gives a purple colour with $FeCl_3$. Aspirin, a carboxylic acid, liberates CO_2 slowly from $NaHCO_3$.
(d) $[\mathbf{D}]/1.00 \times 10^{-4} = 0.40/0.22$ therefore
$[\mathbf{D}] = 1.82 \times 10^{-4}$ mol dm^{-3}

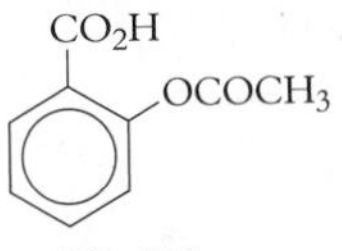

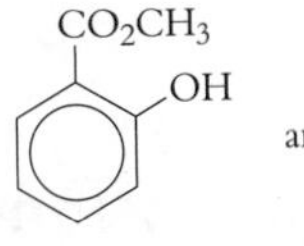

22. *(a)* C_2H_6O
(b) (i) For hydrogen bonds see § 4.8.3.
(ii) $H—CH_2—CH_2—O—H$ [structural formula: H—C(H)(H)—C(H)(H)—O—H]
contains C—H bonds, O—H bond, C—O single bond, no C=O, no C=C and has hydrogen bonds.
(c) peak at 45 = C_2H_5O, peak at 31 = CH_2OH, peak at 29 = C_2H_5
(d) (i) $C_2H_5OCOCH_3$, ethyl ethanoate, an ester
(ii) Work in a fume cupboard. Ethanoyl chloride is lachrymatory, and its vapour burns the skin as well as the eyes. Add a few drops of dry ethanoyl chloride to dry ethanol (about 5 cm^3) in a dry beaker.

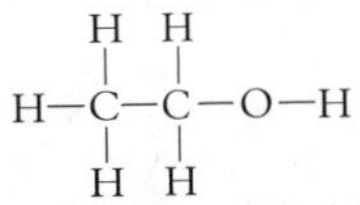

Note the evolution of hydrogen chloride; test by bringing an open bottle of ammonia solution near the beaker. Neutralise the contents of the beaker by adding sodium carbonate solution until effervescence ceases. The alkali hydrolyses any remaining ethanoyl chloride. Note the smell of the ester.

23. *(a)* **A**: IR absorption could be C=O or N—H. Since **A** gives a positive iodoform test, it contains the group CH_3CO— or CH_3CHOH—. **B**: IR absorption suggests O—H or N—H. Possibly **B** is an alcohol formed by reduction of the carbonyl compound **A** by reagent (1), and **B** ⟶ **C** is dehydration to form an alkene with *cis-trans*-isomers. **B** ⟶ **D** would then be replacement of —OH by —Br, making **D** a bromoalkane. **F** is a carboxylic acid, probably formed by acid hydrolysis of **E**. **D** ⟶ **E** could be RBr ⟶ RCN, and in fact **E** has the peak at 2250 cm^{-1} characteristic of —CN.
F: Since 1.0000 g of **F** = $97.90 \times 10^{-3} \times 0.1000$ mol NaOH = 9.79×10^{-3} mol NaOH, it is possible than 1.0000 g of **F** = 9.79×10^{-3} mol, and M_r of **F** = 102. Subtracting 45 for CO_2H leaves 57 which could be C_4H_9, making **F** = $C_4H_9CO_2H$. Then **E** = C_4H_9CN, **D** = C_4H_9Br, **B** = C_4H_9OH, **C** = C_4H_8, **A** = $CH_3COC_2H_5$ with $M_r = 72$
Then **B** has the structural formula $CH_3CC^*HOHC_2H_5$, and **C** has structural formulae

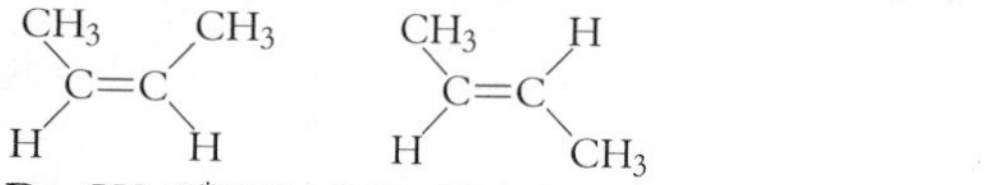

$$\begin{array}{ccc} CH_3 & & CH_3 \\ & C{=}C & \\ H & & H \end{array} \qquad \begin{array}{ccc} CH_3 & & H \\ & C{=}C & \\ H & & CH_3 \end{array}$$

D = $CH_3C^*H(Br)C_2H_5$, **E** = $CH_3C^*H(CN)C_2H_5$, **F** = $CH_3C^*H(CO_2H)C_2H_5$

(b) reagent (1) = $LiAlH_4$(ethoxyethane solution), reagent (2) = KCN(ethanol solution); reflux
(c) Chiral C atoms in **A**, **D** and **E** are shown as C*.
(d) *cis–trans*-isomerism; see § 25.9.2
(e) **A**: C=O, **B**: O—H, **E**: C≡N
(f) 102; see above
(g) C=O: 1500–1800 cm^{-1}, O—H: 2600–3400 cm^{-1}.

24. *(a)* $C_9H_{13}NO_3$
(b) 1 = phenol, 2 = 2° alcohol, 3 = 2° amine
(c) The alcohol group and the amine group both form hydrogen bonds to water so it is likely to be soluble.
(d) (i) Group 1 (ii) Group 3
(e) (i) ethanoic anhydride
(ii) CH_3I, heat in sealed tube
(f) $—NHCH_3 + CH_3I \longrightarrow —N(CH_3)_2 + HI$

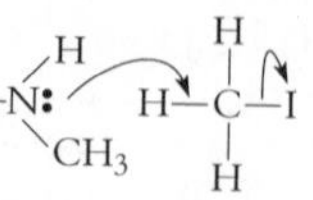

$$-\ddot{N}(H)(CH_3) \quad H{-}C(H)(H){-}I$$

The N of $—\ddot{N}HCH_3$ is a nucleophile. The $C^{\delta+}H_3—I^{\delta-}$ bond is polarised.

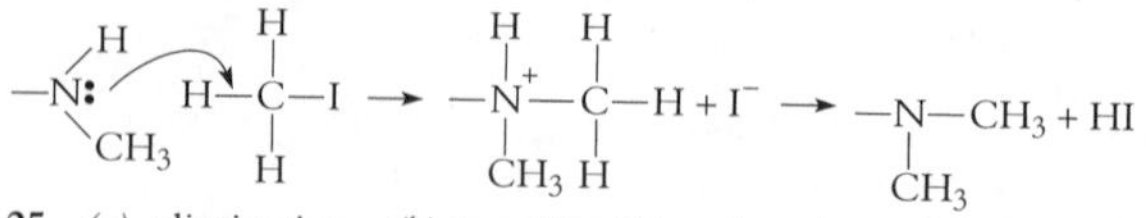

$$-\ddot{N}(H)(CH_3) + H{-}CH_2{-}I \rightarrow -\overset{+}{N}(H)(CH_3){-}CH_3 + I^- \rightarrow -N(CH_3){-}CH_3 + HI$$

25. *(a)* elimination *(b)* two C=C bonds and one C=O group
(c) alkene, cycloalkene, ketone
(d) (i) hydroxylamine, NH_2OH (ii) hydroxylamine, NH_2OH
(e) reduction
(f) [cyclohexanone ring bearing CH_3 adjacent to C=O and $CH(CH_3)_2$ opposite]
H_2 usually reduces C=C, not >C=O
(g) Oxidation by hot, conc. $KMnO_4$ + acid (or ozonolysis); methanal, HCHO
(h) (i) [cyclohexane ring with CH_3 and $OCOCH_3$ on one carbon, $CH_3—C{=}CH_2$ opposite] + HCl
(ii) [cyclohexane ring with CH_3 and OH on one carbon, CH_3CBrCH_2Br opposite]

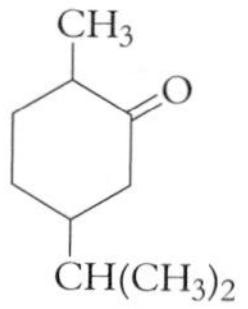

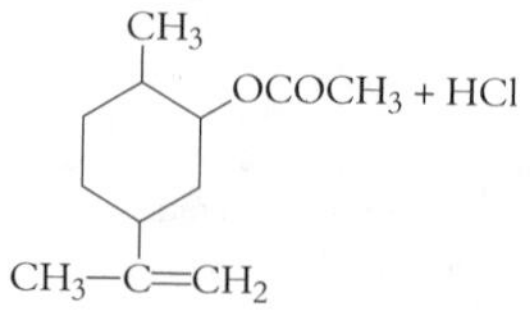

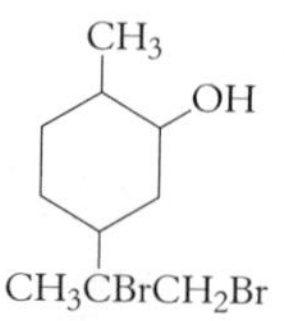

PHYSICAL, INORGANIC AND ORGANIC CHEMISTRY

1. *(a)* (i) 1. Bonds broken: C—H = + 435 kJ mol^{-1}
Bonds made: H—Cl = −432 kJ mol^{-1}
Total = +3 kJ mol^{-1}
2. Bonds broken: C—H = +435 kJ mol^{-1}
Bonds made: C—Cl = −346 kJ mol^{-1}
Total = + 89 kJ mol^{-1}
⇒ step 1 is more likely
(ii) 1. C_2H_6 2. $C_2H_6Cl_2 + H_2$
(b) (i) See § 12.6.1.
(ii) The H—F bond is very strong because H and F are small atoms, so the bonding electrons are close to the nuclei.
(c) (i) $BCl_3(s) + 3H_2O(l) \longrightarrow H_3BO_3(aq) + 3HCl(aq)$
(ii) B in BCl_3 has 6 electrons in the valence shell, and can accept a lone pair of electrons from O of H_2O. Coordination of electrons from O into the valence shell of B is the first step in hydrolysis.

2. *(a)*

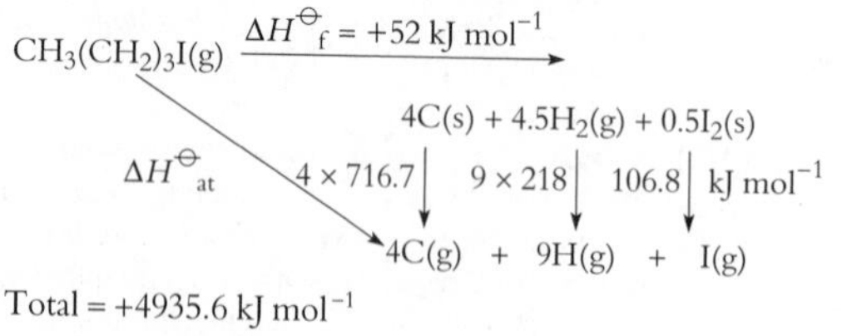

$CH_3(CH_2)_3I(g)$ —($\Delta H^\ominus_f$ = +52 kJ mol^{-1})→ $4C(s) + 4.5H_2(g) + 0.5I_2(s)$

$\Delta H^\ominus_{at}$: 4×716.7 | 9×218 | 106.8 kJ mol^{-1} ↓ $4C(g) + 9H(g) + I(g)$

Total = +4935.6 kJ mol^{-1}

$\Delta H^\ominus_{at}$ = +52 + 4935.6 kJ mol^{-1} = 4988 kJ mol^{-1}

(b) (i)
(ii)

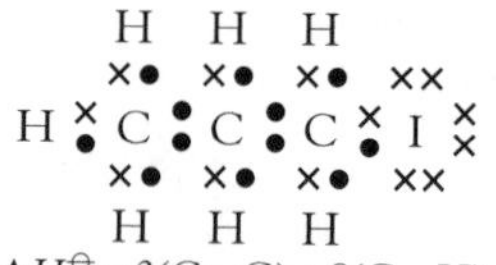

```
      H    H    H
      ×•   ×•   ×•   ××
  H × C •• C •• C × I ×
    •    •    •  •    ×
      ×•   ×•   ×•   ××
      H    H    H
```

$\Delta H^\ominus_{at}$ = 3(C—C) + 9(C—H) + (C—I)
4988 = 1041 + 3717 + (C—I) ⇒ (C—I) = 230 kJ mol^{-1}

(c) (i) deep yellow ppt
$I^-(aq) + Ag^+(aq) \longrightarrow AgI(s)$
(ii) butan-1-ol
(d) The C—Cl bond is stronger than the C—I bond.
(e) (i) $(CH_3)_3CCl$
(ii) white ppt of AgCl(s)
(iii) Tertiary halogenoalkanes are more rapidly hydrolysed than primary halogenoalkanes. In a 3° halogenoalkane the intermediate has a positive charge spread over 3 C atoms, whereas in a 1° halogenoalkane the charge is located on one C atom; see § 29.9.2.

3. *(a)* (i) $Cu(s) \longrightarrow Cu^{2+} + 2e^-$
$4H^+(aq) + 2NO_3^-(aq) + 2e^- \longrightarrow 2NO_2(g) + 2H_2O(l)$
$Cu(s) + 4H^+(aq) + 2NO_3^-(aq) \longrightarrow Cu^{2+}(aq) + 2NO_2(g) + 2H_2O(l)$
(ii) oxidation of Cu, reduction of HNO_3, redox reaction

(b) (i) $[Cu(H_2O)_6]^{2+}$ hexaaquacopper(II)
$[Ni(H_2O)_6]^{2+}$ hexaaquanickel(II)
(ii) $Cu(OH)_2(s) + Ni(OH)_2(s)$
$[Zn(OH)_4]^{2-}$ zincate(II)

(c) (i) $[Ni(H_2O)_6]^{2+} + 2OH^-(aq) \longrightarrow Ni(OH)_2(s) + 6H_2O(l)$
Lewis acid–base reaction

(d) 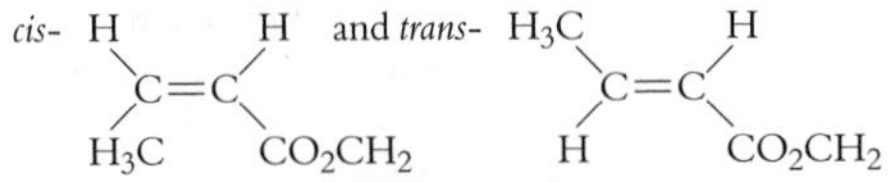 *cis*- $H(H_3C)C{=}C(H)(CO_2CH_2)$ and *trans*- $H_3C(H)C{=}C(H)(CO_2CH_2)$

(e) 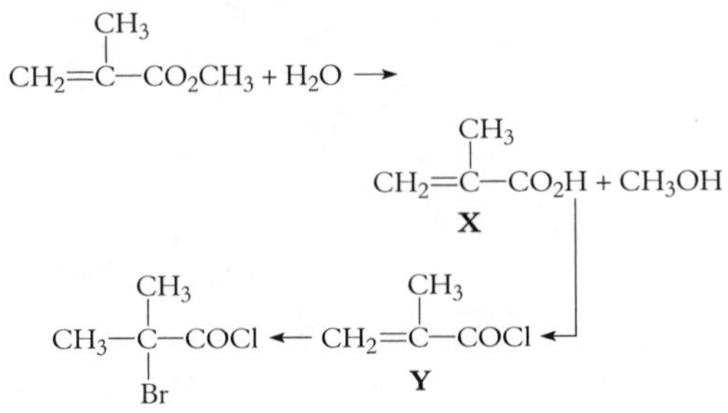
$$CH_2{=}C(CH_3){-}CO_2CH_3 + H_2O \longrightarrow CH_2{=}C(CH_3){-}CO_2H + CH_3OH$$
X = $CH_2{=}C(CH_3){-}CO_2H$

$$CH_2{=}C(CH_3){-}CO_2H \longrightarrow CH_2{=}C(CH_3){-}COCl \longrightarrow CH_3{-}CBr(CH_3){-}COCl$$
Y = $CH_2{=}C(CH_3){-}COCl$

(ii) Step 2: PCl_5, anhydrous conditions; Step 3: HBr
(iii) See § 27.8.6.

(f) 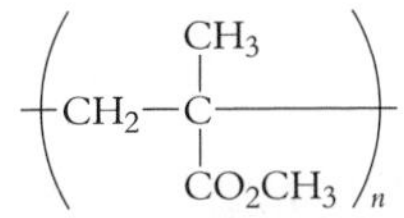
$$\left(\!-CH_2-C(CH_3)(CO_2CH_3)-\right)_n$$

4. *(a)* See § 14.5, variable oxidation state
(b) (i) $2I^-(aq) + S_2O_8^{2-}(aq) \longrightarrow 2SO_4^{2-}(aq) + I_2(aq)$
(ii) Collisions are between two ions with the same charge, therefore in many collisions the ions separate without reacting.
(iii) $2Fe^{3+} + 2I^- \longrightarrow 2Fe^{2+} + I_2$
$2Fe^{2+} + S_2O_8^{2-} \longrightarrow 2Fe^{3+} + 2SO_4^{2-}$
(c) Scandium always has +3 oxidation state. Zinc always has +2 oxidation state. The elements in the middle of the series have many oxidation states, e.g. Mn +7, +6, +5, +4, +3, +2.
(d) Pt/Rh, CO
$2NO + 2CO \longrightarrow N_2 + 2CO_2$
$2NO_2 + 4CO \longrightarrow N_2 + 4CO_2$

5. *(a)* $K_c = [N_2H_4(g)]/\{[N_2(g)]\,[H_2(g)]^2\}$
(b) Rate of forward reaction = Rate of reverse reaction
(c) All the substances are in the same state (gaseous in this case).
(d) no effect, no effect
(e) (i) −2 and +4
(ii) $2N_2H_4 + N_2O_4 \longrightarrow 3N_2 + 4H_2O$
(f) (i) 109.5°
(ii) $H_2NNH_2 + 2HCl \longrightarrow H_3N^+N^+H_3 + 2Cl^-$
(ii) The lone pairs on N of hydrazine can coordinate into the 3d subshell of Co^{2+}.

6. *(a)* (i) The first ionisation energy decreases down the group because the electron to be removed becomes further away from the positive nucleus; see §§ 15.2, Figure 15.2E, § 18.2.
Electronegativity [Figure 15.2F] decreases down the group as the number of electron shells increases. All the elements are electropositive.
(ii) $Na_2O(s) + H_2O(l) \longrightarrow 2NaOH(aq)$
$P_2O_5(s) + 3H_2O(l) \longrightarrow 2H_3PO_4(aq)$
Sodium oxide contains O^{2-} ions which react with H_2O: 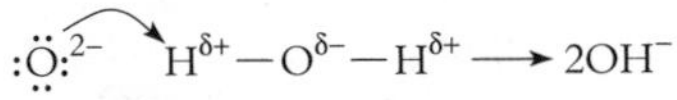
$$:\ddot{O}:^{2-} \quad H^{\delta+}{-}O^{\delta-}{-}H^{\delta+} \longrightarrow 2OH^-$$
P_2O_5 is covalent. P uses its $3s^23p^3$ electrons in bond formation. A lone pair of electrons on O of H_2O can coordinate into the 3d subshell of P as the first step in the formation of H_3PO_4.
(b) (i) Rate = change in concentration/time; see § 14.11. Molecules/ions must collide in order to react; for concentration see §§ 14.2.2, 14.3, 14.13.2. You know the concentration which relates to the initial rate; it is the initial concentration (at the start of the reaction).
(ii) Compare 1 and 2. [**D**] is constant. When [**C**] doubles, rate quadruples ⟹ rate is second order in **C**. Compare 1 and 3. $[\mathbf{C}]_3 = 3 \times [\mathbf{C}]_1$ therefore the rate goes up by a factor of 9. $[\mathbf{D}]_3 = 2 \times [\mathbf{D}]_1$ therefore the change in [**D**] has not made a difference to the rate: the reaction is zero order in **D**.
$[\mathbf{C}]_4 = 4 \times [\mathbf{C}]_1$ therefore the rate increases × 16. The change in [**D**] has no effect.
Rate = 16.0×10^{-6} mol dm^{-3} s^{-1}
Rate = $k[\mathbf{C}]^2$
0.10×10^{-6} mol dm^{-3} s^{-1} = k (0.01 mol dm^{-3})^2
$k = 1.0 \times 10^{-3}$ mol^{-1} dm^3 s^{-1}
(c) $CH_3CO_2CH_3(l) + NaOH(aq) \longrightarrow CH_3CO_2Na(aq) + CH_3OH(aq)$
The $[OH^-]$ changes from 2.0 mol dm^{-3} to 1.98 mol dm^{-3} during the course of the reaction, a decrease of 1%. This means that $[OH^-]$ can be can be considered to be constant, and Rate ∝ [ester].

7. *(a)* (i) See §§ 3.8, 3.9.
M_r of $CH_2O = 30$
Molecular formulae: CH_2O, $C_2H_4O_2$ and $C_3H_6O_3$
H = HCHO, oxidised to HCO_2H, methanoic acid (**M**) and reduced to CH_3OH, methanol (**N**). **M** + **N** form HCO_2CH_3, methyl methanoate (**J**).
L = CH_3CO_2H, ethanoic acid,
K = $CH_3CHOHCO_2H$

H: $H{-}C({=}O){-}H$ **J**: $H{-}C({=}O){-}O{-}CH_3$

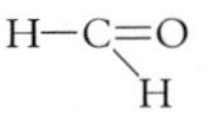

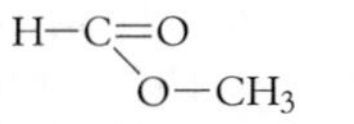

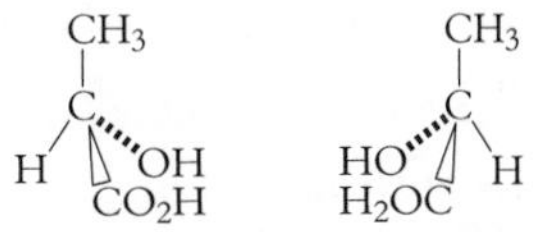

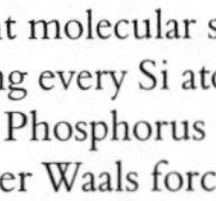

K: CH_3, H, OH, CO_2H on C (two mirror-image forms: CH_3, H, OH, CO_2H and CH_3, HO, H, H_2OC)

M: $H{-}C({=}O){-}O{-}H$ **N**: $H_3C{-}O{-}H$

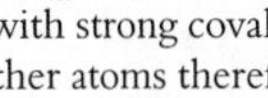

(ii) $C_6H_{12}O_6(aq) \longrightarrow 2C_2H_5OH(aq) + 2CO_2(g)$
(b) (i) From left to right the additional electrons all enter the $n = 3$ shell. They are held closer to the nucleus because the nuclear charge increases from left to right.
(ii) From Na ⟶ Mg ⟶ Al, the number of valence electrons increases and the strength of the metallic bond increases and therefore T_m increases. Silicon has a giant molecular structure with strong covalent bonds joining every Si atom to 4 other atoms therefore T_m is high. Phosphorus consists of P_4 molecules with weak van der Waals forces between them, therefore T_m is lower. Sulphur S_8 units pack into crystals of rhombic and monoclinic sulphur, with stronger van der Waals forces between them, therefore T_m is higher than for P. Chlorine consists of Cl_2 molecules with negligible forces of attraction between them and is therefore a gas. Argon consists of single Ar atoms which are less polarisable than Cl_2 molecules and therefore have weaker van der Waals forces between them.
The strength of the metallic bond increases and T_m increases Li ⟶ Be ⟶ B. The bonds are stronger than in Period 3 elements. T_m increases B ⟶ C because the macromolecular structure of diamond and

the layer structure of graphite involve strong covalent bonds. N, O and F are gases consisting of individual molecules. T_m values are low, lower than in Period 3 because there are fewer electrons to polarise bonds and give rise to van der Waals forces. Ne consists of individual atoms and has a very low T_m.

8. *(a)* (i) $K_a = [RCO_2^-][H_3O^+]/[RCO_2H]$
(ii) $7.4 \times 10^{-4} = [H_3O^+]^2/0.200$
pH = 1.91
(b) (i) to resist changes in pH on the addition of small amounts of acids and alkalis; see § 12.8
(ii) Can accept OH^- ions:

$$H_3O^+(aq) + OH^-(aq) \longrightarrow 2H_2O(l)$$

Can accept H_3O^+ ions:

$$H_3O^+(aq) + CH_2CO_2^-(aq) \rightleftharpoons CH_3CO_2H(aq) + H_2O(l)$$
$$\quad COHCO_2H \qquad\qquad COHCO_2H$$
$$\quad CH_2CO_2H \qquad\qquad CH_2CO_2H$$

(iii) $pH = pK_a + lg\{[Salt]/[Acid]\}$
$= 3.13 + lg(0.400/0.200) = 3.43$
(c) (i) Reacts with PCl_5 to replace —OH by —Cl and form HCl(g) (—CO_2H also does this). Reacts with Na to give hydrogen. Reacts with $K_2Cr_2O_7$, acid (—CHO also does this).
(ii) e.g. conc. NaOH(aq)
(iii) Liberates CO_2 from $NaHCO_3$.

9. Box: $2Na(s) + H_2(g) + 3O_2(g) + 2C(s)$
$\Delta H_3^\ominus = -1131 - 394 - 286 = -1811$ kJ mol^{-1}
$\Delta H_1^\ominus = 2(-951) = -1902$ kJ mol^{-1}
$\Delta H_e^\ominus = \Delta H_1^\ominus + \Delta H_2^\ominus$
$\Delta H_2^\ominus = -1811 + 1902 = +91$ kJ mol^{-1}
(c) (i) CO_3^{2-} (ii) H_2CO_3
(d) yellow
(e) The K flame is lilac.

10. *(a)* In photodissociation free radicals are formed, e.g. (B), (C). In photoionisation, ions are formed, e.g. (A).
(b) 50%
(c) 10^{-1} ppm
(d) 40 km
(e) $CF_2Cl_2 \longrightarrow CF_2Cl. + Cl.$
(f) initiation **D**, propagation **E**, termination **F**
(g) There is a lower concentration of O_2 molecules for O atoms to collide with.
(h) Ultraviolet B, 290–320 nm is absorbed by nucleic acids, leading to skin cancer in humans.
(i) UV of wavelength >240 nm because UV of wavelength <240 nm is absorbed by O_2 molecules.

11. *(a)* (i) CuF_6^{3-}, octahedral
(ii) +3. Only when stabilised by complex formation is the +3 state stable.
(b) (i) $E^\ominus$ for $Cu^{2+} + Cu \longrightarrow 2Cu^{2+}$ is
+0.52 V − 0.34 V = +0.18 V therefore this reaction happens.
$E^\ominus$ for $2Ag^+ \longrightarrow Ag^{2+} + Ag$ is
+0.80 V − 1.98 V = −1.18 V therefore this reaction does not happen.
(ii) $Cu_2O(s) + H_2SO_4(aq) \longrightarrow CuSO_4(aq) + Cu(s) + H_2O(l)$
A reddish brown ppt of Cu and a blue solution form.
(c) (i) A 56.36, B 56.42, C 46.11. A and B agree well, average 56.39 cm^3 g^{-1}.
Amount of thio per g of crystals =
$56.39 \times 10^{-3} \times 0.100 = 5.64 \times 10^{-3}$ mol g^{-1}
= Amount of Cu^{2+} per g of crystals
Mass of Cu^{2+} per g of crystals = $5.64 \times 10^{-3} \times 63.5$ g and % = 35.8%
(iii) The whole of the Cu^{2+} in the crystals was titrated.
(iv) $2Cu^{2+}$ require $4I^-$
(v) Possible errors involved in making up to exactly 1.00 dm^3 and in pipetting are avoided. Weighing is performed three times, which is time-consuming, and there is no increase in accuracy because weighing is the most accurate part of the measurement.

12. *(a)* $CO_2(g) + KOH(aq) \longrightarrow KHCO_3(aq)$
(b) (i) Sum the bond energies (a) of the bonds broken: 4(C—H) + 2(O=O) and (b) the bonds made: 2(C=O) + 4(O—H). The difference = $\Delta H = -698$ kJ mol^{-1}.
(ii) 5×10^3 moles CH_4 need 10×10^3 moles
$O_2 = 22.4 \times 10^4$ dm^3 at stp
Volume of air = $(100/21) \times 22.4 \times 10^4$ dm^3 at stp = 1.07×10^6 dm^3 at stp
(iii) e.g. $2CH_4 + 3O_2 \longrightarrow 2CO + 4H_2O$ (Other equations could be written, giving $CO_2 + CO + C + H_2O$) CO is poisonous, combining with haemoglobin and preventing oxygen from bonding to haemoglobin.
(c) (i) fractional distillation
(ii) For equations see § 26.4.7.
(iii) Energy and frequency are related by $E = h\nu$ see § 2.3.1. Below a minimum frequency, radiation does not have enough energy to break the Cl—Cl bond.

13. *(a)* I. PBr_3 or $P + Br_2$, reflux, distil
II. acidified $K_2Cr_2O_7$. Distil off the product as it is formed.
III. excess of conc sulphuric acid, 170 °C
(b) I. $(CH_3)_3CBr$ II. No reaction III. $(CH_3)_2C{=}CH_2$
(c)

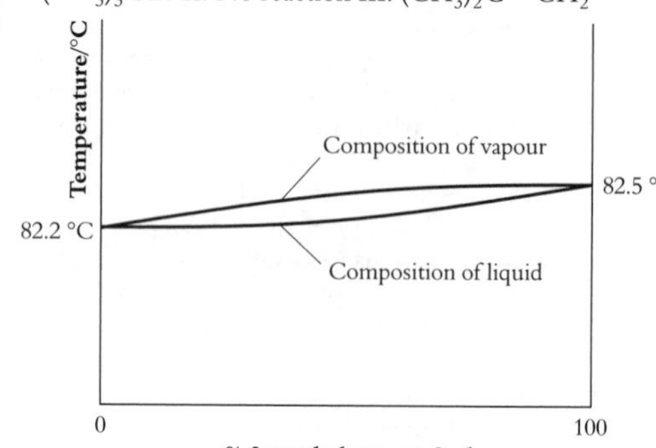

The two alcohols are sufficiently similar to form an ideal mixture. Intermolecular forces will be slightly less strong in the mixture than in the individual liquids but only slightly different. The composition of the vapour will be slightly richer in the lower T_b alcohol, but there will not be much difference between the compositions of the liquid and the vapour. The difference in T_b is so small that it will be impossible to separate the alcohols by fractional distillation.

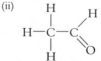

14. *(a)* (i) 750 cm$^3 \times 1/6 \times 12.4 \times 10^{-2} = 15.5$ cm^3
(ii) Mass = 15.5 cm$^3 \times 0.79$ g cm^{-3} = 12.245 g
Amount = 12.245 g/46 g mol^{-1} = 0.266 mol
(b) $Cr^{3+}(aq)$
(ii) CH_3CHO (H—C(H)(H)—C(H)=O)
(iii) 1 mol $K_2Cr_2O_7$ oxidises 3 mol C_2H_5OH
0.266 mol C_2H_5OH is oxidised by 0.266/3 mol dichromate
Mass of $K_2Cr_2O_7 = 294 \times 0.266/3 = 26.1$ g
(c) (i) and (ii) See § 12.6.1.
(iii) $CH_3CO_2H(aq) + NaOH(aq) \longrightarrow CH_3CO_2Na(aq) + H_2O(l)$

(iv) $CH_3CO_2^-$
(v) ethane C_2H_6 and carbon dioxide CO_2

15. *(a)* (i) $K_p = p\,C_2H_5OH(g)/[pC_2H_4(g) \times pH_2O(g)]$
(ii) The value of K_p would remain the same; an equilibrium constant remains the same unless the temperature changes.
(b) The reaction is exothermic: if the temperature rises the yield decreases. The reaction involves a decrease in the total volume of gas: an increase in pressure will increase the yield.
(c) (i) Catalysis takes place on the surface of the catalyst.
(ii) See Figure 14.4A.
(d) (i) $\Delta H^\ominus - (-242 + 52.3) = -46$ and $\Delta H^\ominus = -235.7$ kJ mol^{-1}
(ii) $\Delta H^\ominus = -235.7 + 248 = +12.3$ kJ mol^{-1}

16. *(a)* protein catalyst; see § 14.5.2
(b) (i) 1° one, 2° four, 3° none
(ii) Can form hydrogen bonds to water
(c) (i) nucleophile
(ii) $HCN(aq) + NaOH(aq) \longrightarrow NaCN(aq) + H_2O(l)$
(iii) HCN is a weak acid

$$HCN(aq) + H_2O(l) \rightleftharpoons H_3O^+(aq) + CN^-(aq)$$

When excess HCl acid is present, the position of equilibrium is driven towards the left and $[CN^-(aq)]$ is reduced.
(d) (i) Rate $= k\,[C_6H_5CHO]\,[CN^-]$
(ii) 2
(iii) mol^{-1} dm^{3}s^{-1}
(e) (i) There are four different groups bonded to the central carbon atom so the molecule has no centre or axis or plane of symmetry.
(ii) It is a mixture of enantiomers.
(f) **A** = HCl(aq) dilute, **B** = $K_2Cr_2O_7$(aq), acidic, **C** = $LiAlH_4$(ethoxyethane), **D** = CH_3CO_2H, conc. H_2SO_4

17. *(a)* (i) >C=C<
(ii)

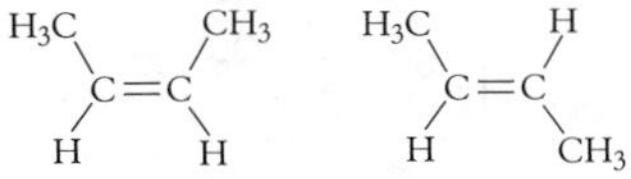

```
H3C       CH3      H3C        H
   \     /            \      /
    C=C                C=C
   /     \            /      \
  H       H          H        CH3
```

(iii) Restricted rotation of groups about the C=C bond
(iv) $CH_2{=}CH{-}CH_2{-}CH_3$
(b) (i) $CH_3COCH_2CH_3$
(ii) $CH_3CO{-}$ and $CH_3CHOH{-}$
(iii) D = $CH_3CH_2CO_2Na$, E = $CH_3CH_2CO_2H$
(c) (i)

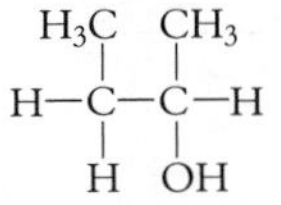

```
   H3C  CH3
    |    |
 H—C—C—H
    |    |
    H   OH
```

(ii) Ion with $m/e = 45$ is $.CH(CH_3)OH^+$
Ion with $m/e = 29$ is $CH_3CH_2.^+$
The molecule splits into $CH_3CH_2\cdot$ and $\cdot CH(CH_3)OH$
(d) (i) similar to Figure 8.5G
(ii) Intermolecular forces in **A** are strong due to hydrogen bonding. Intermolecular forces between **A** and benzene are weaker.
(iii) The peak is due to a hydrogen-bonded —OH group. In benzene hydrogen bonding does not occur.

18. *(a)* (i) Cl_2, UV light, boil, electrophilic substitution
(ii) See § 29.8.3.
(iii) oxidation
(iv) methanol, conc H_2SO_4, warm
(v) $C_6H_5CO_2CH_3 + HNO_3 \longrightarrow O_2NC_6H_4CO_2CH_3 + H_2O$
(vi) NO_2^+, electrophilic substitution
(vii) 3,5-dinitromethylbenzoate
(b) (i) See § 1.9.
(ii) $CH_2{=}CHCO_2^+$
(iii) 27: $CH_2{=}CH^+$, 45: CO_2H^+, 55: $CH_2{=}CH{-}CO^+$
(c) (i)

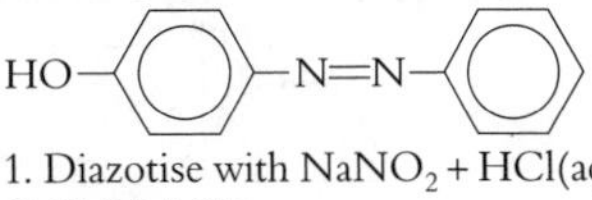

HO–⟨benzene ring⟩–N=N–⟨benzene ring⟩

(ii) 1. Diazotise with $NaNO_2$ + HCl(aq) <5 °C to form $C_6H_5N_2^+\,Cl^-$
Warm some of the diazonium compound to form phenol, C_6H_5OH.
2. React the benzene diazonium salt and phenol.
(iii) $C_6H_5NH_2$ ($M_r = 93$) $\longrightarrow C_{12}H_{10}N_2O$ ($M_r = 198$)
1 mol (93 g) phenylamine gives $0.5 \times 198 \times 0.68$ g dye = 67.32 g dye
1 tonne (1×10^6 g) of dye needs $1 \times 10^6/67.32$ mol phenylamine = 1.49×10^4 mol = 1.38 tonnes

19. *(a)* pent-1-ene, $CH_3CH_2CH_2CH{=}CH_2$
pent-2-ene, $CH_3CH_2CH{=}CHCH_3$
4-methylbut-1-ene, $(CH_3)_2CHCH{=}CH_2$
4-methylbut-2-ene, $(CH_3)_2C{=}CH{-}CH_3$
1,2-dimethylpropene, $(CH_3)_2C{=}CHCH_3$.
(b) e.g. pent-1-ene $\longrightarrow CH_3CH_2CH_2CHBrCH_3$; for mechanism see § 27.8.6
(c) Mass spectrum of **E** has peaks at $43 = C_3H_7^+$ and at $71 = M - 15 = M - CH_3$.
IR spectrum of **E** shows the peak at 1700 cm^{-1} due to >C=O
The mass spectrum of **E** shows $C_3H_7^+$ and $C_2H_3O^+$, which could be $COCH_3^+$, making **E** $C_3H_7COCH_3$. Since **B** is branched, **E** is $(CH_3)_2CHCOCH_3$.
$(CH_3)_2CHCOCH_3 \longrightarrow (CH_3)_2CH^+ + COCH_3^+$
To give this ketone, **D** must be $(CH_3)_2CHCHOHCH_3$.
The IR spectrum of **D** at 3200–3400 cm^{-1} suggests the OH group of an alcohol.
B must be $(CH_3)_2CH_2CH{=}CH_2$ which with HBr gives **C**, $(CH_3)_2CH_2CHBrCH_3$

20. *(a)* (i) **A**, butanal; **B**: 1,1,6 = 3 peaks; **C**: 3,2,3 = 3 peaks
(ii) **A** reduces Tollens' reagent; **C** does not.
(iii) $CH_3CH_2CH_2CH_2OH + [O] \longrightarrow CH_3CH_2CH_2CHO + H_2O$
further oxidation $\longrightarrow CH_3CH_2CH_2CO_2H$
(b) **D** has formula C_nH_{2n+2} and $M_r = 72$ therefore **D** is C_5H_{12}. There is only one environment for a H atom in **D** therefore **D** is $C(CH_3)_4$.

21. *(a)* (i) I The solution is decolourised; the C=C bond reacts.
II A white ppt appears. Hydrolysis results in the formation of Cl^- ions and these react with $AgNO_3$(aq) to give AgCl(s); $-CH_2Cl$ reacts.
(ii) ethanol and conc sulphuric acid
(b)

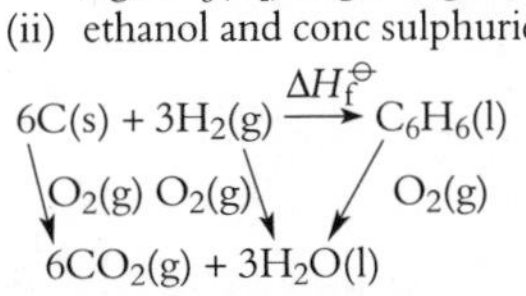

$$6C(s) + 3H_2(g) \xrightarrow{\Delta H_f^\ominus} C_6H_6(l)$$

$O_2(g)$ $O_2(g)$ ↓ ↙ $O_2(g)$

$$6CO_2(g) + 3H_2O(l)$$

$6(-394) + 3(-286) = \Delta H_f^\ominus + (-3273)$ therefore $\Delta H_f^\ominus = 51$ kJ mol^{-1}.
(c) (i) The C—C bond in benzene is between the bond lengths in C—C and C=C.
(ii) I electrophile II nitryl cation, NO_2^+

THE PERIODIC TABLE

Relative atomic mass — 1 H Hydrogen
Proton (atomic) number — 1

1	2											3	4	5	6	7	0
																	4 He 2 Helium
7 Li 3 Lithium	9 Be 4 Beryllium											11 B 5 Boron	12 C 6 Carbon	14 N 7 Nitrogen	16 O 8 Oxygen	19 F 9 Flourine	20 Ne 10 Neon
23 Na 11 Sodium	24 Mg 12 Magnesium	TRANSITION ELEMENTS										27 Al 13 Aluminium	28 Si 14 Silicon	31 P 15 Phosphorus	32 S 16 Sulphur	35.5 Cl 17 Chlorine	40 Ar 18 Argon
39 K 19 Potassium	40 Ca 20 Calcium	45 Sc 21 Scandium	48 Ti 22 Titanium	51 V 23 Vanadium	52 Cr 24 Chromium	55 Mn 25 Manganese	56 Fe 26 Iron	59 Co 27 Cobalt	59 Ni 28 Nickel	63·5 Cu 29 Copper	65 Zn 30 Zinc	70 Ga 31 Gallium	73 Ge 32 Germanium	75 As 33 Arsenic	79 Se 34 Selenium	80 Br 35 Bromine	84 Kr 36 Krypton
85 Rb 37 Rubidium	88 Sr 38 Strontium	89 Y 39 Yttrium	91 Zr 40 Zirconium	93 Nb 41 Niobium	96 Mo 42 Molybdenum	98 Tc 43 Technetium	101 Ru 44 Ruthenium	103 Rh 45 Rhodium	106 Pd 46 Palladium	108 Ag 47 Silver	112 Cd 48 Cadmium	115 In 49 Indium	119 Sn 50 Tin	122 Sb 51 Antimony	128 Te 52 Tellurium	127 I 53 Iodine	131 Xe 54 Xenon
133 Cs 55 Caesium	137 Ba 56 Barium	139 La 57 Lanthanum*	178.5 Hf 72 Hafnium	181 Ta 73 Tantalum	184 W 74 Tungsten	186 Re 75 Rhenium	190 Os 76 Osmium	192 Ir 77 Iridium	195 Pt 78 Platinum	197 Au 79 Gold	201 Hg 80 Mercury	204 Tl 81 Thallium	207 Pb 82 Lead	209 Bi 83 Bismuth	210 Po 84 Polonium	210 At 85 Astatine	222 Rn 86 Radon
223 Fr 87 Francium	226 Ra 88 Radium	227 Ac 89 Actinium†	Db 104 Dubnium	Jl 105 Joliotium	Rf 106 Rutherfordium	Bh 107 Bohrium	Hn 108 Hahnium	Mt 109 Meitnerium									

Series														
*58-71 Lanthanum series	140 Ce 58 Cerium	141 Pr 59 Praseodymium	144 Nd 60 Neodymium	147 Pm 61 Promethium	150 Sm 62 Samarium	152 Eu 63 Europium	157 Gd 64 Gadolinium	159 Tb 65 Terbium	162 Dy 66 Dysprosium	165 Ho 67 Holmium	167 Er 68 Erbium	169 Tm 69 Thulium	173 Yb 70 Ytterbium	175 Lu 71 Lutetium
†90-103 Actinium series	232 Th 90 Thorium	231 Pa 91 Protactinium	238 U 92 Uranium	237 Np 93 Neptunium	242 Pu 94 Plutonium	243 Am 95 Americium	247 Cm 96 Curium	245 Bk 97 Berkelium	251 Cf 98 Californium	254 Es 99 Einsteinium	253 Fm 100 Fermium	256 Md 101 Mendelevium	254 No 102 Nobelium	257 Lr 103 Lawrencium

UNITS

BASIC SI UNITS

Physical Quantity	*Name of unit*	*Symbol*
Length	metre	m
Mass	kilogram	kg
Time	second	s
Electric current	ampere	A
Temperature	kelvin	K
Amount of substance	mole	mol
Light intensity	candela	cd

DERIVED SI UNITS

Physical Quantity	*Name of unit*	*Symbol*	*Definition*
Energy	joule	J	$kg\ m^2\ s^{-2}$
Force	newton	N	$J\ m^{-1}$
Electric charge	coulomb	C	A s
Electric potential difference	volt	V	$J\ A^{-1}\ s^{-1}$
Electric resistance	ohm	Ω	$V\ A^{-1}$
Area	square metre		m^2
Volume	cubic metre		m^3
Density	kilogram per cubic metre		$kg\ m^{-3}$
Pressure	newton per square metre or pascal		$N\ m^{-2}$ or Pa
Molar mass	kilogram per mole		$kg\ mol^{-1}$

With all these units, the following prefixes (and others) may be used.

Prefix	*Symbol*	*Meaning*
deci	d	10^{-1}
centi	c	10^{-2}
milli	m	10^{-3}
micro	μ	10^{-6}
nano	n	10^{-9}
kilo	k	10^{3}
mega	M	10^{6}
giga	G	10^{9}
tera	T	10^{12}

INDEX OF SYMBOLS AND ABBREVIATIONS

A = area
A = mass (nucleon) number
A^* = activated/excited A
[A] = concentration/mol dm^{-3} of A
$[A]_0$ = initial concentration of A
A_r = relative atomic mass
Ar = aryl group
AR = anionic radius
c = concentration/mol dm^{-3}
c = specific heat capacity
c = velocity of light
C = heat capacity
C = charge
C = coulomb
cpm = counts per minute
CR = cationic radius
d = distance
e = elementary charge
E = electromotive force (emf)
E = energy
$E^{\ominus}$ = standard electrode potential
E_a = activation energy
EA = electron affinity
f = force
F = Faraday constant
G = free energy
$G^{\ominus}$ = standard free energy
$\Delta G^{\ominus}$ = change in standard free energy
G.M.V. = gas molar volume
h = Planck constant
H = enthalpy
$\Delta H^{\ominus}$ = change in standard enthalpy
I = electric current
IE = ionisation energy
IR = ionic radius
IR = infrared
k = rate/velocity constant
K = equilibrium constant
K_a = acid dissociation constant
K_b = base dissociation constant
K_c = equilibrium constant in concentration terms
K_p = equilibrium constant in partial pressure terms
K_{sp} = solubility product
K_w = ionic product for water
l = length
l = second quantum number
L = Avogadro constant
m = mass
m_l = third quantum number
m_s = fourth (spin) quantum number
M = molar mass
M_r = relative molar/molecular mass
n = principal quantum number
n_A = amount/mol of A
N = number of molecules
Ox. No. = oxidation number
p_B = partial pressure of B
p_B^0 = vapour pressure of pure B
P = pressure
ppm = parts per million
ΔQ = heat absorbed
r = rate
R = electric resistance
R = universal gas constant
R = alkyl group
R_F value
R.D.S. = rate-determining step
rms = root mean square
rtp = room temperature and pressure
S = entropy
$\Delta S^{\ominus}$ = change in standard entropy
stp = standard temperature and pressure
svp = saturated vapour pressure
t = time
t = temperature/°C
$t_{1/2}$ = half-life
T = temperature/K
T_b = boiling temperature
T_f = freezing temperature
T_m = melting temperature
u = atomic mass unit
U = internal energy
ΔU = change in internal energy
UV = ultraviolet
v = velocity/rate
v_0 = initial velocity/rate
V = volume
V = potential difference
V = volts
V_m = molar volume
x_A = mole fraction of A
X^- = halide ion

X_2 = halogen
Z = proton (atomic) number

Greek letters:
α = position of group

λ = wavelength
ν = frequency
ρ = density